DRY STONE DAYS

DRY STONE DAYS

DAVID D. OGSTON

THE RAMSAY HEAD PRESS, EDINBURGH

First published in 1988 by
The Ramsay Head Press
15 Gloucester Place
Edinburgh EH3 6EE

ISBN 0 902859 95 1

The publisher acknowledges the
financial assistance of the
Scottish Arts Council in the
publication of this volume

Printed in Scotland by
W. M. Bett Ltd, Tillicoultry

Contents

This book is dedicated to
MYRA ELGIN
whose unflinching enthusiasm handselled
this wall of words.

1

'Fut like folk in yon braid Buchan lan?
Folk wha ken their grun like the back o their han,
Divot and clort and clod, rock, graivel and san.'
JOHN C. MILNE: *Fut Like Folk?*

Bondies fae Lan's En tae John o Groats, they said: I steed at my room windae, wytin an hopin. Haar drifted throwe the darklin howe, wuppit its grey claidin roon Broonie's an its cotter hooses. Aa day we'd been penned in bi the coorse widder an the Committee in the hall at Auchnagatt, nae able tae get ootside lang eneuch tae rin races on the weet girss afore the rain cam on again. The bondies wid mak up for't, I thocht – fires for the new Queen bleezin on a chine o hills. 'Faan'll they be lichtit?' I speired, an Mam said faan it wis dark eneuch. Syne it cam tull's – we wis sair made for hills faar we wis, lookin ower tae Broonie's stracht in front o's, Aul Joe at wir shooder, the brae-face up abeen's. We wis boxed in, ower laich. I gaed doon the stair again in an ull teen, nae sure if I likit Coronations.

There wis fame an a name in't, though, for chiels like Tensing an Hillary, staunin wie their Union Jack on the tap o Everest, goggles glintin' in the glare o snaa. Fowk bocht an geddert – photos wis clippit oot o magazines an papers an powkit in ahin their mirrors, fite pencils wie the Royal crest on em lay on mantelpieces, an biscuit-tins or tea-caddies wie the Queen's heid on em wis plunkit doon on tap of presses or on sideboords. Ilka bairn got a tin box fae the Committee wie chocolates in't, it hid the Queen's heid at ae side o the blue lid an Philip's heid at the tither. I began tae think that wis faat wye the mannie on the wireless wis aye on aboot the Heads of State, ye nivver saa em fae the neck doon, juist their heids. Fowk said tae keep the chocolates an they wid be a souvenir tull's, bit it wis a sair torment, an I yokit intae them for fear they'd connach on's gin they wisna etten.

We wis aa echt noo, Tam an Doddie an me, aul eneuch tae be mortified gin we wis made fun o or lached at like we'd eesed tae be for the things we cam awa wie faan we wis littler, like the poem Tam hid likit – 'Fuzzy Wuzzy was a *baar,*

Fuzzy Wuzzy had no *haar*.' Tam an me wis lucky compared wie Doddie, though, we could lauch at faat wir sisters said an mak on we wis sair made at the drollities that quines wis able for. Tam's sister Edith wis ages wie my sister, comin on for five the pair o them. Edith wid be staunin on the kitchen fleer at the fire-side an she wid say 'Sitties doon, Edsie' an plunk her dowp doon on the rug wie a keckle an a flourish. An faan fowk speired at Hilda foo she wis gettin on the day she wid tell them, sober-like – 'A lot the better nae bad' aa at eence.

She wis big eneuch noo, Hilda, tae styter aboot wie's an get a ploy gyaun, though I wis tell't aye tae watch her as if she wis an ornament that roch treatment mith blaud some. We made a bus on the stair-landin – a tea-chest, twa brush haunles an a pair o aul blankets an we wis roadit, but the bus didna laist lang an we wearied o't so we feeriched oot a steen pig fae a bedroom an rowed it doon the timmer stair tae see the soon it made. We climmed up ontae strae bales abeen the soo's pen an they wis mair cobbley than we thocht, for ae meenit Hilda wis sittin nae three feet awa fae's, a douce giglet wie a lauch on her face, an neist meenit she'd tummelt heelstergowdie in amon the pigs an the aul soo wis shakkin her lugs at her an powkin her snoot up, winnerin faa else mith be drappin in.

We focht in the back seat o the car faan Dad an Mam gaed awa somewye, doon tae Methlick on a Sunday efterneen tae see Andra an Nan maybe, or ower tae New Aberdour faar Bob wis the bobby. Ae day, faan there wis juist the three o's coming hame fae Auchnagatt, Dad an Hilda an me, we gaed ower the score some an faativver the stramash we wis up till Hilda dunted the door on the near side, the haunle sprang an she wis flung oot on tae the girss at the roadside a hunner yairds or so by the Crouniehillock road-en. Dad stoppit the car an we ran back tull her: she'd a fyowe scrats on her broo an bits o girss in her hair bit there wis nae sign o broken beens. We got her hame greetin mair fae the shock nor onything, an Doctor

Dickson cam an felt her ribs an meeved her airms up an doon. He plaistered gauze on her sair bits an said nae tae fash wirsels aboot the stour she wis barkit wie, the sticky gauze wid clean the cuts an richt eneuch, faan it wis lifted aff in a day or twa she wis hale an herty, the angry raa marks cowered up an she wis neen the waur. We wis weel warned, efter that, aboot capers in the back seat, an we hid tae content wirsels wie hittin een anither wie cushions for a fyle, syne that wis putten a stop till an we hid tae sit on wir dowps an look at the craps like aaitherbody.

We likit fine, Hilda an me, gyaun tae see relations, ye could compare the hooses they bade in, an their smells o polish an pent, wie wir ain hoose. Best avaa wis faan the big fouk waur deen newsin an it wis suppertime, except that faan we wis awa fae hame it wis tea, nae supper. 'Hiv ye washed yer hauns, David?' some aunties speired, ye wad hae thocht they'd noticed I'd been hine awa fae the kitchen sink aa efterneen. Some aunties aye hid biled ham an lettuce, especially lettuce, they must hae been gey prood o't, there wis sae muckle o't. Some hid breid an cheese, an they cuttit the cheese up intae skelfs for ye, juist tae coont foo mony ye wad rax for. Some-times there wis meat loaf wie salad cream an beetroot, an eggs biled tull they stotted aff yer plate faan ye tried tae haaver em. Wir uncles said, faan we sat doon, 'Stick in , noo, tull ye stick oot!' an we nott nae second tellin, mindin aye tae tak a slice o loaf wie the biled ham or the meat loaf tae add ballast tull't afore the scones or bannocks, syne last avaa, faan we wis ower stappit wie lettuce tae dee justice tae them, the fancy cakes or shortbreid or gingerbreid. Some aunties made Dinnes tae, wie stemm yoamin up fae't, bit some likit it as wyke as sinburned watter an ye could read the papers throwe't. Bit the jams in their gless saacers wis a bonus, ilka jam wie its ain speen: straaberries like saft bools glazed wie sweetness, rasps wie their gritty seeds that stuck ahin yer teeth, or jeelies like the rodden jeely, wauble an spluttery.

Some simmer nichts we'd heid for Knaven tae see Sandy Broon an Babsie an their birn o bairns. We played hide an sik in the corn-yard or the barn, syne faan the gloamin gaured ye tummle ower the trams o barras we gaed inside tae the kitchen an the meneer o

Babsie's washin. She hid a tow for weet hippens hard tee tae the
fireside, a tow for dry claes in the far neuk, a pile here o rippit breeks
wytin tae be darned an a pile there o fite semmits wytin tae be
ironed. The kitchen bizzed like a wasps' byke faan we wis aa
thegither in't – quines kecklin an loons fechtin an the little eens
wie spurtles giein pot-lids laldy. Sandy wad roar fyles 'Haud yer
wheesht, ye orra weeds!' an it wad be quaet, syne, for a half-meenit
or so, the time it took aabody tae get their win back afore they
started again. She wis a lauchin, cheery deem Babsie, there wis
naething got the better o her an ye wad hae thocht that aa the bairns
she hid wis juist a recipe for bein joco. Sandy watched the fitba-
teams that cam tae play at New Deer fyles, he kent faat he wis
spikkin aboot faan he tell't Dad faat the Dons wis up tull an faar
they could improve some.

    Ae nicht at Knaven Sandy brocht ben a rare contraption fae the
endroom: a euphonium. Faar he'd gotten't gweed kens, an faa's it
wis wis onybody's guess, bit he plunkit it doon on tae the kitchen
fleer an we'd aa tae tak a shottie at it tae see faa could mak a soon
come oot. It hid pipes an knobs an furly bits, an a muckle bell like
the biler o an ocean liner. We queued up at the moothpiece, lauchin
in ahin wir sleeves faan the neist een huffed and puffed at it an
nivver a squeak cam for aa their tribble. Een efter the tither, we wis
aa bett, an en Dad oxtered it an steekit his lips ticht an the euphonium gaed oot a blare like a foghorn, an for a blink o time the
kitchen at Hillheid wis struck dumb an we wis aa dusht, even the
little eens. 'Faat wye did ye dee that?' we speired, an Dad said it
wisna win that coonted nor the virr ye blew wie, it wis aa in the wye
ye made yer moo nerra, that wis the trick in't.

    We played fitba on the dryin-green at North Kidshill faan I
wearied o my ain company an held up the park tae see faat Tam wis
deein. We laid jaickets doon for goal-posts an Tam wad hotch fae ae
fit tae the ither in atween them, keekin fyles at his spellin-beuk tae
coont the ffs in 'difference' faan he wisna coontin foo mony goals
he'd latten in. Ae nicht we foregethert, Tam an To an me, doon at
the quarry-hole aside the burn at the mairches o wir laich park wie
Aul Joe's grun. We breenged up an doon the howes an hullocks for

a fyle, syne een o's said, faat wye did we nae try a fry-up? Hame I
gaed for a tattie or twa an a fyowe spunks, fykie wark nippin em fae
the box on the mantelpiece bit I managed it, an faan I won back
doon tae the quarry To hid a smaa dyke o steens biggit tae lat the fire
catch, an Tam hid firewid ready fae foggy fun busses. We kennled a
gweed bleeze, fixed a hub-cap fae a Wolseley on tae the spirkin
sticks, an sliced the tatties on till't. The tatties turned green. To said
it wis fat we winted bit I wis loth tae play the reiver twice an caa
aboot for't in the kitchen-press, I'd deen fine wie the spunks bit fat
wis chuncy. So we kickit the green tatties oot o the hub-cap an
trumpit the aise tae pooder, an lookit roon for a new ploy. We ruggit
roosty pails an ile-drums an broken frames o bikes an connached
tyres up oot o the quarry howe tae the tapmaist lip o the bankin an
coupit the haill rickle doon tae the boddom again.

We played fitba, Andy an me, nearly ilka mornin, faan I gaed tae
Methlick in the simmer-time tae bide wie Nan an Andra in their
hoose at Blackcraig Cottages. The Park wis juist a shortsome dander
ben the road an roon the corner, ower the Ythan, syne throwe the
hedge an we waur there, on the laich side o the village wie the kirk
an kirkyard at the far side. We gaed on tae the teem pitch an made
on we wis playin for the Dons, een o's in the goal (wie real goal-
posts) an the tither een takkin penalties, syne we swappit for a fyle
an got wir ain back, there wis nae quarter socht nor offered. If the
Tawse twins cam doon we kent we wis in for't – they waur fitba-
daft the pair o them, as keen as mustard; they hid short haircuts an
short socks an legs like laarick. They could hit the baa twice as hard
as me, so they waur weel-named: bein goalie faan the twins waur
firin shots at ye wis juist like gettin doses o the tawse, baith hauns at
eence; that made yer fingers stoon. I got wysed up efter a fyle, an I
fluffed ilka save. It didna maitter that I hid tae rin half-wye tae Fyvie
tae get the baa back, at least I still hid aa my fingers.

Gey aften, though, Andy an me hid the pitch aa tae wirsels. It wis
weel kept, aye cutted smooth an even, an the lines easy tae mak oot
fae the saadust they pit doon for the games the local teams played.
The bare grun in front o the goals wis probbit, ilka inch o't, bi the
studs worn bi the big lads. Gin a dyowe lay on the girss or a puckle

rain cam on the baa got sappy an the weet gaed throwe the ledder, an we hid tae lat the panels dry an syne we clarted on the Dubbin. Ae day, faan the Tawses hid made their usual tally – echteen goes, echten goals – Andy pinted tae the New Deer road an said – 'Ere's een o the new buses' an I lookit up an saa this gleamin length o gless snoove by. 'It's caa'd a pan-loaf' said Andy, an sure eneuch the bus wis blunt-nosed and flat at the front-en, there wis nae cab poukin oot an nae snoot faar the injine should hiv been. So like a feel I said 'Faar's the driver then?' an Andy keckled an said losh, he wis in the back seat haein his fly. Andra took the team fae Methlick tae Rosehearty for a game ae nicht, an we gaed wie them for the hurl. Aa the players gaed tae the pub efter the match tae slocken their drooths so we wis late hame that nicht, Andra hid a hard time o't gettin em roadit again.

Andy said they caa'd him Tiger at the Methlick skweel, an I wis teen wie that, yon wis a name tae be prood o. I'm sure Andy wis prood o't, for like as no he'd made it up tae tak the len o me an I wis neen the wiser. His best gag wis faan he said the quine neist door hid latten him see her sair leg. She wis fifteen, maybe saxteen, an we couldna keep oor een aff o her faan she gaed birlin by on her bike or faan she walkit doon Blackcraig Road makkin on she didna ken we wis faain ower wirsels keekin at her fae ahin the tool-shed or throwe the honeysuckle. We tell't een anither faat a dish she'd be in een o yon black goons the quines in the 'Reveille' wore, aa cleavages an bare shooders. We didna ken faat a cleavage wis bit we'd read it somewye an we thocht it hid a hint o danger aboot it. Onywye, Andy said it eence an en he said it twice, he'd seen her sair leg. Like a flech tull a bricht licht I loot masel get gulled an drawn. I speired faar she'd hurted hersel, faar on her leg, an Andy keckled a bit an said it wis abeen the knee. 'Foo faar?' I speired, my een like gobstoppers. 'Oh, I couldna tell ye that,' says Andy, as sober as a kirk elder. 'Na, that widna dee, she's an awfu quine, ye ken' an like a gype I believed him.

Efter supper-time at Methlick, faan I wis doon at Andy's for the holidays in the simmer-time, we gaed oot a bike-run, ben the Haddo Hoose road an up throwe side-roads an single-tracks an hine awa, neen the twa a's wintin tae be first tae say that maybe we should louse an pint the guys back tae Blackcraig for fear o gettin stucken on the road wie nae lichts. Andy wad say 'C'mon min, we'll cut ower here bi Tyanglinford an we'll be hame bi dark'. I hid ma doots aboot it bit we crankit the pedals tull the posts of the palins wis a blur on ilka side o's an we won hame *after* it wis dark, like we baith kent we wid. A cat's lick an we wis beddit, still pechin but fair trickit wie wirsels: doos croo-croo'ed fae the black an secret wid abeen wir gaivel, an the granfather clock i the lobby trimmed the lang day doon tull there wis neen o't left.

Andy nivver cam his leen tae Kiddies bar the eence, faan he bikit up fae Methlick for a day wie's. Seen's he wis in aboot I winnered faat I'd dee wie him, faat I could show him, foo I could make him feel I'd aye the best o't, though I hidna aa his advantages. Foo could I gaur him wish he wis a country chiel like me? The mair I thocht aboot it the mair I winnered: he hid aathing we didna hae, he hid the electric, he hid a bath an laavie, he hid the Park. We hid parks. Parks o tatties, parks wie nowt, parks wytin for the binder, a park wie an aul quarry an a wheen rubbits. I took him doon tae the quarry, tae prove foo thrang wie wildlife my domain could be, bit neither hide nor hair o the wild life wis on show that mornin, the rubbits maun hae gottin wird we wis appearin. I took him tae the burn neist, bit it wisna near saw braw as his braid Ythan. So I tried a desperate tack an took ma claes aff an lay doon in the watter, bit Andy yawned an said I'd catch ma death o flu, an I wis mair nor half-wye sure he hid a pint there. I thocht o the aul mull in the barn, or the strae-shed, faar rats reeshled in ahin the bunches or joukit ben the jists an couples. We snooved in like poachers: 'Caa canny, noo,' I hissed atween my teeth. 'I've deen this afore.' Something meeved. 'Tell't ye!' I said, an syne I saa it wis a dozy hen haudin her heid sidewyes like her neck wis sair. I wished we hid a calfie we could clap or else a sheltie we could kaim, pups tae play wie, a bull tae be feart o, onything. Foo could I tell him foo my wealth wis measured oot in neuks an hidey-holes, secrets naebody wad wint tae ken except masel; foo could I show him, in the hicht o simmer, faar I aimed my snaa-baas at the apex o the garage gaivel, an faat wid he mak o't gin I pinted tae the lowssest slate abeen the corrugated-iron reef o the strae-shed, faar I made on I wis a commando? Faan it cam tull't I wis loth tae lat him ken there wis a place in aa the ferm faar I wis laird an maister, my place – the laft abeen the neep-shed wie its bench an its tapsalteerie smyteral o trock, seerup tins o booed nails, staved hinges, boxes wintin lids, locks wintin keys, gless, roosty files, door-knobs, stourie bottles, staples, teem jam-jars, pent-brushes hard as stookie, an best avaa, a vice. The laft wis like a cave tae me faar I wis Long John Silver an faat I happened on wis pirates' gowd: up there in its mochy, foosty air I wis an engineer, an inventor, a dictator an a hermit. So I said tae Andy we wid hae a scone instead, an we gaed inside: I kent oor scones could haud their heids up wie onything fae Methlick ony day, or Ellon come tae that.

2

'The thin crop is on the iron rock.
The field glitters like a new coin.

This is the land without myth.'

GEORGE BRUCE: *A Land Without Myth*

'What kind of light do the stars have, would you say?'

We steed roon him in the Dominie's room. Mr Milne wis at his desk. It wis awfu quaet. The Dominie wis makkin on he wis writin; ilka squeak o his cheer made a soon like a roosty barra wie a wonky wheel.

'Well. Would you say they shone, or they sparkled?'

We glowered at him. We nivver thocht aboot stars verra muckle. Mr Milne opened a draaer: the mannie wyted. We lookit at his saft hauns an his fite nails. He wis a toonser, we kent fine, he wis weerin a suit.

'Maybe we could say they glow, don't they?' We noddit wir heids. This wis better: the Inspector wis deein some o his ain wark noo. Fremmit fowk like him could fair snorl ye up. We hid it fixed in oor heids, onywye, that bein socht on tae the fleer awa fae wir desks wis likely tae be the signal that a test wis comin, or a check-up, or we wis being brocht tae book for something. It hid taen me a lang time tae cower faat happened ae day faan we wis staunin roon Ma Wilson's desk wie wir readin-beuks, like a bourach o Oliver Twists, heids doon, like we wis wintin something bit we wis ower feart tae say faat it wis. We wis deein a story aboot a hurted wyver, an the peer beastie wis gey far throwe wie't; it wis nearly deid faan it wis my turn, so I peched some an habbered oot the wyver's pairtin wirds aneth my braith. 'What's wrong with you?' Mrs Wilson speired. 'I can't hear you.' I said the wyver wis juist aboot deid an at wis aa it could manage. Mrs Wilson wisna ower taen wie me.

Fan I wis readin Mam's beuks fae the skweel library, though, I

9

wad speir at Mr Milne faat some o the wirds meant, especially the
German wirds in *Boldness Be My Friend.* I wyted tull denner-time
faan the lave wis skailin, throwe tae Rosie Burnett's room. 'Pleezir,
faats a Nazzy?' Mr Milne said ye said it wie a shairp zed, it wis Natsi.
Neist day it wid be a notice in the concentration camp, like Rauchen
Verboten. I aye kept a spare question handy, in case the first een wis
ower easy an ower seen by wie. A haill sentence o German wirds wis
juist the ticket – 'In der nacht sind alle katzen grau'. In the night all
cats are grey, he said. He haunled ilka question, even the een aboot
rape. 'Pleezir, faat's rape?' I speired. Day efter day I deaved him,
either wie some poetry o my ain or wie Richard Pape tryin tae win
awa fae the Natsis.

Oor postie hid been a P.O.W. oot East somewye; he wis gien's a
haun ae day tae get the hey in an he speired gin I wad rin an tak a
suppie caul watter tull him. I forgot tae dee't bit Dad cam up tull's an
said tae rin tae the hoose, an bluidy quick, man, did I nae ken Jack
hid been a prisoner o the Japs an it wis thirst that ailed him? The
magazines wie shiny photographs in the railway cerriage hid picters
o the war time, Hitler an his generals at tea-parties weerin cheese-
cutter bonnets an beets that polished they waur mair like wellintons
faan ye wyded throwe the slush wie em, bricht an bleckit. The
Dominie said the Second War wis in the history beuks an ye could
read aboot it like the times lang seen. I thocht history wis aa tae dee
wie days gey near forgotten, bit there wis history that dreebled oot
in dribs an drabs fae the wireless, names like Korea an the Mau-
Mau, fouk like Eisenhower an Churchill, Marilyn Monroe an Ruth
Ellis.

We wis cuttin hey this nicht in the park abeen the steadins, Dad
an me an Uncle Willie, the detective fae the toon. The mower
whirred an birred its wye roon the squaur shape o the crap, an as the
gloamin fell the squaur wis gettin aye the smaaer in the middle o the
park. I spied a rubbit hirplin doon the bout wie his back legs
mangled, he'd cooried doon aneth the blade an didna bolt in time:
Willie catched him an brook his neck. Faan it wis dark we lowsed an
gaed awa doon tae the kitchen tae the lichted lamp an the scones an
the newsin; the big fowk waur spikkin aboot something caa'd a

reprieve an wid it come afore the morning, an I jaloosed that nicht wis the last chunce for Ruth Ellis. She wis due tae hang for sheetin somebody. There wis a stramash, tee, faan the Bentley case wis on an fowk waur sair made tae mak oot faa hid fired a gun an faa hidna. It wis echt o'clock in the morning that a hanging happened; at nine o'clock the news on the wireless said that so-an-so hid been executed an fyles the mannie mentioned that a puckle fowk hid steed at the jile yetts haudin signs an banners cryin doon the death penalty an Bible texts aboot Vengeance is Mine, saith the Lord.

We gaed tae the Kirk in Methlick, Nan an Andy an me, faan I wis doon at Blackcraig Cottages for my holidays. We steed in the livin-room wytin for the expedition tae get on the go: sheen brushed, hair kaimed, pan-drops in ae pooch an a saxpence in the tither. The saxpence wis a prisoner: it wis for the plate. Nan speired for the tenth time gin we hid clean hankies on's, syne it wis time tae leave. We walkit ben the pavement douce-like, wie the deegnity of Christians. Doon ablow's the pitch wis thrang wie the ghaists o centre-forrits, left-backs an wingers, the air loud wie roars o victory an disappintment. Inside the kirk I sat dumb an watched the fowk come in: they waur dumb tee, fyles noddin faan they saa somebody bit timoursome, as though they'd aa been in an accident an they nott some time tae cower't. It wis a relief faan the meenister cam in, bit I could see straicht aff faat fowk wis gettin at faan they spak aboot him bein 'nae awfu strong, the man' – he hid a chiel tae cairry in the Bible for him. Up he gaed intae the poopit, the mannie sneckit him in, and there wis silence again. I lookit up tae see faat the meenister wis deein, bit there wis nae sign o him. Syne, he powkit his heid up an sat still tull the organ wis quaet, an we waur up an singin. Faan he said we'd say the Creed I wis sair made, aaitherbody kent faat tae dee except me. So I made on I wis sayin't, raxin my moo fae side tae side like I did faan I'd a caramel stucken in my back teeth. I hopit there wisna a penalty for bein the ootlin. Aabody sat doon again wie a pech an a reeshle, the men in dark suits an the weemin in lang cwytes that happit them fae their thrapples tae their cweets. There wis new smells here, new things tae notice – moth-baas an fooshty beuks, the boords aneth yer sheen, the bonny

whorls o the timmer pews. Lord Aiberdeen fae Haddo Hoose cam
an read the Lessons fyles, bit he'd a saft wird and he wad gie a
crochle noo an again, so ye wad miss maybe faat the Philistines hid
deen tae the Amalekites, the coorse deils that they waur. Aabody
sat an hearkened tull him though, like raas o powsers wytin for a
moose tae start; they saved their hoasts up tull he wis deen, it wis the
same wie the prayers – faan the 'Amen' cam there wis a chorus o
barks and bowffs fae ilka airt. Faan the kirk skailed we shook hauns
wie the meenister an gaed ower the road tae get *The Sunday Post* an
hame again. Lord Aiberdeen wis driven back tae Haddo Hoose in
his big car wie the muckle mudgairds an the spare wheel aneth the
wee back windae.

Mam's brither Jim wis chief fireman wie the Ellon Fire Brigade,
an ae Christmas Eve they wis socht ower tae Haddo Hoose tae pit
oot a bleeze i the laird's quarters. They got on tap o things gweed
style, bit he wis black-affronted, the Laird, at crying them oot on sic
a nicht an he wid hae nae refusals bit they wid aa be gweed eneuch
tae tak a dram wie him. So the firemen got a gless o fussky, an seein
foo the first een gaed doon they'd anither een tae be sociable an syne
it wis gey late bit there wis time for a last tooshtie, syne they wis
ready for the road. The Laird shook Jim's haun an thankit him for
their attendance, an he said again foo annoyed he wis at himsel for
takkin them awa fae hame an brakkin up their evenin, bit Jim shook
his heid at that an said he wad hae neen o't – 'Na, na, sir,' he said,
'Yon's the best bluidy fire we've been at in a lang time!'

Ye hid tae watch, fyles, faat ye said tae the Dinnes uncles, they
hid nearly aa the same sense o humour in them, quick an clivver wit
that could mak something oot o naething ataa. Mam said faan they
waur little, on the craft near Fyvie, they wad sit astride the dyke on a
simmer evenin i the gloamin, chaffin een anither an scorin aff a faat
they said, an it wis aye Tom that hid the better o his brithers. He wis
a fairm servant noo, doon Udny wye, bit he hidna tint neen o his
swackness faan it cam tae raggin somebody or cowpin onything they
said tae get a lauch oot o't. There wis a brand o saut, Saxa they caa'd
it, so Tom wad say tae fowk that faan he made his brose he likit sax
speens o meal and sax a saut. They aye fell for't an tell't him he wis

some sair wie the saut, surely, sax speens, min? an syne he hid them.
'Foo's the warld treating ye, Tom?' aye got the same answer –
'Gey seldom, man.' If ye wis daft eneuch tae speir if he wis a hivvy
smoker he wid shak his heid an say 'Na, juist eleiven steen . . . twal,
fyles, wie my beets on'. If ye gaed him bocht jam on a scone or a
bannock Tom wis bound tae say faat a treat it wis tae get the richt
hame-made stuff, naething wis as tasty. The mair sober an serious
his face grew, the mair ye could be sure there wis a topper comin. 'I'm
richt fed up wie secks,' he wad come awa wie, liftin his tae-cup tull
his moo. 'Foo's at, Tom?' said my father, as lood as possible, as if
my mither hidna heard richt. Doon gaed the cup again an he raxed
for a fresh scone. 'I've been baggin tatties aa wik, Jim,' he said.
'Secks, secks, secks.'

Juist as fowk said ye got twa heats oot o firewid – een faan ye
hackit it an the tither een faan ye brunt it – we got twa skelps o fun
fae a gweed joke: eence faan we first heard it an en again faan we
tell't it tae somebody. Jokes at concerts wis passed roon efterhin, an
some jokes appeared oot o thin air as though the win hid cairied
them. There wis een aboot a wifie that hid taen tull her bed an the
doctor cried in tae see her wie his young assistant wie him, an the aul
doctor gaed the wifie a richt gweed gyaun-ower; he sooned her an he
gaured her pit her tongue oot, he flashed a licht intil her een an took
her temperature. Syne he drappit the thermometer and he hid tae
hunker doon tae get a haud o't, an as seen's he'd gotten't he steed up
and said 'There's juist ae thing the maitter wie ye, Mistress, an it's
this, ye'll be as richt as rain gin ye wadna dee sae muckle for the
kirk'. Awa they gaed an the young chiel wis stammergasted: 'Foo
did ye come tae sic a clivver diagnosis' he speired, an the aul man
said 'I saa the meenister aneth the bed faan I drappit the thermometer!' An en there wis the fairmer doon fae Fetterangus tae the
Hiclan Show in Edinburgh an bidin in a hotel wie a hunner rooms or
so. He wis gettin ready for his bed an fulled his het watter bottle,
laid it in aneth the covers an gaed doon the lobby tae the laavie.
Weel, the aul chiel wis kinna dottled kin, an he tint himsel in sic a
braw hotel, bit he cam tull his ain door again, or so he thocht, an he
wis juist aboot tae daunder in faan he heard fowk spikkin, an they

wis on their honeymoon – faat sorra ither? an the man wis saying 'And whose hair is this, my sweet?' an the quine said 'Yours, darling' and the man said 'And whose sweet face is this, my love?' an the quine said 'Yours, darling', an the man said 'And whose shoulders are these, my angel?' and the quine said 'Yours darling' an the aul fairmer couldna stop himsel bit he roared throwe the key-hole 'If ye wark yer wye ony farrer doon an ye come on a het-watter bottle, 'ats mine!'

The bee story got the better o me, tull Mam tell't me faat the funny side o't wis. This bee bizzed aboot ae day an syne it launed on a tansy, faar it fell asleep. Efter a meenit or so by comes this donkey en etts the tansy wie the bee still sleepin on't, bit faan the bee woke up the donkey wis awa. Fowk leuch an said 'Aye, aye, juist at' faan they heard it, an I winnered faat it wis I wis missin in the story, I could see naething tae lauch at. A haill lot o fowk leuch a lot mair nor I did, especially on the wireless faan Ken Platt wis on, they wis roarin their heids aff an the kist o the wireless wad be rummlin wie the soon they made, bit it wis aa gyaun by me, or the maist o't onywye. 'The Glums' wis a bit better, I wis able tae get intae the swing o things faan the aul man stuck his big tae intae the bath-tap an he couldna get it oot again, bit he widna lat onybody come near him tae help him until he'd teemed a packet o gravy-pooder intae the bath-water tae disguise his predicament. Aul Glum's sin, Ron wis an awfu dreep o a chiel, an he wis coortin Ethel bit he nivver caa'd her that, it wis juist Eth. She wis gey near as gormless as he wis, bit ye hid tae feel sorry for em baith, their biggest handicap wis Mr Glum himsel, he wis aye spilin things an showin his brocht-upness, drinkin tae fae his saucer an heuken his thooms intil his galluses, an riftin like a fog-horn.

Faan Uncle Bob wis posted tae the police hoose in New Aberdour we tasted television, Hilda an me, even though it wis at ae remove. The big fowk waur newsin, an Bob said a TV hid come tae Aberdour. 'G'wa an see't,' he said till's, 'It's juist doon the street a bittie.' We said we didna like, we wisna keen tae keek intil a hoose like at. 'Aabody else daes,' said Bob, so that made it respectable, we could say the bobbie hid sent us. So we creepit doon the line o hooses tull we cam tae the richt een, an sure eneuch we saa the squaur kist blinkin in the corner, the curtains wis wide open an we could glower richt in. We leaned sidewyes tae see if the mannie wis at hame, an we wisna disappinted, he wis sittin watchin us watchin him watchin TV.

3

'As busy's a bonnetmakker, smith?' cried Mains.
'Waar nur ony bonnetmakker, Mains,' replied the
smith. . . . 'Sic an unco fash a' this makkin o' new keengs
an' sic wastrifeness o' gweed horse sheen. . . .'
                    WILLIAM P. MILNE: *Eppie Elrick*

Twirr bade in a craft ahin the shop at Nethermuir, an he socht Dad
ower tae cut up a pile o half-backs wie him ae Setterday in October.
We loaded up the circular saa on tae the cairt an aff we set. The saa
blade wis like a bike-wheel, boxed in the centre o a timmer frame,
except of course it wis solid, polished steel that we drave wie a lang
belt wuppit roon the drum on the Fordson. Faan the tractor wis
caain the belt richt the teeth on the blade furled an blurred an the
saa yammered like a banshee; it could ett wid wie a glegsome relish.
We hottered ower tae Twirr's, an the twa o them linkit at it, Twirr
haunin timmer up tae Dad an him feedin the saa squaur on tae the
howlin blade. I dandered aboot, powkin my neb intae Twirr's
neep-shed an laft tull he got scunnered watchin me and he dug a
florin oot o his pooch an said tae ging an get masel a poke o caramels
fae the shop. They waur near deen wie the half-backs bi this time:
aff I gaed tae the shop an got my sweeties, an I wis juist aboot in
sicht o the twa men again faan I heard Twirr lattin oot a scraich. I
raced roon the gaivel o the steadin tae see Dad staunin lookin doon
at his left haun, ye wid hae thocht he hid a reid glove on. My heid an
my beets hid a short argument, an my beets won: I raced awa roon
the neuk, nae able tae mak heid nor tail o't bit I kent it didna look
good. Faat hid happened? Foo bad wis't? I tell't masel I hid imagined
it. It wis nae eese: it wis ower real. Efter a meenit or so a car started
an took aff doon the road, so I kent faat they waur deein, they waur
awa tae New Deer tae the doctor, an he wid mak it aa richt. They
wid seen be back. Efter an oor or so I wis fair famished, stairvin an
twice as feart as I'd been afore. The caul nip o evening wis coming

on an it wis growin darker bi the meenit. I ran hame at the double and met Mam lookin for's at the kitchen door.

It cam oot later on faat hid happened tae them faan they made New Deer. The doctor wisna in so they'd haen tae ging tae Maud, bit the Maud doctor widna tak Dad on seein he wisna een o his patients. So there wis naething for't bit tae ging straicht tae the Cottage Hospital in Peterheid. Twirr drave like the haimmers, roarin doon the road tae the Blue Toon wie the choke full oot, skirling 'Keep i heid, Jimmy, keep i heid!' Dad sat an held his haun steady: the saa hid gotten him faar the thoom jines the loof, it wis hinging bi a threid he said, he could wag it back an forrit like the tassel on a toorie. They kept him in ae nicht at the Cottage Hospital, efter shooin up the disaster area. Alec Riddoch fae Cyarnies cam ower tae see that Mam wis aa richt, an syne Dad wis hame again. His thoom wis stiff an awkward, for a fyle, like he'd staved it, bit he wis gled o't for aa that. Fowk got the haill story faan they cried in, an he wid gaur them grue faan he spak aboot his thoom blawin in the win aa the wye tae Peterheid, an Twirr yelpin on tull him tae keep the heid: it wid hae been mair like the thing, Dad said, gin he'd tell't him tae keep his thoom.

We drave yowes at the dippin time ower tae Nethermuir an up tae Davie Will's place at Chapelstones, Capels as we caa'd it. It wis a gweed traivel, doon by the Dawson's tae the line an up by the wid-side, bit ye'd a new stick tae cut for't tae gie ye wecht an authority in case a yowe brook lowss fae the ticht knot o sheep an made aff her leen: it wis like watchin a pot hotterin, herdin a wheen yowes, ye wis nivver sure the breets widna yoam up ower the nerra lip o the track they waur keppit in. They waur penned at Capels, wytin their turn tae ging ben the throwe-gang doon tae the dip-troch; men riggit oot in ileskins haved them intac the reamin faem o watter that wis neither green nor yalla bit a mixter o the twa, syne they sprachled back on tae their fower feet on dry grun an steed an shook themsels like weet collies, ull-nettered at their drookin an the wye they'd haen their feet caa'd fae them. The bobby steed an took it aa in bit he didna dee naething, he kept weel clear.

We gaed the tither airt faan we nott the smiddy, doon tae Upper

Crichie faar Bill Keith wis. It wis a smaa factory, the smiddy, a warehoose an a stable an a post-office tee, for ye could be sure o news o some kin faan ye wis wytin for yer job tae be begun or feenished. I could hae watched Bill Keith aa day, watched his haimmer dirlin, duntin, tappin, stottin, watched the bellas souchin faan he fired up some heat tae get a daud o metal ready. Bill's tyangs cleekit reid iron fae the forge an heistit it tull his anvil, syne his haimmer swung an his airm's wecht gaed clinkety-clink intae the bouin o the het metal, twa dunts for the shape he winted, the antrin dunt on tae the anvil so's his wark wis mair nor breet micht, it wis a tune tee, a tune played in a race agin the meenit faan the iron tint its saftness an took on the dourness o bein cweeled ayont his pooer. He wis swack, syne, faan he nott tae be, bit he could staun easy faan it suited him, faan he wis wytin for the grey aise o the forge tae heeze intill an eident lowe. He wad newse wie the men ere, maybe een, maybe twa, aboot scandals, subsidies, the government or the price of Bogie. His braid face was blaikit like a sweep's, so that faan he leuch his teeth wis like a raa o snaa-baas sittin on a sleeper. Aa day he vrocht amon stemm an shunners, the smiddy door open tae the win: faan he shee'd a horse, though, he won ootside an his bonnet wad be aff an putten on again back tae front, he turned his back-side tae the muckle breet an fixed the hoof atween his knees, drivin hame the nails an newsin aa the time – faan the shoe was beddit ye wad hae thocht it grew there an aa he'd deen hid been tae faisten't some.

'The horse days is aa by, Jim' Bill wad say. 'Ony bugger noo could dee this.' Nae that lang seen they hid traivelled the pairs tull him on a halter, plooman an strapper, cairter an crafter. He'd been a leveller, the smith – the laird nott him juist the same as the five-echter wie the ae Clydesdale. Nae that lang seen Bill Keith wis in competeetion wie the ither smiddies, an he'd haen tae ken the wyes an naitturs o baith men an horses, mind things, ken things an forget them again for the sake o trade an gweed-wull: noo fowk left implements tae sort, twisted tines tae straichten, draa-bars tae splint, an it wis aa ae sizzen, month in, month oot. Nae that lang seen he wis the maister o his teels, he haunled them an they waur juist as able, juist as skeely as his strength wis: nails an rasp-files,

knives an tyangs – noo the teels grew some, the oxy-acetylene wie
its nozzles an its cylinders, its taps an pipes.

Even so, the aul wirds men brocht tae their horses they brocht still
tae their motors an their antics. Gin a car's tyres wis in gweed nick
fowk said it wis 'weel shod'. Faan a young birkie tried tae turn a
quine's heid an keep her saft on him, an he started giein her sweeties
or a box o chocolates, fowk said he wis at the 'cornin' – spilin her
the wye horsemen fed their beasts a tasty ripp noo an again. If a man
an his wife got on fine thegither they wis 'weel yokit'. An faan ye
brocht somebody intae line again, or ye took the win oot o their sails
some, or ye boxed them in so that they couldna throw their wecht
aboot, that wis 'pittin the hames' on them. Fowk sang still aboot the
Horseman's grippin wird, aboot the pooer it gaed ye tae control
horses an weemin; the weemin sang aboot it tee, for they kent foo
true it wis in ae respect onywye.

The time cam faan they fan oot I nott glesses. That wis a come-
doon, me an Tam Dawson gyaun tae Savoch an gettin draps in wir
een, an him bein latten aff scot-free: they sent me specs wi thin wiry
legs tae wup roon ahin my lugs. Ae day I wis like aa the lave: the
neist I wisna, I'd been disqualified fae the britherhood o game
chiels, the buirdly lads. The glesses divided me fae the ither loons,
as gin I wis less hardy than they wis, waar nor at, they divided me fae
my heroes in the comics an the magazines, the cowboys, an space-
men, an explorers in the jungle. Roy Rogers nivver yet hid tae
squint doon the barrel o his six-gun afore he pumped the baddies
foo o leed. Captain Condor didna zoom throwe the birlin planets,
sort oot the trauchles o a lanely space-station an still get hame afore
supper-time weerin specs aneth his helmet. The glesses wis a badge
I didna wint – Stirling Moss, and Mike Hawthorn or Fangio fae the
Argentine, they hid goggles on, nae glesses, faan they drave their
sleek cars tae fame an glory. Stanley Matthews hidna glesses on faan
he bamboozled Bolton Wanderers at Wembley, passin the baa tae
Bill Perry tae mak the score 4-3 for Blackpool.

Tainted wie the mark o the scholar, syne, I hid nae choice. it wis
aa richt noo tae ken some lang wirds, I wisna ony eese at onything
else. If I loot slip something fae the Newnes Pictorial Knowledge

that I hid nae business kennin, or waar still, that I'd nae eerin tae lat
on I kent, it wis juist pruif that I wis funny that wye, tae be tholed an
peetied. Mr Milne gaed's a composition oot, we hid tae write aboot
a fairmer that wis hame early for his supper ae day an it wisna ready
for him, so the gowk said faat an easy life a wumman hid an he could
easy manage aye tae get throwe his wife's wark in half the time she
did it, an she said she wad change places wie him ony day. She wad
sit on the tractor nae bother if he bade inside like she hid tae dee, an
we wis tae write foo the chiel kept the hoose a haill day. I fair
enjoyed that een: I hid Sandy in a richt sotter, drappin ornaments
faan he tried tae wheech the duster roon em, pittin the lum up wie
ower muckle coal on the fire, leavin pots on the stove sae lang they
biled dry an the denner wis connached. I thocht the fairmer wad be
gey sair made at aa the soss he'd launed in, so I hid him sweirin tull
himsel some, tae be true tae life, like, bit Mr Milne said although it
was authentic it wisna weel advised.

There wis a competeetion fae the Prevention o Cruelty tae
Animals: I wrote an essay for em an they gaed me *Ray of the
Rainbows.* Back hame, in the blue exercise beuk fae Taylor's shop,
I wis draain spaceships an startin up The Hungry Horace Club, wie a
membership o three – Sheila Dawson, Tam Dawson an me. He wis
aye rakin aboot, Horace, for the odd cake that naebody wad miss
oot o the pantry, or bananas, or Swiss rolls dreepin wie jam. The
Club wis nae eese tull's if it hidna secrets, codes for messages an
pass-wirds, an a Club motto. There wis three slogans I wis keen on
for a badge tae weer – 'Yield Not' wis the favourite, an en 'There's
Always Tomorrow' an last avaa 'Good Luck'. I drew them in pencil,
wie a special code for keepin aa wir onygauns weel hidden, bit the
code wis a bittie ower special because eence I'd invented it I could
mak neither heid nor tail o't. I wrote drafts o letters tae the Editor o
the *Lion,* an drafts o thank-you letters tae my aunties in the toon. I
tell't the *Lion* mannie that my pals thocht the *Lion* badge wis mostly
great, syne I scored oot 'mostly' in case he thocht I wis takkin the len
o him. The letter tae Daffy wis only five lines, an it feenished up wie
'This note could have been longer but we have no paper'. The
Dawsons wisna keen on the Hungry Horace Club like I wis, so I said

I wad keep the official journal for em an fill in the details o adventures an so on. There wis juist ae page wie ony Club news an even than, it wis juist ae line – 'Club going on. House built for Club'. The Hungry Horace gang led a quaet life, an naething happened tull's; efter a wik or so we wis nae mair, bit I missed the feelin o conspiracy an the sleekitness of haein something private, something shared bit kent only tae the three o's. I wis ower weel acquant wie my ain company at times, an I cast aroon fyles fir new wyes tae full a teem oor or so.

We made a rare swing, Hilda an me, in the strae-shed faar the reef wis laich an the couples near eneuch: we loopit twa tows fae the reef aboot ten feet fae een anither an tied em ticht so's they hung doon an equal distance fae the fleer. Syne we got a lang boord fae somewye an threidit it inside the loops so that it made a gran seat for showdin on, een o's at ilka en, back an forrit. Faan I wis sair made for a ploy tae keep me oot o langer I wad hunt up a stoot stick, as straicht as possible, wie a comfy grip at the en I held it wie; I geddert smaa steens the size o doos' eggs an made a pile o em, syne I held the stick oot in ae haun, placed a steen on the thick en o't, an the contest wis aa ready. The idea wis tae fling the steen up i the air fae the stick's surface, syne bring up my left haun tae jine the richt een, keepin my ee steady on the steen (on its wye doon bi noo) an swing the stick at the richt speed tae gie the steen a clout that made it fussle throwe the air an dirl on tae the byre reef. A gweed knap made the slates shak, or so I thocht: ye could aye tell faan ye missed, onywye, there wad be nae soon tae register foo gweed the hit hid been.

Ilka picter I could see at the Gatt hall on a Setterday nicht gaed me new material for the dramas I could pit masel in, playin the hero withoot costume or falderals an nae extras, nae audience either; aa I nott wis tae mine foo Alan Ladd hid lookit faan hc wis up against it, baith revolvers teem an his horse shot fae in aneth him. The Frank Sinatra picters wis nae eese tull's, bit the war stories like *Above Us The Waves* or *The Dambusters* gaed me plenty scope; there wis the odd funny picter I could pinch bits o, like the een faar a chiel poukit his fork intil a tattie and held it up afore his een an said 'Is this a dagger that I see before me?' I could see that gyaun doon a treat at skweel denners in Clochcan, gin the chunce cam. Errol Flynn in *The Master o Ballantrae* wis ae picter that I tint masel in, I wis gey lucky tae see't avaa, the wye it happened. I wis doon at Methlick, an my holiday wis nearly deen. Andy an me gaed tae see a picter in the Beaton Hall, an a trailer for *The Master o Ballantrae* cam on, wie sojers in braw tunics, horses an Hielanders, sword-fechts an so on, the haill clamjamfry. I wis due back at Kidshill afore the picter wad be on at Methlick, an I kent we wad be hairstin so there wid be nae spare time for capers like the kin o thing that Errol Flynn got up till. I thocht aboot it aa the time, faan we wis reddin roads an gettin yokit intae binderin. I'd missed my chunce. Syne I noticed i the paper that *The Master o Ballantrae* wis comin on at the hall up in New Deer, only five mile awa. I kent Dad wad nivver stop in fair widder tae tak me tae the picters, bit I speired onywye an he hummed an hawed an said it wisna likely, nae if he wis hashin on wie the binder. So I kent there wis bit ae hope left an that wis coorse widder, rain preferably. Half-five on the day in question cam, an a shooer drookit staunin corn an cut corn alike. Dad said he'd pit in an oor wie Kate an Andra bit I wad hae tae sit maleen an watch the picter bi masel. I could hardly believe it: fae half-echt tae nine o'clock or so I wis Errol Flynn's, an the stooks wis a thoosan mile awa.

CHAPTER

4

'That was another o the times when Hugh Riddel had
felt insulated in a comfort of spirit. . . . Within hand's
touch of a world of men. Yet still safe onlooker, with the
voices of his father and his father's friends droning over
and round him.'   JESSIE KESSON: *Glitter of Mica*

If it hidna been it wis the deid thraa o winter − roads blockit, an the
hill cut aff, snaa driftin day efter day so that we couldna get oot o
Kidshill an the vans couldna get in − it wid nivver hae happened,
ten o'clock in oor kitchen, an fowk sittin wytin for the tae tae come
ben, Alec Smith an Mrs Smith, the Cadgers, an the Dawsons comin
ony meenit. I wisna there, I wis inveesible, sittin in the windae-
seat.

'Nae sign o't brakkin, onywye, so the mannie says.'

Faat mannie? − maun be the wireless mannie wie his forecasts.

'Aye, aye, ye widna ken faat tae mak o yon, its nae eese tae his,
faat he says.'

Fowk aye held tae the notion that a forecast o gweed widder wis
bound tae come true for aabody else, bit nae for onybody that bade
atween New Deer an Auchnagatt.

'Ah weel, there's a gweed mony in the same boat this time,
there's nae mony places hisna catched it.'

There's naething there that onybody can conter, so they keep
mum, its a deid-end.

'Faat aboot the boy, though, wie his bath wie milk in't?'

Aabody lauchs.

I glower at face efter face, tae see foo real this is. Is't true a
fairmer his been storin surplus milk oot o his dairy in his ain bath,
wytin for the Board tae come an get a larry throwe tull him? Nivver,
nivver . . . couldna be . . . syne I start tae think aboot it, aa his
churns is foo an he canna teem them, an the kye keep milkin, so faat
daes he dee wie't, he his tae keep it somewye. . . .

23

'Aye, bit the best o't is his wife hidin his last unce o Bogie so's he widna rin oot, eh?'

Mair lauchin.

'Be a bonny day faan that's the wye o't.'

So it *is* a story: nae wife keeps her man's Bogie for him. Wyte a meenit, though – faa buys the Bogie? it's the wife, usually, richt eneuch. So it wad be easy for her tae keep some back. . . .

Ben comes the big tae-pot, an I winner faat we'll hae tae ett: there'll be nae loaf-pieces because we're gey near oot o loaf, an we hinna seen a bap for a lang time. Faat'll Mam dee, I speir masel, an syne I spy a plate wie shortbreid – Christmas shortbreid, left ower fae a fyowe wiks ago faan naebody cam tull's on Hogmanay tae ett the Christmas stuff.

'Oh, this is rare. . . .'

'Ye shouldna hae deen that. . . .'

I try tae coont the shortbried, tae see if some'll be left ower for me. Aabody'll start aff bein prim, an syne they'll forget themsels an tak a second bit. Stemm climms fae the foo cups as they get passed roon.

'Milk, Alec?'

'If ye hiv't, like.'

'Dyod, man, we've a bath foo o't.'

Aabody lauchs. The shortbreid gings roon an disappears like snaa aff o a dyke.

'Sandy Meldrum gaed awfu quick, eh, Lord, he wisna nae weel mair nor a day or twa.'

Faat wye div fowk spik aboot death an illnesses faan they're ettin? It's aye the same: pit them doon at the table or gie them something tae chaa, an they start in on faa's nae weel, or faa's haen this or that tribble, or faa's deid.

'The thing is, he wis nivver strong, Sandy, I aye said he wadna claa a grey heid an it juist shows ye, he'd hae been echty-fower wis he? echty-five maybe?'

'Echty-five, easy. Faa's yon loon o his mairried on again, aye, Alfie, like?'

Alfie's nae loon, he's nearly fifty.

'Alfie? Jean Pratt, as wis. She wis Jean Pratt afore she got in tow wie Alfie. Jinty Pratt faan I kent her.'

If she wis Jean Pratt faan she mairried Alfie, faat wye wis she Jinty Pratt afore at?

'Aye, Jinty wid hae been at Maad faan you wis ere, wis she?'

'Michty aye, same class as me, man. Her fadder wis the grieve at Timmeryetts, wie Jock Dunlop, aye, Chae's fadder.'

'God, its a cyaard hole yon.'

'Aye, Chae didna thole't lang, best thing ivver he did, gyaun intae Greenmoss.'

'Chae still ere? I heard he wis awa fae ere noo.'

'Na, na, aye, the wife's awa, like.'

Faa'll wint tae ging farrer doon that road? Speir faar, an ye lat on ye dinna ken. Maybe aabody kens. There's a skelf o silence, onywye, so that leaves me mangin tae fin oot faar Chae's wife's gaen. Surely somebody's gyaun tae nail't doon. Surely somebody kens her name – bit maybe nae namin her keeps her oot o favour. If it wis her that gaed awa, that blecks her.

'It wis the traveller, wist?'

'Na faith, O God, ye'll nae get aff wie that een, she wid nivver gie a traveller the time o day. He wis the manager o the place, I think. Na, she wis ower gweed for a traveller.'

'O. Bit o side, wis ere?'

'Oh aye. She kent her ain worth aa richt, an Greenmoss wisna the size o her.'

'Aye, bit Chae wis a bit bigsy, ye ken, in his ain wye.'

'Oh, Chae wis a big, big man, bit a smaa cwyte fitted him.'

That's a gweed een. He wis a big, big man bit a smaa cwyte fitted him. A big, big man bit. . . .

'Faa's he gotten noo, than? His he gotten a pal yet?'

I thocht a pal wis somebody ye played hide-an-sik wie or gaed climmin trees wie. Faat wid Chae wint tae ging climmin trees for?

'Aye, there's some wird there's a deemie fae the Broch he's kirnin wie.'

Again, nae name. She maun be a richt jaud. There's a chap at the back door an Mam says that maun be Dod and Bet noo, she'll mak mair tae. In they come, reid-faced fae the win an fae the tchauve o pleiterin throwe drifts doon tae the corn-yard. Dod speirs if the van's here yet, though he kens fine there's been nae wheels in the close aa mornin.

'God'll michty, I thocht he wid hae been bi noo. I wis tellin Bet we'd missed him.'

'Na, he'll be hinnered aawye the day, wie fowk makkin up for nae haein him for a fylie.'

They mean Bill Robertson, in the van fae Taylor's in the 'Gatt. That's faat they're aa here for, wie teem pilla-cases an bags wie haunles, wytin for Bill tae come as far as his onywye, seein the road wis cassen juist tae lat him win oor wye. Aa efterneen yestreen we opened up twa channels for the van wheels, skimmin the deeper drifts ablow the hicht o his exles.

'He his the wecht ahin him, ony roads, surely tae God.'

Roon comes new shortbreid, an Dod taks a bit; Bet lichts a Woodbine. Either the Dawsons shift the focus noo, or the newsin cairries on as though their comin in hisna made for ony chynge o tack.

'Iss is gey near as bad as forty-seiven, iss.'

'Damn the bit, ye wad be sair made tae be as bad as aa that.'

'Na, forty-seiven wis a coorse een. . . .'

There's nae contest: aa lesser storms, aa tamer winters are brocht tae the bar o forty-seiven to pit forrit their ain degrees o coorseness, bit they faa short, some bi a lang wye. Ony comparison wie forty-seiven is an excuse, mainly, tae howk up memories an in a funny wye, tae tak the sting oot o faat's warst aboot *this* winter. Naething could be as hard tae thole as faat forty-seiven wis.

'It wis up ower the palins, mine, ye couldna see posts.'

'Aye, yon wis a nizzer, yon een.'

'Caul, did ye say! an sae lang o't, months mine, richt up tae the hinner en o Mairch. . . .'

'We walkit ben the tap o the dykes doon tae the 'Gatt, tae meet Presley's van, gweed kens foo we'd hae gotten butcher meat withoot the van. . . .'

'Lord aye, an Dickson comin up fae Aul Deer on his skis tae see tae somebody. . . .'

That's a picter tae haud on tull: Dr Dickson on skis.

'He wis a big chiel, tae, he maun hae hid them afore the bad snaa cam, aye, it wid hae been a sport for him, I wad say. . . .'

'Oh aye. Bit it wis the beasts ye felt sorry for, skitin on yon ice, haill sheets o't, mine, they couldna get purchase on't.'

'Some fowk lost a puckle kye that wye.'

'Some fowk lost mair, there wis a lassie smored wisn't there, walkin fae New Deer tae somewye.'

'The peer quine aye, she ran intae blin drift an that wis her.'

I'm thinkin aboot the Doctor on his skis. Faar did he cairry the black bag? He wis a big chiel, an a big cwyte fitted him . . . the mair i think aboot it the mair true it soons. Dickson widna hae latten a pucklie snaa stop him. For a meenit, syne, castin snaa wie shovels clarted wie caunle-wax disna seem as heroic as it did yestreen, bit I mine foo my shooders creakit faan I rase this mornin – snaa's nae sae lichtsome, nae faan ye're takkin on twa hunner yairds o't. Fower hunner yairds, onywye. Oh, easy. Say half a mile.

'Weel, Davie, ye're nae sayin naething.'

Fowk turn their heids. This is nae time tae say onything, faan ye've juist been singled oot for nae sayin onything. Mak on they're nae glowerin, wytin.

'Missin the skweel, eh, I can see ye're raill doon i the moo aboot it.'

Aabody lauchs. Wie a bit o luck, though, it'll blaw by an they'll get back tae winter-time, or death, or ailments.

'Missin the blonde, mair like, gin ye ask me.'

Mair lauchin. I wish I wisna here. Mam looks oot at the side windae.

'Nae sign o him, the vratch. Ye wid hae thocht he widda been here or noo.'

'Faat time is't onywye?'

'Oh, that clock's nae richt, it's aye faist, that een.'

Alec Smith powks in aneth his jaicket for his Ingersoll. They wyte for him tae read aff the message, as gin he'd been pickit for the job.

'Geen eleiven, though.'

'We've nae wireless ivnoo, canna get the batteries chairged.'

'Ye've aye the paper, hiv he?'

'Aye, aye, bit ye canna fix the time bi the paper. It's the peeps ye need.'

The peeps at sax o'clock, faan the mannie says This is the BBC Home Service, and this is the Six o'clock News, read by Alvar Lidell. He's the mannie wie the plooms i his moo.

'Nae a great miss, the wireless, there's damn all on't.'

He winna get aff wie that een.

'Faa wis girnin there wis nae Jimmy Shan, than?'

'Ach, there's een or twa decent things, bit faa wints a bleiter o dirt like yon boy wie his bath foo o milk!'

So it's true – it's a story.

'Faat wid *you* dee wie yer milk, than, if ye couldna shift it?'

'Oh, Christ knows . . . drink the bluidy stuff, I suppose.'

A lauch.

'Aye, wid ye!'

'Weel, I widna pit it in the bath onywye!'

'Faat wye nae?'

'I hinna got a bluidy bath!'

They aa kent at wis comin, they wis lauchin afore he feenished sayin't. Neen o's his a bath, come tae that, nae a bath wie taps onywye.

'Ye wad miss the wireless, though. Ye wad miss the paper, surely!'

'O, aye.'

If een o the weemin says she listens tae Mrs Dale, they'll aa say they listen tull't.

'I wid miss the Dales, lat me tell ye!'

'Oh, sae wid I!'

Funny thing, Dr Dale's nivver stucken wie yon motor o his. He widna ski tae see somebody, though. Dr Dale's a toonser.

'Ah weel, Bill ma loon, I hae my doots aboot ye.'

This is said tae test the temperature o their optimism. They'll cry doon the thocht that Bill Robertson his laired somewye. It'll be waur still gin he lairs faar we cast yestreen, syne it'll be oor wyte. Gin he disna try ataa, the blame's aa on his shooders.

'Bill winna stick.'

'We should walk, maybe, doon tae the main road in case he taks a look an disna try farrer.'

'Na, na, he's clear eence he's on the level bit.'

'Aye, bit get on tae the level bit!'

'Cyaarnie's been up an doon bi noo, surely. It's only that bit fae the road up tae the brig, ye ken.'

'Nae a gweed turn aff o the road, though, ye're on tull't afore ye ken, there's nae room for a run at it.'

Draa-backs multiply like weeds, eence ye start. Clear een or twa awa, an anither een growes int's place. Supposin his van's up tull't, wull he hae the stuff we're lookin for?

'We're gey low on floor, ye ken, an we're doon tae the last baggie o sugar.'

'Oh, we're needin juist aboot aathing, I think. Ye ging throwe some things faister faan the widder's coorse.'

'Some things. Somethings ye dinna bother wie.'

'Faat things, like?'

'Ach, funcy stuff an so on, caul stuff, ye dinna feel like a caul denner ivnoo, div ye?'

'Na, na, broth's the thing, eh?'

'Like the wifie's broth!'

'Aye, the wifie's broth.'

They aa mine aboot the wifie's broth, an a lauch gets up. She hid a tink come tull her door this day, sayin foo sair made he wis, he hidna etten naething for a lang time, an he speired her could she nae spare a bite, mistress? so the wifie speired at him gin he likit second-day's broth an the tink said he thocht it wis juist rare. Ah weel, the wifie said, you come back the morn than, I've juist made some.

'Naething wrang wie third-day's broth either, sticks tae yer ribs, yon stuff.'

'Aye dist.'

'Weel, we'll be aa here for wir denner yet, if Bill disna show up or lang.'

There's a great chorus o na, na, nivver, bit it could still come tae that.

'Na, na, we'll haud awa hame, we'll leave a line for him, we can aye come back for't.'

'Aye, bit foo'll ye ken tae come back or no?'

'Ach, we'll tak a chunce. We canna bide here aa day, me, me, ye've mair tae dee than hae his in aneth yer feet.'

'Ye're nae in onybody's road, sit still, man.'

Faat's wrang is, the new shape this mornin's takkin, a shape it wisna mint tae hae. First aff, fowk cam tae wyte an oor an syne ging hame again: aa the newsin an the fly-cup bit o't wis supposed tae be temporary. Noo the mornin raxes, an there's nae end tull't. They can aa bide, they ken at. Bit foo lang, on tap o aa the time it'll tak tae hae a pick denner, an syne mair tae? the langer they aa bide, the less pint there is in gyaun hame, in case Bill comes five meenits efter they're awa fae the back door. Better tae mak a clean brak, noo, afore they hiv tull.

'Nae sign o him, is ere?'

An wie that, as gin he'd wyted for the chunce tae fleg aa o's, the injine o Bill's van kittles up wir lugs. He's nae juist on his wye here, he's in the close. Faa his the farrest tae wyde hame fae here? The Smiths, nae doots aboot it. So they get first go, an syne the Cadgers, syne the Dawsons. Faan Mam an Dad ging oot, Mam wie her teem bag an Dad tae newse a meenit, I snoove ben tull the kitchen tae see faat bits o shortbreid mith be lyin aboot.

5

'Syne hey for Cyaak an Cyaarneywhing
Bracklamore an Bennymeen,
Scoor the boords o Leddysfoord
An skum the lums o Glesslaw.'
FLORA GARRY: *Spring Fever*

The tarry poles wis lyin at the roadside, on the lang park as Mam
caa'd it, the girssy bank nowt wis aye raxin their moos tull fae ahin
the palin. Tam Dawson an me steed on them: they waur lang an
heavy, trimmed an planed as smooth as pencils. Neist day we made
on we'd kent aa the time faat they waur ere for: this wis the Hydro.
The 'power'. Fowk spak aboot it like it wis an item amon their
messages – they waur gettin in the 'power'.

Mannies wie tin hats on their heids gaed traivellin throwe oor
parks thegither: I thocht maybe there wis hailsteens forecast bit Mam
said the hard hats wis a badge, like, like the tape-measures an the
three-leggit camera-thing – a kin o uniform. Mannies in green flan-
nels an clean wellintons cam an newsed tull een anither, biros at the
ready, pintin this wye an that wye an gyaun awa again in order to come
back an ging throwe the rigmarole again some ither day. Mannies
wie widden haimmers cam an drave square pegs intae the grun, an
we wis warned nae tae meeve ony o em or else. Syne mannies in
reefer-jaickets cam, howkin the great holes up an doon the parks for
the poles tae get beeried in, as though ilka pole wis a strainer. They
waur a roch crew, some o them: twa chiels took me on an newsed
awa tull's, an afore I kent faat wis makkin em sae gweed-nettered an
sociable they wis speirin gin we'd ony eggs tae spare. So I saved a
half-dizzen an they took em fae's wie a richt gweed wull, juist the
conter wye that Mam took it faan she fin oot faat I wis up till.

Eence the poles wis sunk an they wis ready for the power-lines,
the commando-team got yokit: men climmin tae the cross-trees on
the tap harnessed intae belts an buckles, heistin themsels up the

pole wie a belt haudin them at the waist an their beets spikit wie nails so's they could get purchase on the wid: they wis fleet an sure-fitted as though teem air wis their element an hicht their ain domain. Bi the time they'd feenished, ilka pole wis starred an jabby wie a thoosan nail-prints.

Bill Aitken fae Methlick cam an did the wirin o the hoose an steadins, dapper in his blue biler-suit an his clean sheen that wis as blaik an as weel brushed as his thick heid o hair. Bill smokit Capstans an said 'Absolutely' in his saft, gentle voice. Cables an copper wire sprooted fae the holes he bored intae the plaister-strappin, throwe the waas an in aneth the fleer. Syne the switches cam, trig an neat tae look at: lampshades wis bocht an a kettle like a pot-bellied mirror. I wis mangin for the day faan we wad get some gweed o aa the wark Bill did, an syne it happened: I cam hame fae the skweel an tried the switch aside the stairs, an there it wis, the bulb wis pruif o't: we hid in the power.

Efter the switch-on there wis an evenin in the hall at Auchnagatt for aa the fowk like his that hid tae come tae terms wie the newness o the electric: the wives hid a 'Demonstration' an the men-fowk hid a film. Kettles, irons, cookers an fridges wis laid oot for aabody tae see the range o stuff ye could throw yer siller efter: juist lookin at em, fite an clean an shiny, ye could tell that maet wad taste a treat faan it wis made sic a fantoosh wye. The men said they widna wint for scones an bannocks noo, na, nor cake nor gingerbreid, or even stuff they hidna tried yet. Weemin trickit up in flooery aaprons naebody wad badder wie for fear o fylin them gaed ower the shape an size o ovens an the rings on cookers, an they made some samples so's ye'd ken they wisna leein. Doon i the smaa hall we saa green an polished injines that could knype on throwe fire an flood an dee aa the coorse or clorty jobs aboot a place in half the time that ony man could feenish them: there wis nae wird o foo ye mith be stucken gin the injines foonered on ye, bit they waur aa spleet new so ye didna think aboot em brakkin doon. A fairmer in the film wis on a reef this day, an his laidder skited faan he wis half-wyes doon, an that wis him awa fae hame for a fortnicht bit faan he hirpled back again he wisna neen ahin, the machines hid kept up fine wie aa the wark he couldna dee himsel.

The Calor Gas mannie stoppit. Fowk tell't the story o the aul wifie that thocht the Hydro wis a great improvement – she could see the better foo tae licht her Tilley. We could rin up the stairs noo, Hilda an me, faan we gaed tae oor beds. The close roon the back door wis bricht as day on a dark nicht, an faan a car drave up we pat on the porch licht so's the veesitors wadna hae tae pleiter throwe the dubs faan they cam in. I could read in my bed noo, the *Newnes Pictorial Knowledge* an the beuks fae the skweel library. There wis a twa-barred fire noo in front o the teem grate in my bedroom, so's I could tak my claes aff as slow's I likit: faan I switched the fire aff I loupit in aneth the covers an watched the reid bars fade tae orange, syne tae grey, tull faar the fire wis wis juist a glint o metal an the shaddas claimed its space again. Ilka day for a wik or so I ran hame fae Clochcan winnerin faan we wid be suppert like the wifies in the hall hid shown the fowk, bit maybe Mam hid nae been peyin muckle heed tae them or faat they said, the fancy recipes wis slow-kin in comin tae the fore. Hen broth tasted the same efter the power came as it eesed tae dee, an sae did stovies: the only betterment we kent wis makkin toast aneth the grill o the 'Jackson' – bit even that hid a queer thraw till't. The aul wye hid aye been tae sit hunkered doon like a puddock wie the lang fork in yer haun, poukin the slice o loaf as near the fire as ye could win withoot drappin't in or gettin aa yer knuckles brunt, an the stob tae *that* rose wis ye could easy nae draa back the breid in time an it wad be weel sung afore ye kent it, bit there wis this gweed pint in its favour: wie the aul fork ye could cut loaf as thick's ye likit, an the toast wad be het crust on the ootside an het breid i the middle – noo the slices aa hid tae be thinner for the grill tae cairry them, an there wisna the same chaa in them, they wis bruckle noo an lichtsome.

Tam Dawson an me wis comin hame fae Clochcan ae nicht an we spied some roosty nettin-wire, the kin o wire ye wad keep chuckens in wie, an we thocht faat a gran ploy it wad be tae rowe the wire up some an see fae could fling it farrest. Faan we'd tried that a fyowe times we hit neist on the contest o faa could fling it hichest. Syne we couldna gree aboot faa wis winnin, for we'd nae guage tae measure wie, an we micht hae left it at that hid it nae been for the electric line. We wad see faa could clear the line wie't – an we tried that shot aboot tull een o's wearied some an his airm didna caa the roosty wire far eneuch intae the air. We blackit oot Lambhillock an the Cairtney's place an Geordie Fyvie tee, aa wie the ae snorl o wire. It wisna aften that I gaed hame feart, bit yon wis ae time. Geordie Fyvie maybe winnered faat wye we'd sic an ul wull at him, for aa the pieces Mrs Fyvie gied's if we cried in at the back door on wir wye by, bit Tam an me hid a faa-oot wie Geordie faan we fulled his waal wie sods and divots ae nicht. 'Faat the hell d'ye think ye're deein?' he roared at's. We'd nae answer tae that. We cut sticks fae his rodden trees an we nivver thocht twice aboot it, bit Geordie mith hae been roosed up aboot that anaa for aa we kent. I got a kittlen eence fae Mrs Fyvie an I cairried it back tae Kiddies in my bosie, it wis a grey haunfu o a craitur an I took peety on't faan Mrs Fyvie said she'd hae tae droon the wee smout. He nivver thrave, the cat, bit he wisna tied intill a pyok an haved intae the burn.

I nivver baddered wie bandies in a jam-jar or hatchin tadpoles – the jeely sotter mined me on sago puddin an I wisna taen wie sago. Doddy Smith hid guinea-pigs an rubbits at the back door at hame, bit I hid juist the ae rubbit for a fyle in the lythe o the byre waa roon fae the neep-shed. Tae-leaves an oatmeal hid sic a fine smell fyles I wis half inclined tae try some tae see faat it tasted like. The hens' mash, steered in a pail like brose in a caup, gaed me the same notion; best avaa, though, wis feedin milk tae calfies, trystin their heids doon tae the milk – ye dippit in yer haill haun an gaed em yer weet fingers tae sook, an they seen got the hang o't faan yer haun wis lickit bare an ye loot it faa tae the fite froth, their moos sank intae the real thing an they wis roadit, powkin the pail gey near oot o yer grip in their hurry tae get ilka drap. Cattle-cake wis like bullets, hard an lumpy, bit corn wis an odd mixter, quick-silver the wye it ran an lowpit, happin yer haun easy like a second skin faan ye stappit yer fingers intill't, stottin like hailsteens faan ye fed the hens an walkit in amon them an rained their denner doon, crying 'Tuck tuck tuck tuck tuckie'. Doon tae the hinmaist haunfu o the corn, I kent I wad dee't again an I tried nae tull, bit it aye happened – my nails scratted on the boddom, an a caul, shairp stang dirled throwe my nerves an gaured me grue. Ilka ragged, wauble lenght o corrugated iron did the same mischief faan ye loot yer nails scrape on't – yer back-been took the shivers for a second or twa.

A new loon cam tae the skweel an brocht a new scare tae some o's, we'd nivver seen the wye fowk wie his ailment could change sae quick: ae meenit i the playgreen he wis racin aboot an en for nae reason we could ivver pint till he wad be streekit flat oot an shakkin like a breem buss that a gale o win plays wie. The fit lasted nae time at aa, really, bit tae his it seemed a gweed fyle aye. Tam Soutar hid tae pit up wie being hicher nor the lave o's, heid an shooders: it wis fyles an unchancy thing tae be noticed or tae staun oot ony, tae mak ower muckle o a mark. Bit Hugh Milne tell't me ae nicht tae bide ahin faan the bell gaed, an he took me roon the side o the skweel-hoose intill his gairden. He wis wintin me tae see foo tae growe flooers: he showed me the beddin plants in front o his windaes, an I could hardly look at em for noticin the heids poppin up ahin the green fence of the playgreen. Tam Thooms an Alyssum – the names hid a queer ring tae them, especially Sweet William. I couldna see foo onybody could be prood o growin Sweet William. Syne he pinted tae some daisies, Livingston daisies he caa'd em, an he said they opened oot faan the sin shone. I thocht there wid be some raggin in store for me faan he loot me awa again, bit no, nae this time, my pals must hae thocht it wisna my wyte the Dominie wis a gairdener. I planted Tam Thooms an faan I gaed tae see em efter a wik or so there wis nae sign o them, so I thocht nae mair aboot it tull Mam cried on's tae ging intae oor gairden this day wie her, an she took's ower tae the hedge an sure eneuch, the Tam Thooms wis there as large as life. So that wis me startit noo, an there wis naething for't, I hid tae dell the borders and get on wie the classy stuff, even Sweet William if the warst cam tae the warst. Peter Dinnes gaed me straaberry plants an reeled aff a list o tips an pints tae me, aboot snippin runners an wuppin strae roon the green berries tae keep em aff the grun an so on, bit he nivver tellt's aboot the spurgies an the blackbirds, my first crap was aa hairsted afore I set hauns on em.

So I got cocky sine an startit in on catalogues o roses, bit the 'ifs'

an 'buts' got the better o's, there wis ower mony details tae see tull
aboot faar yer grun wis facin an the depth o tilth an as for prunin em
an graftin em, I could see my days as a rose-expert wis aa ower afore
I'd yokit. Bit the catalogue idea got a haud o me, an I sent awa for
catalogues o air-guns an catalogues fae a joke-factory, Ellison's, the
name wis. As far as I could mak oot the jokes wis mair dangerous
than the air-guns. They advertised onything that the coorse side o
yer naittur micht be trickit wie – 'SURPRISE YOUR FRIENDS'
the beuk said, showin ye horny-gollachs made o plastic ye could pit
on somebody's denner faan they wisna lookin. Rubber snakes for
hidin aneth cushions wis a winner, they said – 'SEE THEIR
FACES!' They hid conjurers' sets for hame-made magic, card-
tricks an trick-cards, speens that melted faan ye pit em in yer tae an
fried-eggs that skirled faan ye probbit a knife intae them. The
gadget I wis maist taen wie wis a thing nae bigger nor a button for
hidin in yer moo – 'BE A VENTRILOQUIST! THROW YOUR
VOICE WITH EASE!' So I sent awa for't. Faat a secret I wad hae
faan the postie brocht the parcel – I could see masel bein the star
turn at Christmas parties in Clochcan an aa wir relatives gettin awfu
prood tae say they kent me. The gadget, faan it cam, wis even
smaaer than the picter o't, an it wis naething mair nor a washer wie a
bevelled rim an a wee drum that ye could wheeple intae faan ye
threw yer voice. Faan ye pit it in yer moo the first thing ye winted tae
dee wis tae spit it oot again an the second thing ye wis like tae dee
wie't wis tae swalla't. I read the instructions a fyowe times an winnered foo it wisna as easy as they said it should be. 'Control it with
the tongue,' the caird said, bit I wis sair made tae joogle the washer
an even mak a soon o ony kin, lat aleen speech. 'Fit's adee, man?'
Dad said, faan I gaed roon an roon the kitchen, thinkin maybe
motion wis an aid tae ventriloquism, 'Sair teeth?' I started tellin him
faat I wis up tull, bit the washer broke lowss an gey near chokit me.
'That loon's nae richt,' Mam said. 'There hisna been a wird oot o
him for an oor or twa.'

6

'Gradually, after the age of about six, children . . . begin
to expect and depend upon cycles of events; but even
then their unit of measurement is so small – their
impatience, if you wish to call it that, is so great – that
the foreseen still seems too far off to qualify the present
to any important degree: their attention still remains on
the present in which things constantly appear for the first
time and are constantly being lost for ever.'

JOHN BERGER, JEAN MOHR: *A Fortunate Man*

Some days naething happened. Some days I wid hae fenced wie my
faither wie a richt gweed wull, even haudin posts straicht for him or
heftin the mail-haimmer or cairyin staples; some days even fullin
neeps wis a sicht better nor fullin in an efterneen. Some days the
fairm gaed soor on ye, it wis a teem pooch wie nae ferlies left tae rax
for. I wid pine, stuck in a dowf mood, for something new tae tak my
fancy, some fresh angle on faat I kent so that my maist weel-
traivelled grun wid come awa wie some surprises. There wis naewye
I could ging tae get awa fae faat it wis that ailed me, it wis me masel
that scunnered me. Hilda wisna big eneuch tae draa me intae devil-
ment, an aa my roch ploys wis special onywye for the verra reason
that she couldna jine in em or match me at em. In my *Book of
Heroes* it wis Nelson that I minded on faan he wis still a loon an far
fae hame ae nicht, they fand him sittin on a loupin river's bank an
faan they speired him gin he wisna feart he said he'd nivver seen it,
fear, an faat wis't? So I wid think foo gran it wid hae been hid
Kiddies haen a river close at haun an syne I could hae gotten tint like
Nelson. There wis eence faan I wis tint at a skweel picnic at the
Broch, bit I wis ower little tae enjoy the feelin, I didna ken foo tint I
wis till a bobby fand me, an syne it wis ower late.

The skweel picnic aye gaed tae Cullen or Macduff; it wis een o the
fyowe times we wis on a bus, so we waved at aabody, waggin
hankies oot o the windaes at men hyowin in the parks, or gin there

wisna fowk tae wave at, we saluted stirks an yowes as gin they kent
we wis aff on the ran-dan. A peer breet on a push-bike wid get sic a
flappin o hankies he wid winner faa it wis that kent him, an he wid
maybe lift his haun till's afore we waur oot o sicht. Doon on the het
saan the mithers spread their rugs an plunkit doon their bags an
yokit intae wyvin, tull een wid dare the lave tae ging an try the
watter wie her, an they wid hyst their frocks up an styter doon tae
the caul waves tae get their taes weet. We ran races on faativver livvel
grun we got a haud o: the egg-an-speen race wie a Golden Wonder
or a Majestic instead o an egg, the seck race, the three-leggit race an
the wheel-barra race. We played fitbaa or rounders, syne the baker's
van appeared an aa the pyocks wis laid oot on a table for's – aye the
same pyock ilka eer, wie a bridie an a cream-bun an maybe a
fly-cemetery. We got ice-cream later on, bit we gaed an bocht wir
ain tee, we drank fizzy ale oot o wee bottles an sookit ice-lollies.
Faan it wis hame-time there wis aye somebody that wis tint an
somebody that thocht the bus wis coming at half-seiven, nae half-
sax, an of coorse they waur bound tae be awa roon the shops maybe
or they'd cried in at their man's sister's hoose for a fly-cup an
naebody kent the address so we couldna ging an get em. Faan we got
roadit, though, the big eens at the back for a caper tae themsels an
the little eens at the front, ready fir the time faan they started
spewin, we waved an waved an we waggit wir hankies again. We hid
saan inside wir pooches, in wir lugs an in wir hair, atween wir taes an
even in aneth wir teeth.

It wis aye hyowin-time faan the picnic cam roon, an syne the
holidays. I nivver thocht aboot it aforehaun, gin I wid get tae Andy's
or no: it juist happened. He hid gotten wired intae the piana an he
wis makkin a gran job o't, he wis aye practicin. There wis ae tune I
wis fond o bit I could nivver mine the name o't. 'Play yon een, min.'
I wid say. 'Faat een?' he wid say, kennin fine. 'Och, yon een,
toodle-toodle-toodle-oo,' I wid say. 'Minuet in G' Andy wid tell
me, nippit-like bit fine pleased that I wis ignorant. Granny Dinnes
wid be there fyles, an this day we wis aa sittin roon the table at wir
denner faan the big fowk yokit intae girnin aboot foo the paper in
the laavie wis aa deen. Again, I peyed nae heed, syne I lookit up an

they wis aa glowerin at me, so I jaloosed it wis my wyte. Granny cam richt oot wie't. 'Faat div ye use sae muckle paper in the placie for, loonie?' she speired. Lookin at it ae wye, surely she wis bound tae ken, I thocht, it wisna juist the kin o thing tae mention at yer denner. So I boxed clivver an I said 'The same thing as ye use a little pucklie paper for, Granny'. Andra leuch an said 'Juist at,' an at wis praise eneuch. He nivver blew, Andra, or threw his wecht aboot, bit gin ye contered him an he wis richt aboot a thing an you wis wrang he wid shak his heid an tell ye 'Aye, ye canna kid the kid that kidded millions'.

He wis hashin on ae day tae get awa tae the depot. He hid his fite sark on, bit nae tie. 'Watch this.' he said. 'Shut yer een.' I couldna faddom foo tae watch wie ma een shut bit I did it onywye. 'Look noo!' he said, an faan I opened ma een again he hid his tie on, knotted an snod aneth his collar. 'That wis quick,' I said. 'Show me foo tae dee't.' Andra ruggit the tie doon an inch or so an syne he pinged it back again, it wis a dummy knot an the haill tie wis held on wie elastic. He wore a blue uniform, like a bobby, bit on het days he could pit on a jaicket that wis lichter nor the thick, offeecial een. I wis awfu keen on a real fitbaa, a ledder een an nae neen o yon orra rubber efforts, so I began tae speir Andra gin he saa baas in the shops in Aiberdeen an foo muckle waur they? I gaed him aa ma pennies an he brocht me hame a baa. It wis ledder aa richt, bit faat a snorl-up I got intill faan I hid tae pump some win intill't: I hid tae lowssen the laced-up bittie an get a haud o the winpipe, blaa the bladder hard syne fecht an get the pipe tied, stap the haill thing back aneth the laces an powk it doon so's there wis nae bump or else the baa lookit like it hid a gumbile. I wisna juist as keen on fitbaa faan I hid tae tchauve tae keep it workin.

We gaed ower, fyles, fae Methlick tae see Nan's relations in Ellon, they bade near haun tull a toon park wie short girss so faat else could we dee, we played cricket wie the Ellon cousins. They hid real stumps an a real bat, an a broon baa that wisna like a baa I'd ivver seen afore, it widna stot bit it could fair kittle yer cweets for ye gin ye furled the bat wrang an missed it. I wis mair feart o the broon baa than I'd ivver been o a fitba, even een wie the Tawses' beets ahin't. I wis sair made, tee, tae faa in wie the palaver that gaed intae cricket, aa this rinnin forrit wie yer shooders showdin like yer semmit wis yokie, turnin side-on tae keek by yer left funny-been afore ye brocht yer richt airm up throwe a wide arc tae throw the baa richt, except ye didna spik aboot throwin, it wis bowlin noo, an the chiel staunin ere wie his bat in baith hauns as though he hid tae hing on tull't in case he tummelt. The loons roared 'Howzat!' nearly ilka time they bowled at me, an 'L.B.W.!' ilka time I missed. I could see I wis ower roch for cricket, it wisna juist a new game tae me bit a new language anaa. We gaed back tae the hoose for the tae an pieces, an there wis mair palaver ere, poorin tae throwe a wee sieve an drappin lumps o sugar in't wie the shiny tyangs, an a wee bowlie for caul tae wie flooers on't, I'd nivver seen the like afore. I thocht it lookit like a leprechaun's chunty.

Ella King, Nan's neepor at Blackcraig, bade on the Fyvie side o Nan's hoose. She gaured me ging an eerin for her ae day, ower tae the grocer's on my bike for a jar o beetroot. I wis juist pickin't up faan it slipped throwe my fingers an dunted doon on tae the fleer. I could see the gless wis broken, bit the label kept the jar egither an I biked hame wie't, in the hope that Ella widna notice. There wis a craft neist, in the raa o hooses, an syne a straicht road that took ye ben tae Woodhead an doon tae Fyvie. Cars on this road hid tae slow doon as they waar passin Andy's, an I wid lie in my bed fyles at nicht an winner faat wye fowk wis oot at sic an oor. The odd car its leen wisna oot o the ordinary, bit twa or three cars wis a different maitter, they wis traffic. We full't note-books, Andy an me, wie car numbers. We biked ower tae the shops for ice-lollies, an cried in on Mrs Miller up in Timmer Street, abeen the depot. We plotted costumes for the Fancy Dress Competition at the Methlick Flower Show, bit I wis tell't I couldna pit my name forrit because I wis fae Auchnagatt an I wisna local eneuch. Nae lang efter the Flower Show it wid be time for the Dons tae start playin again, an time for the skweel tae start. Dod Dawson hit on a new ploy, he wid be a hirer an drive bairns tae Clochies. He bocht a green Bedford, wie slatted seats in't, an the days o wir stravaigin doon by Kiddies tae the burn an up the brae tae Geordie Fyvie's wis by wie. Hilda an me got pickit up at the en o wir ain road, at the prairie gate. We laid raas o smaa steens across the road tae see faa could jaloose best faar Dod wid stop. The een wie the raa nearest the front wheels wis the winner. The best seat wis the front een, aside Dod, an it wis aye Tam or Doddie Smith that got plunkit doon in't, tull ae day I girned aboot nivver bein up front wie the driver so neist morning, sure as egg, faan the van stoppit for's the front seat wis teem an wytin for me. I walkit straicht by an sat doon at the back. 'D'ye nae wint the front seat?' Tam speired, ull-nettered like. 'Ye made a richt flap aboot it the streen.' 'Och, disna maitter tae me,' I said, 'I'm nae fashed.' So the front seat wis teem for a half-mile or so afore Tam plantit his dowp on't, sayin I hid hid ma chunce. Efter Dod's speed o drivin we thocht Dod haimmered on like the clappers; he maun hae been deein fifty juist, bit tae his it felt like echty. Gin we stoppit in the Gatt, fyles, for a poke o sweeties or a bag o crisps, an there wis een o's wie nae siller, Dod widna lat onybody be an ootlin, he wid claa far doon in his dungers' pooches for a spare threepenny.

Wie aa the ins and oots o drappin kids near haun their ain doors, Dod didna hae's back hame aa that seener than afore, it juist felt that wye. Gin there wis some time tae full in afore supper-time I micht be yokit intae gedderin growth on the breist o the lang park in front o Cadger's, or spreadin muck on the brae-face atween his an Aul Joe's mairch-dyke. Muck wis a lang tchauve, fullin cairt-loads fae the midden wie the Fordie backit back as far as she wid ging an the cairt-fleer as laich as possible so's ye wisna liftin ony mair than ye nott tull. Rivin sharn oot o a rank midden, trumpit wie barra-wheels an its ain wecht, wis a sair fecht; yer feet sliddered an ye laired yersel, the mair ye focht for purchase the mair ye stytered, an aye the graip haunle an the shiny shaft birsled the saft howe atween yer thoom an yer fore-finger tull the blister started an ye could hardly thole the heat o't. We riggit the foo cairt tae the park-face, pat the Fordie intae neutral, an haved muck aff the back o the load intae raa efter raa o smaa heaps, wytin for the neist phase o the stramash, the hinmaist phase − spreadin aa the piles graipful bi graipfu, shakkin the sharn lowss so's it wisna ower knotted, tryin tae mak an even job o't. If ye didna pace yersel, an tak it slow an easy, een o twa things wid befaa ye – ye ran oot o win, or yer thoom ran oot o skin. Fowk wie false teeth hid tae watch, tee, in case aa yon shakkin made their plates drap oot. Gweed sharn wis clorty, sappy an weel-sizzened – 'the mither o meal,' fowk said.

We cowpit weet stooks roon tae the win ae nicht, bi the licht o the meen, in the park abeen the hoose. It wis a rare feelin, like an escapade: like we wis fechtin-chiels, oot on a nicht manoeuvre, the shaves wir faes, sentries sleepin at their post. I crept up on em an breenged at their heids an warsled em tae the grun. Afore they kent faat wis happenin I'd cut their thrapples an they wis aa goners. 'Caa canny, min,' my faither said, 'Ye're some roch.' I thocht o tellin him we'd nae time tae loss or the machine-guns opened up, syne I thocht better o't. Better tae keep thinkin the stooks wis sojers than tae be tellt that they wis juist stooks. Like the time we hid plumbers wie's, an they said the job wid tak a fylie langer nor they'd thocht an they wid wark throwe their denner-time; Mam said she widna see em stucken, she wid rustle something up. Seen's I heard it, I could see in my mind's ee faat a denner could be like gin it wis *rustled* up, it wid be bound tae be the kin o maet that cowboys hid, a muckle steak on a tin plate, or baked beans sweeled doon wie coffee! In the hinner-en it wis spam an a fried egg, bit even spam could taste like it hid been made on the camp-fire, if ye tried hard.

We wis left tae wir ain devices, Hilda an me, mair aften nor we winted fyles, it wis gran tae hae cousins come withoot warnin, Pat an Jeanie maybe, wie their clean frocks an their pig-tails. Ae spring nicht Dad an me wis fencin nae far fae the hoose faan a car cam in aboot, an twa chiels dandered doon the park tull's an newsed for half-an-oor. We tidied up faat we wis deein, an syne the twa chiels said they wid hae tae be awa noo, an they gaed back tae the close an the car started. Dad fand a post that hid a lowss staple, an syne he raised a wire some an fichered aboot wie't. The car left. Still he scuttered, though he wis aa deen. 'Are we nae deen yet?' I speired. 'Aye, aye,' he said, 'I juist thocht we wid lat em clear awa afore we made for the hoose.' An syne I kent he hid been loath tae speir the lads in, he wis maybe feart they wid forget tae ging hame again.

The nicht I rescued the collie I wis rale prood. I wis roon at the back-en o the aul railway-cerriage faan this eldritch soon began, an I hid tae airt masel tae faar it wis comin fae for a meenit, syne aff I set. I fand him staunin on his back legs at Broonie's palin on the far side o the burn, heukit ontae the tap wires bi ae front paw – he'd been tryin tae loup ower the palin an he'd catched ae fit atween the wires, sprung the bottom een tae ower-lap the een abeen't an he wis held, ilka meeve he made makkin the tension tichter. I raced back tae the hoose tae tell Dad, bit he wisna tae be seen. So we gaed doon, Mam an me, wie a stick an an iron bar, tae free the peer breet. We levered the wires apairt an he fell syne, the trappit paw hingin like he'd broken't, bit it wis juist numb fae being grippit for a fyle, he hirpled awa efter a lick or twa.

7

'Twa set o wires for weavin shanks –
Wi' worset, baith in hanks an clews –
An' linen, mair than thirty ells –
An' plaidin to mak coats an trews.
Sic lots o buttons – bits o twine –
Auld keys and corks, you'll seldom see.
Now, wisna this a gay auld kist
My Luckyminny left to me?'
WILLIAM ANDERSON: *My Luckyminny's Kist*

Atween the button-box (a smaa pine-wid kist, wie a hinged lid an a half-meen bress haunle on't) an the box o photographs (a lot bigger, made o varnished timmer) there wis nae likeness in size or colour, bit they waar sib tae een anither, for aa that, for they waar fullt, baith o em, wie the relics an remains o times an places lang seen left ahin, deid days an sometime fashions lang bypassed. There wis ilka shade an size an circumference o button in the wee kist – some as big as draughts-men an some dainty eneuch for a dall's semmit, ledder eens that lookit like green fitbaas haavered, gold eens wie pattrens, clear eens made o gless, coloured eens that waar as smooth as Smarties, squaur eens as roch as Spangles, metal buttons an bress buttons like the twa braw lads that micht hae been in uniform eence, they hid 'Pigott and Co's Fast Shank' on the inside. The odd penny and ha'penny, a bress chine, a thermometer, a padlock an a kilt-preen wis beeried in amon the mixter-maxter o hunners an hunners o buttons, a gweed lot o em still wie stray tufts o threid wuppit roon their eyelets, as though they hid been riggit fae their finery an drappit in amon the smachrie, their wark deen an their heyday feenished.

The box o photographs wis a diary o prood days; the prood faces ringed in a semi-circle on a waddin-day, the steady set o men's shooders as they sat on a lang deece, their place's name pented on a shelvin in front o them, littlins in their Christenin-goonies, motor-

44

bikes polished an ready for lang roads, horses kaimed an at the halt, bridles bleck as ink, nurses lauchin at an open door, hooses sittin solid ahin hedges; a rowth o faces, smilin or serious, an a dearth o lanscapes, as though perspectives didna traivel weel on tae paper, an they waar better lived in nor lookit at. There wis bit ae picter wie a lang view – Kidshill fae aneth the steadins half a park awa, my granfaither David staunin farrest forrit bit still a lang wye fae the camera, Granny Ogston haudin a hen's pail in the middle o the frame, an my faither atween the ploo shafts on the brae-face, heidin up tae Cadger's.

'Faa's at?' I speir Mam, haudin up a post-caird stampit 'Milne, Turriff' in the bottom richt neuk. Twa sober chiels, solemn as kirk elders, sit at a laich table, smored aneth thick suits an weskits, their sarks ticht at their thrapples. Een o them's left airm lies crookit on the table, his fingers gruppin teem air in a lowss neive. The tither een looks by ye, awa sidewyes tae space naebody's fullin. They dinna sit easy: they're nae there for themsels bit for the sake o aa the fowk wytin tae see them as they were that meenit faan the shutter meeved. Deep in their een, maybe, lies a question we canna answer, they baith look as if they wyted for a verdict. 'Faa's at?' I speir, an Mam supplies the names o her twa brithers, the place faar they waar sittin, the reason for't.

A still auler picter : this time, in bonny gowd type, the name 'T. Milne' an the place 'Turriff, N.B.' This is a man sittin, a wumman staunin aside him, her left haun on his richt shooder. They're at richt angles tae een anither, nae side bi side : she looks by me ae wye, the man likewise, bit in the conter airt. Faat mith their ages be? the early twenties, maybe, they look saft-skinned, the pair o them, bit there their sameness stops aathegither. She shines in bleck silk, in a dress wie lang sleeves an a hich collar, the texture sliddery an licht – he sits in a roch suit as thick as a calf's lug, nae crease tae the breeks on him, they look like nae iron wid mak ony odds till em. His left leg, crossed ower his richt knee, can be seen doon tae the sheen an twa inch fae the bottom there's a clear lirk tae show they've been lat doon for this day. Their hauns, tee, tell a story : his quaet, drappit on tull his lap – hers busy, een touchin him an the tither een raxed oot tae grab on till a fire-screen that blocks half o her richt leg, an in front o that a plant near as hich as the man's watch-chine. The wid o the cheer, close tee tae the marled surface o his jaicket, looks bricht an smooth, smooth like the bleck goon the wumman stauns sae straicht, sae still in.

The loon stauns bi the car's rinnin-boord, his heid nae mair nor an inch or twa abeen the haunle o the back door. His richt haun hauds a stick, or a toy maybe, its nae easy seen faat it is. His shadda, his reflection, can be seen ahin him, on the warm metal o the car's side. His sheen's laces look ower lang, his socks ower short : his face tells me he disna hope for onything tae come fae the box they've pinted at him. The haill picter measures three inch bi three, an there's a border o fite cardboord roon the photograph, a quarter inch o yalla, creamy fite. On the back, in a thin, firm haun, somebody his screived 'Woodside, August 1948'.

Ootside a hoose (her hoose?) on a steen slab, a wumman lookin saxty, maybe sivventy, heid back, een level, her chin firm an steady. Only the merest hint o fite lace saftens the stern frock she's in, bleck fae her thrapple tull her cweets. This is a stoot face; her een daur ye tae look awa fae her. Her left haun lies on a cheer's back, an the size o her ring on the waddin finger says as muckle aboot her as the jaunty set o her : it's a wide ring, bi some trick of the licht mair a man's nor a wumman's, unless faat his happened is that she's been tell't tae haud her haun forrit an there's some distortion. Ae look at her richt haun, hingin doon aside her, an ye begin tae winner : her hauns are a man's hauns, nae doot aboot it, muscled an gurly wie aul age bit capable, they signal wark an willin-ness. Jet beads hing on her braid breist, faistened bi a roon pin that draas them ticht at her neck. She micht be staunin at attention, this lady; faativver ulls she's kent, faativver dool an wae she's met wie, she's a lang wye fae lyin doon aneth em.

On a grey boord, thick an made tae laist, a picter o twa bairns maybe nae an eer aul. They're weerin Christenin-goons, an they hiv bare feet powkin oot in front o them. The reid letterin at the richt side o the picter says 'A. J. Norrie, The Studio, New Deer'.

I cam on strangers, young an aul alike, an thocht them fremmit fowk, little kennin them tae be the friens they waar, little kennin foo near bi bleed an kinship their faces wis. A fyowe Haddo Hoose picters, faan Mam wis a nurse ere, hid fowk in em that waar nae relation – bit them apairt, the box o photographs wis the femmly story, history nae in narrative bit in expressions, times loupin up tae meet me so that faan I sat an haunled em the picters played a trick wie calendars an distances. Ae meenit I wis lookin at my faither on his Ariel aside the stable door at Kiddshill, his Brass Band uniform on, an the neist meenit he wis kecklin on a furry rug aside his sister Daffy, weerin goonies for the man fae Norrie's tae record the Christenin o the twins thegither. Ae meenit the picters showed me faar I lived an ran an climmed an tummelt; neist meenit I wis far fae hame an face tae face wie fowk that I hid neither map nor compass close at haun tae airt me tae them wie.

Hairst days an ploomen : the men o Seggat 1923. There's twa picters o this toun, an Uncle Bob in baith o them : een teen in front o the cairt-sheds, wie eleiven men lined up, sax staunin an five sittin, a shelvin at their taes faar somebody his clarted the fairm's name in a gey hurry, the letters are uneven an roch deen. Bit the men are a braw sicht, great bannocks o bonnets on their heids an a watch-chine on the weskit o a chiel in the front raa, the grieve maybe. The tither picter's the opposite : only seiven men noo, an nae near sae weel turned oot. Bit the shelvin this time his 'Seggat' lettered trim an bonny, wie a horse-shoe on the richt an a horse's heid on the left. Fower o the seiven chiels hae pipes luntin, though fient-a-hair o rick can I spy. This is the posh picter, teen at the muckle gate wie a wheen trees ahin't : the caird says 'David Smith, Photographic Artist and Picture Frame Maker, Marriages and Picnics Attended By Appointment'.

We think, noo, faat a careless thing it is, tae staun still for a picter tae be teen – spile een, ye tak anither, anither twa; the better the machinery his gotten, the less we trust it. We multiply the choices, noo, at waddins, so that nae lassie in her best claes his tae tak second-best faan it comes tae the image o hersel she keeps. We think, noo, faat a lichtsome thing it is, the camera – in baith senses. It can be cairried in a pooch, a haun-bag, like ony article we pit awa

until the meenit faan its nott an used, syne pit awa again; an bein
teen, haein wir picter teen, disna cairry noo the wecht it eesed tae
hae, its nae momentous an we dinna feel momentous faan we dee't :
bit in the picters in the box o photographs, I could see in faces an the
stances o the subjects foo they hid turned themsels as near tae
statues as they could manage, gey near inanimate, subject fadin
intae object, the het bleed cweeled, their pooer as maisters o their
destiny lifted fae them. They wis under orders faan they steed there,
sat there, lookit this wye, that wye. They hid tae be tell't faat wye
tae be, fowk that nivver thocht aboot a wye tae be : fowk that made
claes, made breid, made things intae something else, fowk that
plooed parks, drave cars or larries, sorted broken things an made
things chynge for them – they hid tae be tell't faat wye tae be, faat
wye tae haud their heids an faar tae pit their hauns. It wis like gyaun
back, for them, tae the days faan ither fowk took chairge o them,
showed them foo tae manage, pat them throwe initiations.

The loon reflected in the motor-car, the loon in the seat o the
green Fordson, shadin his een fae the bricht sin, wis me. The third
picter faar I wis centre-stage wis in the gairden at Kidshill, an I wis in
dungers, styterin doon fae the front door. There wis a street-
photograph, though, fae Aiberdeen, faar Mam wis haudin bags o
messages, an a wumman that I didna ken hid teen me bi the haun.
Granny walkit in ahin the three o's, wie anither wumman aside her,
haudin a case in her richt haun. My cwyte hid a double raa o buttons
an a velvet collar; I wore fite socks an bleck sheen. Only me an
Granny look the mannie in ahin the camera in the face; the lave mak
forrit, like they're nae wintin tae be hinnered. The big photograph o
.me an Hilda, baith o's sittin, wis teen in Ellon in a studio. I nivver
thocht aboot it then, bit noo it strikes me, foo there's nae a picter o
my faither an me : juist me maleen, or wie my sister, or Mam aside
me, ahin me. An faat wis't I'm haudin in my haun, this prize that
seems a pairt o August 1948, in the picters at Woodside? It could be
a larry, a larry wie wee wheels an a laich cabin. My richt haun shows
my knuckles ticht an siccar : my larry wisna gyaun naewye, nae if I
could help it.

Gyaun back in time again, a picter o my Granny Ogston an three quines, an my faither at the far side, deen up like Fauntleroy in his hose an breeches, an a shiny buckle on his belt. His twin, Daffy, stauns aside him, ahin the pair o them their Auntie Kate (she wisna mair nor ten eer auler then em), syne Granny Ogston an the aulest quine, Patricia. It micht be 1916, 1917. They aa look as gin the day's for naething ither than this purpose, it's an outin an an occasion. By contrast, the hairst-park photograph marks an interruption tae the day; the men an weemin an the three horse mak a tableau, staunin stock still an watchfu. Their stillness is reeted in the bunn shaves lyin roon aboot them, nae stookit yet. Here the camera his geen oot tae them, tae meet them on their grun. The men are aa ages; a halflin wie a shafe in his left oxter, an aul man wie a baird an mowser, twa mair chiels in atween these twa extremes. Twa weemin staun thegither, their hauns ahin their backs. They're gey weel dressed for wark, some braw for the day's darg. I winner gin they've been socht for fae the hoose tae full oot the haill picter o the toun's strength. Their douce companionry adds blitheness : they're weel-faured, ilk een in her ain wye. The three horses staun quaet in their pykit collars an lang hames.

I look at the haill picter, for that's faat it is. This is the story of a place, a country, nae in narrative bit in expressions. This is faat yokit man an beast thegither, men an their weemin-fowk, aul men an young. The shaves lyin faar they drappit gie the continuity; they indicate faat happened afore the man cam wie the camera an faat happened faan he left: the binder meeved again, the stooks rase fae the cut stibble, the sweat dried in their oxters an they lowsed the beasts faan it wis weerin on tae nicht. This picter is nae life frozen, bit life, for a brief meenit, bringin intae focus aa the loyalties, the loves, the meanins an the values that faistened them tae een anither an the braid laan that ringed them.

8

'The land which happened inside us no one can take
from us again, not even ourselves. But God, such a long
journey ahead for you and me. Not a question of
imagination, but of faith.'
ANDRÉ BRINK: *An Instant In The Wind*

I could mine things, spell some an dee composition, bit I couldna
draa. The dominie hid tae ging awa fae Clochcan fir a day or twa, an
we got in a wifie tae tak chairge o's. She wis awfu keen on geography,
so we did toons o Scotland : Thurso hid pavin-steens, Cromarty wis
faar Hugh Miller cam fae, an Perth hid dye-works an a railway-
centre. We did rivers neist, an as if that wisna bad eneuch, tributaries
o rivers. She winted us tae draa wir ain maps free-haun, an I couldna
get the hang o't, my Scotland lookit like a rubbit wie three lugs.
'What's this?' she scraiched, clatterin an atlas doon first ae side o my
heid, syne the tither. Maybe she thocht she could drive geography
intae me the hard wye.

Maist nichts faan I gaed tae my bed I wheepled lines o poems tae
the reef abeen me, tryin rhymes an lines tae get a verse tae start.
Neist day I'd pit it doon on paper, or forget the haill thing tull the
neist nicht. Deaconess Anna wis due tae veesit us again, so I did a
poem for her.

'Every year she visits our school
To present to us our prizes,
And every visit that she makes
Our appreciation rises.'

It wis read oot on prize-day. Bi this time, haein poems broadcast
tae the haill skweel an aa the Mams and Dads anaa, an weerin glesses
aa the time, I wis weel by the stage o bein ony eese for onything, so I
knypit on wie the poetry. Faan fowk wis girnin aboot the price o tae
I cam up wie –

50

'We'll need tae dee athoot wir fly
We'll need tae tak wir chatter dry
The reason is we havna tea
The price o't (I'm sure) is higher than Benachie.'

Some poems wis in English, like the Mrs Ritchie een.

'There was an old man who lived in a house
Infested with mice an rats.
And so for the special purpose
He kept a dozen cats.'

Faan I got stuck fyles, in my bed onywye, I gaed tae sleep; bit writin the poems doon, faan they widna gee wie's, I wid chynge pens tae see if at improved things some. I thocht fyles that gin I wrote better, the poem wid rhyme better; it wis aye a bad sign faan the writin wis copper-plate. I likit history, an the names o the kings an queens o Scotland, an the fowk that they brocht intae the limelight wie them – Edward I o England wis 'Langshanks', John Balliol wis 'Toom Tabard', an the Earl o Angus 'Bell-The-Cat'. Mr Milne tried science wie's, bit we hid nae test-tubes or explosions, so it wisna aa that interestin. I wis gey haunless faan it cam tae makkin things; ither loons could mak an injine oot o pirns an rubber-bans, bit nae me. Takkin things tae bits wis aa richt, as lang's there wis nae chunce I'd hae tae pit em back thegither again. I made a TV eence. I drew three picters on three pages fae an exercise-beuk, an ilka picter hid a story or brocht the story forrit. There wis juist ae programme, bit it wis a cracker. Picter No. 1 hid a mannie speelin up a laidder wie a tin o pent in his haun. Picter No. 2 – the laidder cowpit. Picter No. 3 – the mannie sat on the grun wie the pent-tin on his heid an the pent rinnin doon his shooders like custard on a dumplin. I jined up the pages wie Sellotape, side bi side, syne I cut a squaur windae in a card-boord box an ruggit the picters ben by the windae, lookin in at the same time. It wis sair on the airms, richt eneuch, bit it wisna sair on the een, it wis aa by afore it hid really started. I tell't Mr Milne ae day, faan he hid socht me tae come oot o the class tae ging tae the skweel-hoose tae cairry jotters for him. Seen's we wis ootside he wis raxin for his tabacca an the papers he rowed his fags in, and he strade on, furlin his fingers at a great rate. I said, as modest-like as I could manage, that I hid made a TV. 'What with?' he speired. I tell't him aboot the box an the mannie's meshanter. 'Ah well,' he said, 'You know what they say'. I said I didna. He said necessity wis the mither o invention.

We got the phone in. It sat on the dresser an we wyted for the thing tae ring. It wis a novelty for a wik, maybe, syne it wis a pest. It wis waar, fyles, tae ken aforehan faat relations wis comin tae see us. I took it in my heid that I wid like tae try Weetabix, I'd seen an advert for't an it wis made oot tae be the best o breakfasts. Wid Taylor's hae the stuff, I speired Mam, an she said tae phone em an fin oot. So I phoned Maisie an I speired gin they hid Weetabix. Oh aye, she said. Dad said, ahin me, that he thocht he'd heard me sayin 'Hiv ye weet yer breeks?' bit I said na, it wisna at. Maisie said she wid lay a packet by for's, an I could hardly wyte tae pree this rare mixter. Sure eneuch, neist time we wis in Taylor's Maisie hid it ready for me. Hame I gaed an try'd it. It lay there on the plate like twa Brillo pads, an it nott twa speenfus o sugar tae ilka moofu tae gie't ony taste ataa. There wis juist the ae packet o Weetabix in the hoose at Kiddies, it wis like chaain strae.

Tam Dawson caa'd the feet fae me ae day faan he said the reason we hid belly-buttons wis that that wis faar ye wis shooen up again faan ye wis born. I took oot o that that gin ye didna watch yersel faa wis tae say the stitchin widna get unraivelled faan ye least expeckit it, like faan ye played at cowp-the-cat or ye wis climmin ower a yett. Ye wid tine yer skin, syne, an ye wid be left as nyaakit as a peeled banana. I started gyaun aboot gey canny-like for fear o bein shoogled, tryin nae tae rax my wyme mair than I nott tull. I couldna bring masel tae peek at my ain belly, in case o lowss stitch wis startin. I'd seen faat happened faan a maazie or a pullover tint a daud o wool – the mair ye riggit it the mair it ran. I'd seen my Granny at her wyvin; I'd haen tae staun in front o her wie my hauns apairt so's she could wup her worsit back intil a baa again, an I wis nae neen keen on the idea that they'd hae tae rowe me aathegither again if my belly-button lat me doon.

It wisna aften we wis nae weel, ony o's, barrin Dad maybe – he hid this ulcer an it fulled his craa wie brash watter an made him fite-faced. A rift fyles wid gie him ease fae't, bit he wis trauchled wie sair heids tee, for oors an oors. We wis aa lean kine, the Ogstons : my granfaither David wis ull-faured for wecht an nivver a strong man, Granny bocht him Tonic Wine an droggit him wie't ilka morning, a lippin egg-cupfu, tae gie him virr for aa the day took oot o him. She made him tasty fare tae try an tryst him intae ettin mair. His wyke stammack hid come doon tae Dad, some days he wis bad wie't an ye could see foo sair made he wis. There began tae be some wird o's meevin fae Kidshill, gyaun tull a smaaer place an a chynge o air. Some days, withoot me or Hilda kennin, Mam an Dad wis awa in the car tae ging an look at places. They seldom spak aboot it, or at least nae faan we wis near by. Syne ae day we wis tell't we hid tae come a run wie them, we wis gyaun ower tae Geerie wye an look at a craft. It wis a smaa place, sure eneuch, bit the great thing aboot it wis the trees at the road-side an roon the steadins, mair trees an closer at haun than Kiddies hid. The sin shone an the new smells, the new feel o the place we gaed tull wis aa rare an gleesome : bit we left in the car that efterneen an nivver socht a second look, so the deal didna come aff.

Colonel Nasser made the news, nae eence bit nicht efter nicht. He hid blockit aff the Suez Canal an said it wis Egypt's. Fowk spak aboot it even mair nor usual, this wis serious an they wis aa for deein something, they said Nasser nott a hidin noo tae stop his bauld an sleekit impedence. It gaed on an on for wiks on en : fae July onwards, throwe August an September an October tee. Israel pat its sojers intill't, an a war wis brewin. Syne there wis a cease-fire, bit the British an the French invaded onywye. They gaed in wie an airborne invasion o Suez an Port Said, an it lookit like it wis a straicht an easy path tae tak the haill Canal bit syne they stoppit, the government wis bein gaured tae pull oor sojers oot o't. The campaign tae save the British flag fae shame juist peetered oot, an there wis rage an blame fleein thick an faist, especially for Eden. He wisna a weel man, Eden, fowk wis sorry for him bit they couldna credit foo he'd latten aathing rin awa fae him, he'd latten ither countries tell him faat tae dee an foo tae dee't. Waur nor aa that, though, wis the

news he'd geen tae Parliament wie, tae say that Nasser hid surren-
dered faan he hidna. Eden gaed the government the wrang impression, an syne the country-fowk thocht the stramash wis aa deen faan
it wis naething like it.

Ae mornin, faan the Suez business wis at its hicht, Mam said
tae Hilda an me faan we cam doon the stairs that there wis nae
skweel for us that day, we wis gyaun tae see a craft ower bi Kintore
somewye. We drave throwe Auchnagatt tae Methlick, syne Old-
meldrum an Inverurie, an aboot three mile by Kintore we cam till't,
the sign at the road-en said 'Windsor Park'. Efter a quarter-mile or
so we wis in the close, an the car stoppit. The place wis caa'd Broomhill an the fowk that bade there wis caa'd Silver. They waar gettin
on, the Silvers, an they said it wis a wee hoose they waar wintin, hine
awa fae craft wark. Mam an Dad newsed tae them an we sat an
listened, latchin on tae facts an snippets faan they wis mentioned.
Broomhill wis aboot ten mile fae Aiberdeen, half the size o Kidshill,
an the butcher cam on Setterdays. We wis three mile fae Kintore an
a mile fae Blackburn, sax mile fae Inverurie an did we like an
Abernethy biscuit? We wis weel placed for a view o Benachie, the
neepors' name wis Massie, an the skweel in Blackburn wid suit the
bairns fine. There wis twa roads tae Blackie, either doon the main
road or ye could tak the double dykes aside the rubbish dump. The
big fairms roon aboot wis Cairntradlin an Kirkton, an we hid heard
o the Campbells, hid we? Dad say Oh aye, an it wis mair nor likely.
Efter Mrs Silver offered tae again an mair Abernethies it wis time
tae be awa; I noticed an aul pump sax yairds fae the back door so I
speired Dad if it wis still workin. 'It hid better be, laddie' he said,
'That's oor watter.' Broomhill hid nae rinnin watter in the hoose,
an nae power either. The Hydro wis comin, said the Silvers, bit sae
wis Christmas.

Mam an Dad tell't us nae tae spik aboot the trip we'd teen or faat
they hid newsed aboot. Syne ae day Alec Smith cried in wie his sin
Jimmy, an there wis nae mair o a secret in't, Kidshill wid be Jimmy
Smith's an we wid be in faat they spak aboot as the Geerie. The date
for flittin wis fixed for November; Dad an Jimmy struck a bargain
aboot faat we'd leave an faat we'd tak wie's. I wis disappinted that

there widna be a roup at Kiddies, for I hid aye likit roups. Mrs Cadger cam tae the back door ae nicht tae say Cheerio tull's –Mam priggit wie her tae come in an hae a fly-cup bit Mrs Cadger widna, she bade at the back door. Unless the roads wis blockit, an fowk cam tull's tae wyte for the vans tae come, there wisna an awfu lot o comin an gyaun atween the weemin fowk on the hill. It wis maistly the men that micht meeve aboot wie freedom, an even then it wisna seen tae be a veesit bit an eerin, an ahin ilka eerin, wytin for't tae be sorted oot or seen tull there wis aye the chunce o a fly-cup an a ginger snap tae ging wie't. Ye hid tae mine aye pit a snap ontae the palm o yer haun an syne dunt it wie yer funny-been : three broken bits wis gweed luck. It wis only snaps ye could try that wie, Rich Teas wisna hard eneuch an ye caa'd em aa tae crockanition.

Faat wis ere tae dee noo bit tae wyte the time oot; tae coont the fite steens. Faan a man dee'd, the aul Greeks hid it, ye coonted the fite chuckies he hid cassen in a bowie aa the days o his life – a fite steen for ilka gweed day. That wye ye could measure foo content he'd been, foo blithe a life he'd kent. Leavin a place ahin is a smaa daith – though at the time it disna feel like at. It's only later, faan ye traivel back tae the kent grun, eers auler maybe, that ye see that there's a stoot yett barrin the wye back, a yett that wis nivver ere afore. The yett wis haimmered intae place faan ye wis lookin somewye else, faan ye wis bein faa ye are. Yer ain ghaist his teen a Gordon's shullin an listed wie the ither ghaists o aa the yester-tales. We gaed oot o Sooth Kidshill in the November o 1956, intae Broomhill, Kinellar.

9

'In our house we lived with old times; concurrently in the 1910s and Twenties as well as the Fifties. The past sustained us in a physical as well as mental sense. It came home from work every evening in its flat cap and dirty hands. . . .'

IAN JACK: *Before The Oil Ran Out*

Aul times were near at haun, nae oot o sicht, nae oot o mind. They threided in an oot o things the big fowk newsed aboot, leuch at, shook their heids ower.

We heard o them, my sister an me, an we grew acquant wie them. They were brocht forrit, fyles, tae gie the shadin o comparison tae this life o oors, so that faat happened *noo* hid aye a conter-wecht, a balance cowpin either tae the side o better or the side o waur. They could be straicht admonishment, an cairry mense an coonsel. They pented for's the colours o the days an nichts that lay ayont oor ken : tae Hilda an tae me, the lang ago – tae Mam an Dad, yestreen or else the day afore yestreen.

Aul times cam in fae the weet parks an sat doon wie's; they gaed oot aside us tae barn an byre, corn-yard an broken grun. They steed their flauchter-spaads against a waa an left them stannin there, laid doon their brechams in a quaet neuk, lowsed the aul gig ahin the railway-cerriage so that we could mount the seat an flay the sheltie's ghaist in front o's wie imagined wheeps.

Aul times wis fowk. 'My father,' Mam wid say. Nae 'faither', bit the wird that hid authority. He wis a man like that, William Dinnes, in his ain hoose an in his femmly : a man nae tae be gainsaid, nivver contered faan he spak his mind. He took his seat at table first; he wis the first tae leave his cheer again. He wis a Plymouth Brethren man, stinch at the Meetin on a Lord's Day mornin faan they gethered, the Meetin fowk, tae brak breid ahin the steekit doors. Their Gospel wis the sterk an aefauld truth o Christ the sacrifice for sin, man the sinner

tint forivver or he won till Calvary. A notice-boord afore a Meetin-
hall hid aye the letters pented, efter oors o worship an so on 'D.V.'
Deo Volente. Nae times were siccar, nae places there bi richt. That
wis their creed, an it wis William Dinnes's: naething wis deserved,
naething guaranteed. God's Will could come like a Mey mornin, or
it could blatter doon an caa ye heelster-gowdie. William Dinnes
didna shape his days an sizzens – he took them piece-meal fae the
hauns o mercy, in the hope that faan the hauns wis rochest they wis
pruif o providence.

On July the seiventh echteen ninety-fower William Dinnes merried Jeannie Adam at Rosehill, Inglismaldie, Laurencekirk. William
worked the fairm at Flyingwells, Lethenty, Fyvie wie his ain fowk,
an he took ower the place faan they dee'd. They hid nine o a
femmly; the first, Willie, wis born on the twentyfirst o June echteen
ninety-five; Adam, on the twentyfifth o January ninety-seiven;
Tom, on the twentyfirst o January ninety-nine; Jean on the twenty-
first o November, ninteen hunner; Bob, on the twentysecond o
February nineteen three; Peter, on the seiventh o June nineteen
five; Andra, on the echth o February nineteen seiven; Jim, on the
third o October nineteen ten; Mary on the twentysixth o Mey
nineteen thirteen.

The craft of Flyingwells at Lethenty (juist kent as 'Lethenty') wis
twenty-seiven acre. Faan William Dinnes married, it wis on the
Haddo Hoose Estate. Fae echteen seiventy tae nineteen hunner the
seiventh Earl, John Gordon, raxed oot the moggan tae the tune o
twa hunner thoosan poun, improvin the grun an the warkin o't. For
aa that, aiblins for that verra reason, a muckle swatch o grun
belangin Haddo Hoose wis offered up for sale come the en o the
Great War, an William Dinnes bocht his craft in nineteen nineteen.
He wis his ain maister noo. It wis a mile-steen, nineteen nineteen :
the three aulest loons wis aa meeried in that eer. Willie tae Margaret
Cowie o Cairnbanno, New Deer, in the Kerr's Hall, Maud; Adam
tae Margaret Gerrie, at Banchory; Tom tae Elsie Grant, a fairm-
worker's dother, in the Temperance Hotel, Huntly.

He wis a bobby, Willie, in the City Police in Aiberdeen. Peter
jined the Police tee, on the ninth o July nineteen twenty-five, startin

in at a salary o three poun ten shullins a wik. Adam got a post wie
the firm o Clark an Chapman. Tom gaed in for fairm wark an he
bade in fairm wark aa his days. Bob fee'd for a fyle an chaumered
wie the men at Seggat tull he took a scunner at the ploo-shafts an
jined the Coonty Police in nineteen twenty-echt for the same pey as
his brithers. Bob wis peyed monthly; bed an boord wis a poun a wik.
He wis posted tull a wheen toons an villages – Peterhead, Inverurie,
Bucksburn, Turra, Cruden Bay an Aberdour. It wis in Peterheid
that he got married, in the April o nineteen thirty-twa, in the Royal
Hotel, tae Ethel Reid, a fairmer's dother fae Ravenscraig, Inverugie.
Seiven eer gaed by afore anither waddin – in thirty-nine, Andra
married Agnes Henderson fae Chapelhaugh, Methlick. He bade at
hame, Andra, helpin his faither wie the jinerin jobs that William
Dinnes took on for neepors faan he retired tae Hillbrae, Braiklay in
nineteen thirty-three. In nineteen thirty-five Andra gaed tae drive a
float wie a haulage firm in Methlick, French an Shand.

Jeannie worked in the shop at Lethenty for Mr William Chapman,
syne she meeved tae Aiberdeen an got a post wie a dentist bi the
name o Hewer. In nineteen forty-one she married George Florence
in Ruthrieston Sooth Kirk. Neist it wis Jim's turn; he gaed abroad
wie the Army an focht in Palestine, an in the July o nineteen
forty-three he married Jeannie Ritchie at St Mary's on the Rock at
Ellon. In less than a twal-month Mary wis married tee, tae James
Ogston o Sooth Kidshill o Auchnagatt. An en it wis Peter's waddin,
an the haill femmly wis awa an sattled : in the April o nineteen
forty-five he married Mary Rait at Tulloch, Aulmeldrum.

Nineteen forty-five. Hitler hid gaen tae earth in his bunker, still
pinnin faith on phantom sojers, still plottin faar tae bring forrit
shreds an tatters o battalions. I wis born on the twenty-fifth o
Mairch, a Sunday, at half past twal, in the Maternity Hospital in
Ellon. I wis a peer craiter, barely able tae haud my ain. They pat me
in an incubator, exiled fae contact an contamination. Naebody wis
latten near eneuch tae touch or haunle me : my faither drave tae
Ellon ilka day tae staun an look at's in the plastic cave I lay in. Eence
I wis able for't they loot me hame tae Kiddies an a cot aside the
kitchen Rayburn. On the twenty-fifth o November the minister o the

Sooth Kirk, New Deer, Dr Matthew Welsh Neilson christened me in the kitchen at Sooth Kidshill at half-past three in the efterneen. He christened me David Dinnes – the Dinnes for my mither's fowk, an David for my father's father, David Ogston.

My father spak o him, his wirds, his mainnerisms, as though tae wise me in the name I cairried. David Ogston wis brocht up at Gordon Cottage, Auchnagatt bi his granda an grannie; it wis the hoose they hid retired tull fae the fairm at Cairncummer, Cyaarnie's we caa'd it, the place at the road-en faar the railway brig wis. David's granfather hid the sheds at Auchnagatt faar they haunled goods an stores fae Aiberdeen bi rail – grain an coal an sic like. He hid the chunce, my granfather, o takkin ower the sheds faan he got merried in the eer o echteen ninety-nine, bit David gaed his ain gait an gaed intae Sooth Kidshill. His bride wis Helen Jean Philip, the dother o Mr and Mrs George Philip o West Mains, Nethermuir, New Deer. The Philips leased the fairm fae John Dean Leslie, o the Nethermuir Estate. David an Helen Jean gaed intae Kiddies on the twenty-echt o Mey echteen ninety-nine an started dairyin wie saxteen kye an a pair o horse, the Clydesdale an a licht-leggit beast for the deleeveries.

Their first bairn wis a quine : Patricia Philip Ogston, born on the ninth o Mey nineteen three. Faan she wis three she got the stirkie's staa; James an Davina wis born on the twentieth o Mairch nineteen sax. Helen Jean wis sair made tae manage twins an James wisna a strong bairn : Davina gaed tae Granny Philip at Wasties tae be lookit efter an tae gie her brither mair o Helen Jean's attention. Aa throwe the time she wis at the skweel at Clochies, Davina – Daffy as they caa'd her – hid a hame at Kiddies an a hame at Wasties. George Philip, come a Freday, took her ower tae Wasties an she bade wie them tull the Sunday, syne she gaed back tae Kiddies.

Faan Patty left the skweel she bade at hame an helped her mither. She jined the New Deer branch o the Scots Girl Friendly Society. Later on she gaed tae London tae be lady's maid tull a Lady Sybil Middleton, syne she came hame an took a post as maid ower at Kennethmont, wie Mrs Leith Hay o Leith Hall. James an Daffy gaed tae Maud skweel efter Clochcan, faar the dominie wis R. D.

Robertson; James walkit barfit in the simmertime tae Clochies, an
at hyowin-time he took a dreel fae the steadins up the park tae the
tap road in the mornin. At nicht the hyowe wis wytin for him faan he
walkit hame. Doon at Maud the dominie wis Major John Law. He
gaed them poetry tae learn, like 'The Slave's Dream' –

> 'He did not feel the driver's whip
> Nor the burning heat of day;
> For death had illumined the Land of Sleep
> And his lifeless body lay
> A worn-out fetter, that the soul
> Had broken and thrown away'

My father wid say that fyles, wird for wird. He left Maud skweel
faan he wis fowerteen tae help his father. He wis sent doon wie twa
horses an cairts tae the railway sheds in Auchnagatt for the eer's
coal, twal hunnerwecht a cairt, at thirty-echt an saxpence a ton.
Daffy left the skweel an worked at Wasties wie her Granny an her
Auntie Kate. In nineteen twenty-twa she pat in sax month at Craib-
stone College, near Aiberdeen. In nineteen twenty-sax she danced
at New Deer wie Robert Boothby. This wis the wye o't : Boothby
wis new on fir the Member o Parliament, an he toured his consti-
tuency in his braw weskits an his yalla ties, meetin fowk an takkin
tent o faat they said tae him – he took the funcy o the weemin tee,
for he wis young an swack-like, braid-shoodered an a bauld birkie :
he could turn heids, an he kent it. He cried in at West Mains tae see
George Philip, an he noticed Daffy in the kitchen an spak tull her.
He speired gin she wis gyaun tae the Dance that nicht in New Deer,
the do they laid on for their new Member. She said she wis. Boothby
said tae mind an keep the second dance for him. Faan the nicht
started, the M.P. gaed roon the fleer wie the President o the local
Association's wife, as he wis honour bound tae dee. Fowk watched
his ilka step. The second item wis announced, an the band struck up
the tune; the men meeved tae get their pairtners. Boothby kept his
promise : he made straicht for Daffy.

Daffy merried Joe Davidson fae New Deer : his fowk hid the Earl
o Aiberdeen Arms. James took up the cornet, an played in the New

Deer Brass Band at dances near at haun an hine awa, aawye fae New Blyth tae Alford. They played at Armistice Services; my father took the 'Last Post' solo twice. 'Ye hid tae watch yer top lip,' he said tae me, 'in case ye cut yersel shavin. Ye'll aften see that on a trumpet-man, a mowser tae proteck the lip.' The Band wis James Crichton, Alec Yule, Alec Cruickshank, James Ogston, Alec Crichton, Harry Yule, Charlie Simpson, Dod Dunbar, Alec Mutch, Leslie Taylor, Bill Johnstone, George Munro. They were plumbers, fairmers, railway-men, jiners, motor-hirers, posties. 'Some nichts' my father said, 'ye could hae played lang eneuch an lood eneuch tae be heard fae Aul Deer tae Fyvie, an they still widna tak the fleer. Some nichts ye kent ye hid a gweed crowd wie ye seen's ye'd gotten intae the first reel. There wis nae tellin.'

David Ogston wis a fiddler, an my father took the fiddle up, though he nivver played in public. Faan I wis little there wis still a fiddle in its ain case in the hoose at Kiddies, an a knot o rozett in the wee boxie faar the spare brig wis keppit.

Efter a lang time tholin the stounin in his nether wyme, my granfather socht the doctor an he wis patten tae the Infirmary in Aiberdeen. There wisna muckle they could dee for him, an he lay nae weel throwe the winter an the spring o nineteen thirty-echt. Daffy bade in the toon at this time an she lookit efter him, takkin twa trams tae ging an see him ilka day an bring him tasty mett tae tryst him intae ettin some. He did a great notion on sweetbreads so she wid cook them in her ain hoose an tak them up tae Foresterhill an heat them in the oven for him. She brocht him brave an cheery wirds, a souch o hame. On the nineteenth o April David Ogston dee'd at the age o saxty-fower. In the June o the same eer Patty married George Stables fae Holywell, Kennethmont. His fowk hid Bankheid at that time, an George an Patty gaed in there faan the aul fowk retired.

My father wis the last tae mairry o the Ogston femmly, sax eer efter his father's death an a year efter his sister Daffy lost her man, Joe, in a motor accident in Aiberdeen. Ae Sunday nicht in nineteen forty-three James wis on his wye hame on a push-bike fae Methlick tae Kidshill, on the stey brae oot o Methlick, the New Deer road,

faan he passed a woman walkin her bike up the lang slope o the brae-
face. He pedalled on a fyle bit the incline got the better o him anaa an
he hid tae come aff the saiddle tae catch his win again. The woman
cam abreist o him, an they got on tae newsin. He speired her name,
an she said Mary Dinnes. 'Some frien o Jim,?' he speired again,
mindin on the James Dinnes he hid met at dances at New Deer or
Pistligo. 'He's my brither,' said Mary, 'an faat micht your name be?'

A fyowe wiks gaed by an James wis cryin in at Braiklay wytin for
Mary tae come aff duty at Haddo Hoose. She wis an Auxiliary
Nurse ere, hid been sin nineteen forty, faan the Marquis o Aiberdeen
an Temair had gien the Government a bit o Haddo Hoose for
mithers up fae Glesca to come an hae their bairns awa fae the
stramash o war. There wis saxteen beds in the Hospital pairt for the
weemin come tae term, an room for five-an-twenty mair that were
still wytin, in the Hall pairt. The weemin cam bi rail fae Glesca tae
the Joint Station in Aiberdeen, faar they were met bi a Sister an a
nurse, an they were teen for lunch at Mitchell an Muils Restaurant
afore the private bus took them oot tae Haddo Hoose.

James an Mary fixed their waddin for the simmer o nineteen
forty-fower. The clash on ilka side wis aa the same, faativver airt it
sprang fae — there wis tae be a big offensive an the Allies wis gettin
ready tae throw aathing intil an invasion. Mary stoppit wark at
Haddo Hoose in April. Faan an Auxiliary depairted Lord Aiberdeen
made siccar that he saa the quine tae thank her an tae wish her weel,
bit he wis awa fae hame faan Mary left. Faan he won back tae
Haddo he fand oot she wis awa an sent her wird tae come an see him
at the earliest opportunity. He speired faat their plans wis an faar
the waddin wid be held. They couldna get a full reception, naebody
wis takkin bookins for meals sae near tae D-Day on the saxth o
June, an the date that James an Mary winted wis the third. They
hidna fixed on faar the waddin wid be either, so Mary said tae Lord
Aiberdeen that they hid still tae see tae some things. Straicht aff he
said, 'Why not get married in the Chapel, Nurse Dinnes?'. Mary
said that neither Mr Ogston nor hersel wid ivver think o askin sic a
thing. Lord Aiberdeen said she wisna askin, he wis offerin. Mary
said that she wid spik tae Mr Ogston.

They were merried on the third o June nineteen forty-fower bi Dr Matthew Neilson, James's meenister fae New Deer. Jean Dinnes, merried the eer afore tae James, gaed Mary the fite dress she hersel hid worn. A nurse at Haddo Hoose len'd her a veil an a pair o fite sheen. James left Sooth Kidshill in a hired car; he wore a blue suit wie a faint stripe. Efter the ceremony in the Chapel they gaed doon tae Methlick tae the Ythanview Hotel, faar they hid tea an hamebakin. Their cake wis made bi Mrs Roy o Bucksburn.

James an Mary gaed hame tae Sooth Kidshill on the saxth o June. Helen Jean, my father's mither, made room for the new bride: she gaed up tae Kate an Andra Watt at 7 Auchreddie Road, New Deer an bade wie them till forty-nine or fifty, syne she gaed tae Patty up at Bankheid o Kennethmont. Mithers tae dothers: in nineteen forty-five the same thing happened at Kidshill, faan William an Jane Dinnes sell't their craft at Braiklay an cam tae bide wie Mary in the April, the month efter I wis born. They bade in the room-end an their bedroom wis the middle room aff the lobby : efter a wik or twa they were draain their cheers intae the fireside in the kitchen an my father wis advised on a fyowe maitters that he kent himsel, like the best time tae sell nowt, maybe, or the richt wye tae spen calfies. James an Mary tholed the arrangement as weel as they were able, tull the aul fowk jaloosed that they wis maybe raxin ower far intae the on-gyauns o Kidshill, an they gaed intae Aiberdeen tae bide wie Willie an Maggie. They spent some time wie George an Jean efter that, bit the toon's steer didna suit them an they cam back tae Kiddies; William Dinnes dee'd there, in the end-room, on the seiventeenth o Mairch nineteen forty-echt, at the gweed age o sivventy-nine. He hid nivver kent saft livin an he dee'd in hard widder at the hinner-en o winter.

My sister Hilda wis born on the thirtieth o September nineteen forty-nine. She wisna a peer smout like I hid been, an she thrave nae bother. She wis christened on the twenty-second o January nineteen fifty in the Sooth Kirk, New Deer. Jean Florence made a cake for her wie a wee stork on the tap o't.

My father's mither dee'd at Bankheid o Kennethmont on the echth o Mey nineteen fifty-three, the Eer o Capital Letters : the Coronation o the new Queen, the Ascent o Everest, the Ashes Won bi England. She wis a quaet woman, Helen Jean, timorous in company : nae een tae coort the centre faar she mith be noticed. She wis laid tae rest faar David Ogston lay, on the breist o the Hill o Culsh abeen New Deer.

Aul times, my times. There were yokit thegither, there wis a grippin wird that made them baith as een. I grew tae scance at them that hae the past is hazed wie glamourie; bit I kent, tee, that I could nivver lichtlify the warsle that hid geen tae be the makkin o the warld I wis at hame in. Nae roose o mine is nott, noo, tae be the heid-shafe o their story; facts be their warrandice, their fact my watchwird.

To my daughters,
Brooke and Amanda,
and my
grandson Marco

Foreword

WHEN someone like Maggie Tabberer, who has been in the public eye for nearly forty years and is a household name, writes an autobiography, most people feel that they already know her. In a sense, of course, they do.

A good autobiography, however, should reveal what lies beneath the gloss of fame. Few public faces are brave enough or fearless enough to do this and settle instead for the occasional glimpse or coy insight into the private world of their fears, their insecurities, their frailties. What sets this book apart from the rash of memoirs is Maggie's extraordinary honesty and her total lack of artifice and pretension.

Having spent most of her life in the world of fashion and PR, a world notorious for fabrication and fantasy, Maggie has managed to remain essentially true to herself. This self is an intricate interweaving of complexities and contradictions, which Maggie has not shied away from revealing to the reader. Writing honestly about oneself is often a traumatic, painful and humiliating experience. Digging up old hurts, mistakes and insecurities is like pressing down on a sore tooth, and I have witnessed the many tears that have been shed during the writing of this book.

There have also, however, been just as many laughs. For unlike those public figures whose egos dictate that they take themselves incredibly seriously, Maggie has never lost the ability to laugh at herself, heartily and with humility.

The Maggie that all of her friends and family have known is here in this book, a living breathing blueprint. There is Maggie the Baptist from suburban Adelaide, who will look aghast at something you have done or said which she thinks is not quite respectable or proper. 'What will the neighbours think?' was very much a part of her upbringing.

There is Maggie the Larrikin, who will be the first to speak the unspeakable or tweak the nose of pomposity and then scream with laughter at the shock of what she has done. She is still very much the daughter of the father who turned the hose on his disapproving sister.

Maggie the Sensualist runs like a golden thread through the fabric of the book. All of her senses quicken to the stimulation of choosing what to wear or setting a table or decorating a house or cooking a meal or dancing to music or smelling a rosemary bush or stroking a loved one.

Maggie the Perfectionist was evident from the first time she refused to go to school unless her hair ribbons matched her dress and she is constantly being teased by her friends for the never-ending tidying of her house and theirs, the plumping of cushions, the ironing of clothes, the re-arranging of objects. Near enough is never good enough, which is one of the ingredients for her success in whatever she undertakes. She will always spend extra time, energy and concentration to push herself and others to do their utmost to make it simply the best.

But always present through the public triumphs and personal heartaches is Maggie the Vulnerable, the warm, the generous, the gutsy, the big-hearted woman that everyone who has ever known her will recognise. This book is Maggie and reveals why she has gained what so many other people who have also achieved wealth, fame and admiration never attain. She not only loves, she is beloved.

Susan Mitchell
Writer and Broadcaster

Contents

Sunday, Bloody Sunday

I was alone at Greenville, my home in the Southern Highlands in New South Wales. It was 13 April 1997. Steve, the manager of the property, had called in to see if I needed anything, he was going into Bowral. 'Just the newspapers, Steve. Thank you.'

The newspapers! I knew the story was about to break, a friend had warned me the previous evening. Please don't let it say 'Maggie T's ex' again, I thought, but predictably it did. Both Sunday papers carried the 'shock story' — Richard Zachariah, the man with whom I'd shared ten years of my life, and had bitterly, publicly and painfully broken up with eighteen months ago, was to marry 'the other woman'. The phones will run hot today, I surmised. I was right.

I made coffee and walked out onto the verandah. For seven years I'd lived at Greenville and I still couldn't believe how beautiful it was. It was a clear, cold, autumn day, the trees were dressed in vivid gold. I stood and watched a flock of ducks glide in and swoosh to a perfect landing on the lake. Those bulrushes were really taking over the lake. I'd have to think about clearing them this winter, and I made a mental note to talk to Steve about them. The phone rang. Here we go, I thought. My friends and family have been wonderful, so concerned for me and the lousy time I've had adjusting to Richard's betrayal. It will be my daughter Brooke, or a mate — Pete, Barb, Georgie, or perhaps Vicki or Ken. It wasn't. It was my stepson, Nicolas.

'Maggie,' then a great sob.

'Nicolas?'

'Maggie, Pappi, he — '

'Nicolas, Nicolas, what? What about Pappi?'

'Oh, Maggie, Pappi died last night.'

'No, oh no!'

Not today, please not today, I thought, I can't handle this today. Then no, not any day. In the next few minutes Nicolas told me how his father, Ettore Prossimo, a man I'd spent twenty-nine years with, had died suddenly of a heart attack in Italy.

'Maggie, could you please tell the girls? I can't.'

'Of course, Nicolas, I'll call them. Darling, I'm so, so sorry.'

'Yes, I know. But, Maggie, now all I've got in the world are you and Brooke and Amanda.'

'Nico, we will always be a family, I want you to remember that. I'll call you after I've spoken to the girls. Will you be OK?'

'Sure, it's just so, so …'

'Yes, darling, I know, it's hard.'

We hung up and I sat and cried, then I rang Brooke in Sydney. This was not going to be easy, she absolutely adored Ettore. Her first words were, 'I must go to my brother, right now.'

'Good, darling. I'll call you there after I've spoken to Amanda.'

I knew it was hideously late in Italy, but I dialled my younger daughter's number anyway. She had in fact just spoken to Ettore's sister, Franca, and had been sitting staring at the phone, wondering how to tell me. We cried and I told her to try to get some sleep and we'd speak again in a few hours. Sergio, her husband, sent all his love.

I then rang my best friend, Barbara. She loved Pross even though we'd flown a lot of emotional missions together. She had seen me through a turbulent courtship, a marriage, the birth and ten days later the death of our son and many years later the cruel break-up of our marriage; because of a redhead, a younger red-head. They're always younger, aren't they? We both cried. The phone went feral in the next couple of hours. The humiliating headlines, 'Maggie T's ex to marry', paled into insignificance as I told my friends about Pross' death.

I walked to the bathroom and splashed my face with cold water. I was shocked at my reflection — red nose, swollen eyes and I looked scared. I was scared. My Rock of Gibraltar had just crumbled. Pappi dead. We hadn't been together for years, but I always knew he was there.

The phone again.

'Hello.'

'Margaret?'

Margaret. No one calls me Margaret, except a couple of mad friends and then only in jest.

'Yes.'

'Margaret, it's Chas.'

Chas! I don't believe this, Charles Tabberer, my first husband — he had always called me Margaret. We hadn't spoken for years. It was an awkward, stilted conversation. He had phoned to see if I was alright: he had seen the headlines. I told him about Ettore. He expressed his sympathy and added, 'I mean, this man brought up my daughters, didn't he?'

'Yes, Chas, he did.'

'My God, Margaret, you've certainly had a life of great highs and lows, haven't you?'

'You could say that, Chas, yes.'

'It seems to me your greatest mistake has been that you've picked the wrong men, starting with me.' And he gave a nervous, embarrassed laugh.

'Yes, Chas, you might be right.'

THE SKY had turned a deep charcoal grey. It intensified the light. I watched the noisy sulphur-crested cockatoos wheel in and land in the big oak tree. Destructive little devils! How dare they look so beautiful, stark white against the dark sky. I stood watching them for a long, long time, my head scrambled with so many painful memories. And then through my tears I suddenly started to laugh. I mean you had to laugh. The irony of it hit me. Consider this: number one phoned after we'd been apart for thirty-something years.

Number two died.

Number three announced his impending marriage!

Margaret was definitely *not* having a good day.

Childhood

MY CHILDHOOD home, where I grew up and lived until I married, was a typical Adelaide bungalow. Eighty years old and built of stone, it looked like a child's drawing of a house, with a door in the middle, a window at either side and a verandah across the front. I was the youngest of Alfred and Molly Trigar's brood of five; clearly a mistake. Times were tough in 1936 and another mouth to feed had obviously not been planned. But I was born and took my place at the end of the line: Ronald, Joan, Betty, Nancy and Margaret May. Margaret after Princess Margaret and May after my stern-faced Grandmother Ryan. I hated the 'May'. Years later my sister Nancy would intone, 'Margaret May ... but then Margaret may not.' Rather prophetic really.

Alfred had come from a large family of Cornish descent. He was blond, tall, long-limbed and lanky, with a wonderful aquiline nose and incredible sky-blue eyes. Mother had a mysterious look — long, very dark hair which she wore in a thick twist, olive skin and big, sad black-brown eyes. I can still see those sad eyes. Her illegitimate birth and unhappy childhood were responsible for much of the sadness in them. Added later was the everyday struggle to make ends meet.

Molly never looked Australian. For years I was asked, 'Where does your mother come from?' How, as a child, was I supposed to answer that? 'I don't know,' was all I ever said. Eventually, I did find out, or partly. Annie Ryan, her mother, was said to have had an affair with a foreign sailor. He left the country and sailed off leaving Annie pregnant in a time when 'nice' girls didn't do that sort of thing. She suffered all the shame and indignity of bearing her daughter out of wedlock. The family must have moved into damage control. Annie handed over her tiny daughter to her brother and his wife, and went away.

Mary, or Molly as she became known, spent her first years with them until they fostered her out. I guess that's where her sadness began. I have no affection in my heart for Grandma and Grandpa Ryan, as we called them. They were dour. I have a sense of ugly black lace-up shoes, thick lyle stockings, dark dresses and a tight mean little bun on my big, grim, square-faced Grandma. Grandpa always wore a sombre suit and a mood to match.

My mother grew up with a strong sense of shame, she was made to feel more than illegitimate. Insecure and feeling unworthy, she was fostered out and pushed around, having to move on again and again, never fitting in. I don't know if this is correct, but the family folklore is that she was only taken back into the Ryan household when she was old enough to help in the house and later to work and bring in money. I hated Grandma and Grandpa Ryan for what they did to Molly. When we were little, visiting them was a nightmare. 'Sit up straight.' 'Don't talk.' 'Don't be loud.' 'Say thank you.' We were never invited past the kitchen. There was no joy in their house. It seemed as dark and shuttered as they were, and I could never wait to leave.

My mother's baby photograph shows the most adorable little girl. For years I've stared at it and wondered how could they?

Molly's deep sense of inferiority contaminated her entire life. I suspect that despite her incredible efforts to protect, love and serve her family, she passed on some of that 'not good enough' feeling to her children. As I grew older I was very aware, as were my sisters, that if we had differences of opinion we should keep them to ourselves. Mother's pride was so bound up in our family that she wanted us to be close-knit and loving, always. Things she obviously never experienced as a child, but so longed for.

Our mother had an overwhelming sense of respectability. In later years, when Dad would call by the pub on his way home and so be late for tea (it was never dinner), she would stand, impatient and anxious, at the front gate. We kids would be wailing about being hungry but we always had to wait for Dad. Finally, around the corner from Unley Road he would appear. My father must have held the record as the slowest bike rider in the world. How the bike stayed up was a miracle. He would weave very, very slowly from one side of the road to the other, and I'd watch my mother's face grow dark with anxiety and her eyes moist with humiliation. She'd mutter through clenched teeth, 'Get inside, Alfred. How dare you come home like this? What will the neighbours think?' It was always what will people think? I loved him anyway.

But life wasn't all sad and anxious. We were known as the rowdy Trigars, and we were. There was always footy on the radio, barking dogs, screaming kids, doors banging, aunts and uncles coming and going. While we visited our maternal grandparents only when it was absolutely necessary, we used to see our paternal grandparents almost every weekend, and we regularly visited Dot and Frank, Mum and Dad's best friends. My father and Frank had become mates when they both worked building roads. Frank and Dot lived in a large rambling house set on a hill above the Centennial Park Cemetery, where they were the caretakers.

As kids we loved going there because we were free to run through the cemetery and play hide and seek amongst the tombstones. My parents are now buried there and it is as cold and unfriendly as Grandpa Ryan's house. The Trigars' house, however, was full of warmth. My father's father was a towering great man with a big droopy moustache and a neat way of flipping it into a disciplined curve with his forefinger. My grandmother was a round little woman, literally half his height, with snow-white hair neatly worn with a side part and finger-waves.

They owned the last dairy in the inner-city area of Richmond. The property, while not large, bordered onto railway land where they were able to graze their cows. At the back of their house was a coolroom where Grandma churned the milk into the best cream and butter in the area. Customers would come to the back door with a billy can to buy their milk and cream. Grandma always wore a pinny, tinkling with a pocket full of small change. She kept chickens and ducks and sold their eggs. At one stage she also had turkeys and some very bad tempered geese who terrified me with their savage charges at my skinny legs. With all of us seated around a big table, Dad and Grandad would enjoy a beer, the women would have tea, the kids a glass of fresh milk and always delicious scones with lashings of Gran's fresh cream and homemade jam.

My father had a horse called Gifty, and through most of my early years we went everywhere with Gifty pulling the trap. All my girlfriends' fathers drove cars while we went by horse and buggy. We would leave our grandparents' house at dusk and have to light the little oil lamps on the side of the buggy. Nancy and I would sit facing our parents in the dicky seat with our backs to old Gifty's bum. When Dad tickled Gifty with the whip to get a move on across a busy road she usually let us know what she thought by issuing a large fart, warm and smelly, on the back of our necks. We'd all laugh, hold our noses and clip clop home, tummies and hearts full.

I don't know how we all fitted into our old house. At one stage Nancy and I shared a big double bed. We would write notes to each other and hide them in one of the brass knobs on the bedhead, and read with a torch under the blankets after the lights were turned out. But we could never fool Mum. She'd yell from her room across the hall, 'I know what you two are up to. Now put out that torch and go to sleep.'

The centre of the house was a big square room with a fireplace at one end. In it was Mummy's cherished big polished wooden table. Although it was used only for special occasions, such as Christmas or when visitors came, it was always set with a linen and lace doily and a vase of flowers fresh from the garden. There was a settee on one side of the room, a sideboard on the other and two big chairs for Mum and Dad at either side of the fire. There Mum would sit with her never-ending basket of mending, Dad with his newspaper and the big bakelite 'His Master's Voice' radio tuned to our favourite programmes, including 'Saturday Night Theatre', 'Dossier on Demetrios', 'The Quiz Kids', 'Pick a Box with Bob and Dolly Dyer' or 'Jack Davey's Quiz Show'. The whole family always tried to answer the questions, dreaming about winning one of the big prizes.

The kitchen was a small room off the enclosed back verandah. For years Mother cooked on the wood stove. Later, her joy was a new gas cooker, but she never got rid of that old stove. The gas was supplied by a meter in the front hall. You paid as you used, and there was always a search for pennies for the damn thing. We had no refrigerator, just a large, old icebox in the corner of the kitchen, serviced by the iceman, a big, loud, cheerful man with huge arms.

Washing up brought on a nightly squabble amongst the girls. Joan would be going out, Betty had friends to see, Nancy had a mountain of homework and Margaret May was at the end of the line. To this day I would walk a country mile rather than wipe up. For many years there was no running water in the kitchen. We had to fill a kettle from the small brown sink off the back verandah and boil the water. When water was eventually connected to the kitchen, it was cause for a big celebration.

My two favourite places at home were Gifty's stable and the roof of the big shed next to the house. The trap was kept there, as were the family bicycles, Dad's tools and the wood-fired copper where Mum boiled the life out of the endless piles of laundry that went with having five kids. I can still see her copper stick, its timber turned white and furry from a zillion dunkings in that big soapy pot. She washed every day. A visiting aunt once counted twenty-something little dresses flapping on the clothes line.

A trapdoor in the floor of the shed led to a cellar where occasionally we would hide. It was dark and damp and a bit scary. But the shed roof, I loved. It was covered in the most luscious grape vine, and the grapes would lie on the iron in the hot Adelaide sun and grow fat and golden. I enjoyed clambering up there and simply stuffing my face. I was a fearless climber, much to my mother's horror; climbing over the roof, the top of the water tank and up into the big fruit trees that grew by the side of the house. I'd happily sit up there for hours.

Each day milk and bread were delivered to our house by horse and cart. I loved the smell of the baker's van when he opened the doors. The vegetable man and the rabbito came weekly. An ancient Chinese man sold fish from his handcart, and every now and then a man who sharpened knives and scissors, and another who sold clothes line props would come by.

Mum and Dad grew as much fruit and vegetables as they

could to help feed us, but both loved flowers. Dad grew the biggest dahlias in the district and Mum loved her carnations, but none of us kids enjoyed the relentless rhubarb that seemed to thrive, despite a concentrated effort by my sister Betty to kill it off. She stamped on it every morning and night going to and from work. If you're intent on growing rhubarb try stamping on it twice a day, it sure as hell worked for ours. Rhubarb and apple, rhubarb and tapioca, rhubarb pie and rhubarb with rhubarb. And we all hated it. Mother would simply say, 'Waste not, want not,' and we just shut up and ate it. In fact we ate everything at her table. She didn't have to spell it out to us, we knew we were poor and life was a struggle.

Dear Molly, she had to be the worst cook of all time. She'd boil the vegetables to a nice shade of tasteless grey, she'd grill the chops to a state of char. There was tripe in white sauce, my all-time favourite gag food, and lamb's fry like boot leather. But I loved the leftover dripping. Hidden beneath a congealed layer of fat in the bottom of the pan, the dark jelly was delicious spread on a thick slice of fresh white bread, topped with a slather of tomato sauce. The payback for this decadence was having cold roast lamb sandwiches for lunch three days straight. I'd use all my charms to try to swap them with some school friend, even for plain jam jobs. Anything was better than grey lamb.

Mother's best effort was roast rabbit with herb and bread stuffing, never enough stuffing to my mind. Sometimes Dad would go out the back and catch a chook. I'd watch through the flyscreen door as he walked into the hen house. There would be lots of squawking and some bad language from Dad, then he'd emerge with a flapping white hen, grab the tomahawk and lop off its head on the woodblock. Inevitably the hen would jump loose and, to my fascination, run around minus a head with blood spurting in all directions. Then Dad would fling it in a bucket and Mum would pour a kettle of boiling water over it. Dad would sit on the edge of an old sink in the backyard with the bucket between his legs, one of his hand-rolled skinny fags in his mouth, and merrily pluck out the feathers. I couldn't bear the smell of those wet feathers; it was disgusting. Mind you, it didn't stop me eating the chook. To this day if I buy a free-range chicken and there's so much as a skerrick of a feather, it triggers the memory of that awful smell.

While my mother was not a gifted cook, she was a great housekeeper. The linoleum in the hall was always polished to a hazardous shine and the furniture buffed to a gleam. Even now I can picture her cleaning the windows with methylated spirits and crunched-up newspaper. Molly didn't know what it was to sit still.

She always had certain routines to 'freshen up' the place. Lace curtains in the front bedrooms were washed, starched, pressed and rehung with monotonous regularity. A new piece of oilcloth with some terrible pattern would be bought for the kitchen table. And then there was the bath. The bathroom was set off the verandah opposite the kitchen, little more than an add-on really. It had unlined corrugated-iron walls — an oven in summer and an icebox in winter. It contained a tin bath and a cranky chip heater, which was always blowing up. There was a shower over the bath, but we never used it because Mum said it was a waste of water. Nearly every week she would paint the bath 'to freshen it up'. Friday night was family bath night, and as usual I was last in line. Mum would often have painted the bath the day before, and by the time I got in the paint would be soggy. Inevitably I would get out with white paint stuck to my bottom. I hated being last.

My eldest sister, Joan, was something of a surrogate mother to me. I guess because poor Molly was out working, or just plain worn out. Joan would wash and cut my hair, and tweezer splinters out of my bottom, a legacy from scaling the back fence. She was first on hand with the Dettol when I scraped my knees and later knitted my sweaters and sewed my best dresses. But by golly she could be tough. If I talked at the dinner table she would lean across and whack my fingers with the bread knife, not that it stopped me talking.

In summer we were an outdoor family, with trips on the tram to Glenelg beach, being burnt to a crisp in the sun and returning to one of Mum's home remedies. Sliced tomato halves or white vinegar soothed burnt backs but certainly didn't heal them. Peeling skin was a favourite pastime, and Nancy and I would compete to peel off the biggest piece. I had inherited my mother's olive skin, and I'd burn black each summer. It somehow offended her. In later years I wondered if she suspected that she had some 'coloured' blood, or had she just been taunted as a child because of her black hair and dark complexion? I didn't really care. But she would nag me with: 'Stay out of the sun'; 'Put on a hat'; 'Keep under cover'; all pointless advice to a headstrong brat. Summer nights meant mattresses dragged out onto the back lawn. I'd lie in the crook of my father's arm and he would point out the Milky Way, the Saucepan and the Southern Cross. I never look up at a starry sky without thinking of him, my dear old Dad.

As I grew older I became fed up with being last in line and turned into a bit of a ringleader. I had my gang, which consisted of Natalie Pike, the prettiest girl in class, Beverley Berryman, who was sweet with Ginger Meggs red hair, bossy Patty Wickes and gentle Judy Holmes. Over the back fence were my constant playmates, Ronnie and Denny Wilson, two snow-white blond brothers. When they left, Barbara Loader moved in and became a close friend too. Years later she married my first boyfriend, dark-eyed Maurey Crocker. Down the street was a tall, handsome boy called Don Harris, my first crush.

Don and I would escape from the other kids and climb the huge peppercorn trees that grew in a vacant block on the corner of our street. He'd be Tarzan, I'd be Jane. Years later, after I had moved interstate, I was at the Adelaide races and this tall, good-looking guy stepped out of the crowd and said, 'You Jane? Me Tarzan.' We fell in a heap laughing. Don swears that on one occasion, after he'd fought off an imaginary lion and swung to my rescue in the peppercorn tree, I had looked down at the lion then looked up at him and said, 'Well! Kill it!' From that moment on he said he knew I was not going to be a tame little Adelaide housewife.

On really hot days we'd beg to be allowed to go to the local swimming pool, which was in a huge tin building. A high balcony circled the pool, and when the older boys used it as a diving board the attendant would scream blue murder and they'd be banned for a week. One day I actually crawled out onto it, but even then I must have had a keen sense of survival. One look down was enough to send me clambering back on my shaky little pins. But all the other rough stuff — the dunking, the splashing, flicking with wet towels — I adored. Only when I had been in the water so long my toes and fingers had shrivelled like crumpled paper and turned dead white did I know it was time to get out and spend my ha'penny on a bush biscuit. They were big oblongs, dry as a tack and totally tasteless. I loved them.

At school I was always getting into trouble, mainly for talking in class. I spent a considerable amount of time sitting outside the headmaster's office waiting for some kind of detention to be dished out. Usually it was writing one hundred times, 'I will not talk in class.' I found a way of tying three pencils together with a rubber band so I could write three rows at once. I don't believe it fooled the headmaster one iota.

Although my teachers never actually said as much, it was implied that I wasn't like the rest of the Trigar girls. What did that mean? Not as bright? Not as committed? I never dared ask, but I knew I was out of step. I always felt a sense of difference. I loathed school and I particularly hated homework. I'd fudge it and beg my sister to help me. I never came to grips with arithmetic. My spelling to this day is appalling. Geography was threatening and history simply a mystery. However, I was a mean defence basketball goalie and I adored art class. Somehow I scraped by with a pass each year.

Now when I look at my school pictures many of the names have faded but I remember the faces. That one was Miss Goodie Two Shoes, that one a bully, that one with the blond plaits used to sit in front of me and I'd watch the nits do somersaults up and down the part in her hair. Of course we all got nits. Mother would go into a spin, dreadful smelly solutions would be bought from the chemist along with a fine-tooth comb, and we would be dunked and combed and dunked and combed.

I don't know where such traits come from, but from an early age I had definite ideas about how I wanted to look. I refused to go to school unless the colour of my hair ribbon matched that of my dress. Poor Mummy. She had four daughters to contend with, and this little monster with a stubborn colour sense. If the dress and ribbon didn't match I'd march to the end of our street and hide in the doorway of the bootmaker's shop. Then mid-morning I'd wander home and say we had been given a half holiday. Mother would eventually take the ruler to my legs and whack me back up the street until I went off to school.

When I was about six years old, the Second World War was a daily subject in our house. The 'Japs' and the Germans were discussed at length, battle headlines were read aloud, radio reports were tuned into, and I felt the threat. The 'what if?' questions were often in my mind but never really spoken. At school I wore a little blue fabric 'safety' bag which Mummy had sewn for me. It hung around my neck and contained a bandage, ear plugs and a small pad to bite on if the bombs started to drop. It was all terrifying. We had air-raid drills, during which a siren would sound and in an orderly fashion we would file out of class and go and sit in a big cement irrigation pipe half sunk into the playground. On air-raid drill days my imagination would conjure up all sorts of horrors. After school I would hop on my bike and pedal like blazes to get home to the safety of my family before the bombs dropped out of the sky. Years later, of course, I realised that I did live in the lucky country; we had never known real war, just the threat of it.

At the movies in the old Unley Town Hall, where I regularly went with Mum and Dad, I would cover my face with my hands when the war newsreels came on. I didn't want to see bombed buildings and bodies. I remember the food coupons, too. Mother would sit at the kitchen table, working out how to feed her family and constantly thumbing the pages of her coupon book, as if by some miracle it would double in size. It never did. Frequently we were sent to do the shopping. Often she didn't have the necessary coupons and just as often not the money, but who could say no to children? The local shopkeepers never did. It would 'go on the tab'. They knew Mrs Trigar would settle when she could, and she always did.

I don't remember my childhood birthdays but I do remember feeling disappointed that my Christmas present came in a plain brown paper bag and would be something sensible, such as socks or knickers and singlets. Now I am obsessive about wrapping my family's gifts — coordinating the colour of ribbons and paper. My kids love to send me up but they have never had a sad little gift in a brown paper bag.

My brother Ron, nineteen years older than me, had gone off to join the Navy. He trained as a hard-hat diver, which terrified my mother. We would anxiously watch the mail each day and there was always great excitement when his letters arrived. His homecomings were as exhilarating as his departures sad. I thought he was the ant's pants. He would slip me a coin to press his trousers. I would make sure that his navy-coloured, serge bell-bottoms were perfectly creased in the traditional manner with the help of a damp cloth and Mum's old-fashioned iron. I would also run his bath. Wanting it to be a big, deep bath I'd pile on the woodchips until they were roaring. Mum would run outside and yell, 'Margaret, the flames are coming out of the chimney, you're going to burn the house down.' I never did, but there were some anxious moments.

Ron was a real larrikin. He arrived home once with a bunch of sailor mates and told Mum we had to put them up. We simply didn't have room in the house, but they were quite happy to roll out their sleeping bags and doss down in the shed. They had cracked open some bottles of beer and I can still see my father sitting on an old stool with his worn beautiful hands, rolling a fag and looking up at Ron, laughing and laughing at all his yarns. He adored his only son. Another time when Ron was home on leave he convinced my father he had the best way to use up that bloody rhubarb. He would make rhubarb beer. It was to be a family effort.

We collected all the Woodroofe's lemonade bottles we could find, those unique to South Australia with the little stone stoppers. Then we washed and dried them, and picked the rhubarb and chopped it up. The old copper was stoked, and the red brew boiled and bubbled for hours. Finally the bottles were lined up like red soldiers along the window ledge on the back verandah and Ron went back to fight the war, telling Dad how long he had to wait for the fermentation to be complete. He needn't have worried. A few nights later, *bang! Bang!* They exploded all over the walls and ceiling. There was broken glass, stone stoppers and pinky-red liquid sprayed over everything. Mummy was furious. It took hours to clean up and she didn't hold back telling Dad what she thought of him and his son and their cockeyed idea. Dad just gave me a big wink and laughed.

My sister Joan worked as a clerk in an office. She married her handsome soldier Ray Clark, who was a dead ringer for Tyrone Power. I always thought he looked gorgeous. Still do. They lost their first child at birth, a boy, but this was kept from me and Nancy because we were young. All we noticed were the many whispered conversations behind closed doors. Once when I was playing in the shed I spied a large bundle on a high shelf. Scrambling up I discovered a bassinette. I dragged it down and had started to put my dolls in it when Joan came into the shed and began to shout hysterically, tears pouring down her cheeks. I stood there, stunned. Why was I always doing something wrong?

It seemed I was always in trouble. Like with the butter. I loved butter but it was in short supply in our house; the food coupons, not to mention cash, saw to that. My mother was too proud to ask my grandmother for butter, aware that it was their only means of support. I came home from school one afternoon to an empty house, and as usual I was starving. I pulled a chair over to the dresser, took the butter dish down and made myself a couple of sturdy sandwiches. When my mother returned home she burst into tears. It was all the butter she had saved for the family for an entire week, and I'd eaten the lot. She didn't yell or hit me. If only she had. She just sat there, quietly weeping. I hung my head and tried to say I was sorry. My sense of shame was almost unbearable. To this day if I tell this story, my eyes fill with tears. And now if you open my fridge you will always find three tubs of butter. I made her very sad and she was so caring for all of us. She tried so hard to look after everyone in the family:

going out to work cleaning other people's houses, and cooking, cleaning, washing, ironing and carrying out endless tasks at home. She scraped, saved and went without even the smallest pleasure for herself. On top of that she cared about all the aunts and uncles, the grandparents and her friends. This wasn't the first time I had made her cry and it certainly wasn't the last, but it is imprinted indelibly on my mind. I'll never stop regretting my greed for that butter.

My father's drinking became his way of coping with the disappointments in his life. It was increasingly hard for him to make a living, feed a large family and pay off the house. There was the war, the Depression and the uncertainty of any employment. I do know, though, that he loved my mother very much. They always slept in the same bed and he never left or came back into the house without giving her a kiss. They had met on a tram. Dad was making eyes at Mum and began to show off, really acting up, until the conductor put him off the tram. Dad must have been about nineteen years old. He ran along to the next stop where Mum usually got off, and that was the beginning of their life together.

My father always spoke lovingly about how beautiful Molly was when they met. She was seventeen when they married. Their wedding photos show Alfred tall, blond and handsome, and Molly small, dark, with heavy black hair caught in an orange-blossom veil. Just after their third child was born, Molly saw an advertisement in the newspaper: 'Wanted: human hair for wig making.' She went off and sold her hair and came home with a perky bob. I'm sure she still looked gorgeous but Alfred didn't speak to her for a week. It was the biggest argument they were ever to have. Mummy claimed that with the babies she had no time to groom her long hair. Also, she believed that no sacrifice was ever too great for her family.

As time went on Dad found a good job as a groundsman at the Unley Oval and later at the Adelaide Oval. There wasn't much my Dad didn't know about growing grass. I adored those summer evenings when, after tea, he'd 'dinky' Nancy and me on his bicycle over to the Unley Oval, a few blocks from our house. We would wear our swimsuits under our dresses, and at the oval we'd run in and out of the sprinklers. Dad would squelch around changing their positions and then go back and do it all again before dawn.

I adored Dad's sister Thelma. When I was about ten years old I travelled miles by tram just to spend the day with her. She had married late in life by the standards of those days and had one son, my favourite cousin Lyndon. I thought Thelma had style. She drank whisky, smoked, wore red nail varnish and dressed with a sophisticated difference: beautiful pleat-front slacks and little handknitted cardigans over silk shirts. Once she and my father had a row and she stormed out of our house. At the gate, as she turned to give him a final earful of abuse, Dad grabbed the garden hose and let her have it. She was drenched and naughty Alf just laughed. Mummy was appalled by this behaviour.

My mother was also irritated by the regular visits of Dad's friend and drinking partner, Robbie. He was a bachelor and would come calling to the back door, always it seemed at tea time. Mummy allowed him to sit just inside the kitchen door by the icebox; he kept his bike clips on and his hat propped on his knee. I don't remember him being anything but quiet and polite. He only ever stayed a short time and he'd back out of the room thanking Mum as he went. I always felt sorry for him. There was a great loneliness about this man, and as humble as our house was, we had companionship. There were kids, pets, noise, a meal being cooked. I never knew where or how he lived. He would just slide off into the night until his next visit.

'Always at tea time, Alf. Why does he always come at tea time?' Molly would carry on. Never did she weaken and ask Robbie to stay.

Dad would quietly retire to his chair at the head of the kitchen table, which is where he was one howling winter's night when we were all eating the evening meal. The old ceiling began to moan and groan. A few seconds later a little river of dust streamed down onto the table. One of my sisters yelled, 'The ceiling's going, get out!' There was a stampede for the door as the entire ceiling caved in and eighty years of dust followed. We did a quick headcount — Dad was missing. When the dust cleared, there he was, sitting at the table with his drink in his hand. As still as a statue and shrouded in grey dust, he was not in the least perturbed.

Dad was always first up. By around four-thirty he'd be sitting at the kitchen table, listening to the news on the radio, his long legs crossed, rolling his fags for the day, which he kept in a little tin. He had a metal roller and he would feed the paper into one end, stack in the 'baccie', give the roller a twirl and out would come a cigarette, of sorts. A couple of years ago Nancy gave me this little machine, together with Dad's old corkscrew. Both were weapons for his death one way or the other. I can't look at them without missing him.

When I was very small I used to give him hairstyles. He'd sit in his corner of the kitchen and I'd brush his, by then, very fine, wispy hair. I'd spit on my fingers and shape big kiss-curls onto his fore-head, or one big sausage curl down the centre. The family would roar with laughter. Dad had limitless love and patience with me. I was his baby, his centenary model as he used to say, and he called me 'Skeeter', claiming I was as skinny and little as a mosquito.

We used to go to the Parkside Baptist Church. Father rarely, but Mother and all the children every Sunday. In fact, three times, for Christian Endeavour, Sunday school and evening church. Even at a tender age I considered this to be overkill. The evening service was best because I could stand close to my mother and hear her sing. She had a marvellous contralto voice and eventually joined the choir.

I never felt comfortable in the Baptist Church. The sermons were all hell and brimstone. It was scary and no one seemed very happy. It was like a visit to Grandpa Ryan's. I became wilful, or as the family would proclaim, 'Margaret is very single-minded.' I refused to go. I know this hurt my mother, but Daddy didn't say a word. We'd just look knowingly at each other when the subject came up.

I thought a lot about clothes, probably because I lived in hand-me-downs. My sisters sewed well, and my first 'new' dress was one Joan made for me to wear to her wedding in 1944. It was blue silk with little yellow pears and red apples all over it. About an hour before Joan was to go to the church she went to press the dress. The iron was too hot and she burnt the sleeve out. I was heartbroken. Joan just grabbed the scrap fabric, chopped out a new sleeve and quickly sewed it in. I went off to the wedding, one sleeve slightly on the bias, but it was my dress and it was *new*.

When I was about nine years old I spent a lot of time at my friend Natalie's house. She was everything I wanted to be, pretty with curly blond hair. I always felt gawky, all arms and legs. If I was called home from play for lunch I'd scoff it down and be back at Natalie's in a flash. Her mother would ask, 'What did you have for lunch, darling, a glass of water and a swing on the gate?' I loved their house, it seemed smarter than ours, and Natalie and her family were very sweet to me. One year Natalie was chosen to ride the float of the black horse, Nipper, in the John Martins Christmas Pageant, one of the great annual

Adelaide events. Mummy took me in to see her. I had mixed emotions when my pretty friend, dressed in a white tulle fairy dress with a silver star wand, went riding by. I was proud that she was my friend but so envious.

Several years later I got to dress up in costumes. At about thirteen years of age I joined the Combined Churches Physical Education Group at our local Baptist church. We did coordinated marching, floor exercises, clubs (where we swung black and white-striped clubs in a set of exercises) and rods (where we performed with shiny silver rods). When I was measured for my rod, from the centre of my neck to the tip of my longest finger, a message came back to say it couldn't possibly be right, no one had arms that long! That did a lot for my confidence. Then there were the musical numbers, performed in costumes.

I had only been with the group for a short time when auditions were held for the state team to compete in the national titles in Ballarat. I knew my parents would find it hard to pay for the costumes, travel and accommodation, but I wanted so badly to compete. My mother agreed that I could, and when I was chosen to join the state team there was high excitement all round. Once a week I had the local group's rehearsals and state rehearsals. However, my dreams of wearing a pretty fairy costume like my friend Natalie were dashed when I was chosen, probably because I was the tallest, to play the 'Big Baboon' in our musical number. The song lyrics were: *'And the big baboon one night in June, he married them and very soon, they went upon their Aba Daba Honey Moooooon ... '* Photographs of the performance show a tall, skinny girl in a tight, brown jersey costume with funny little red pants and braces, and a face with big ears peeking out of the headdress. Coming out from behind her was a very long, stuffed tail. The number brought the house down but I was ragged by all the kids for a long time afterwards.

In the same competition I was lead girl in the marching routine. Having practised in the local hall, in my mind I had choreographed the routine to fit the hall's interior features — turn right at the dreadful green curtains, left at the fire-hose, cut diagonally across the floor at the staircase. I was the perfect leader, until we found ourselves on the big stage in Ballarat, where there were no green curtains, firehoses or staircases to guide me. With growing panic I led my charges on a pathetic shambles zig-zagging all over the stage. I wanted to die, and almost did when the South Australian official gave me a withering look as we lurched off stage, deflated and penalised.

Travelling to and from Ballarat by bus was very exciting. Away from my family for the first time, it was the start of my love affair with travel. When my friend Patty Wickes' parents suggested I travel with her to visit her relatives scattered from Port Lincoln across to Ceduna in the centre of the Great Australian Bight, I was keen to go. How I talked my parents into it I don't know, but suddenly Patty and I were waving goodbye from the deck of a steamer and sailing out of Port Adelaide for the overnight crossing to Port Lincoln, where we were to catch the train for the rest of our trip. We both felt very grown up.

On board we had tea in the dining room, then decided to take a bath. By this time we were well out into the strait, and the old tub was really starting to rock and roll. I began to feel squeamish and just had time to yell a warning to Patty to get out of the bath before I heaved and lost my entire three-course meal. We were both happy to get off that boat. The train ride seemed endless; three rickety carriages that slowly wound their way north. At one property we were shown two little beds made up in the grain shed. 'This is where you'll sleep,' said Patty's stoic-looking aunt. My mother will have a fit when she hears about this, I thought.

They were hot, sunny, funny days spent exploring the huge machinery used to harvest the wheat and riding the draught horse to see the salt lakes. We both came back with blisters on our bums and Patty's aunt had the perfect cure — a good douse with metho. Jeez, we jumped! Then back on the train and off to visit more relations in strange little towns with even stranger names: Wudinna, Minnipa, Wirrulla. They were mere specks on the vast, sparse landscape. We were away for about three weeks. It was then that I determined to leave school at the earliest opportunity.

I still felt like the ugly duckling of the family, with my gangly arms and legs, and dead-straight hair. Nancy, with big brown eyes like our mother's, was the beauty. She was closest to me in more than just years. She hated to be held responsible for me but that's normal for sisters. She had joined the Girl Guides, so I became a Brownie. Daddy would give us a penny each and we'd spend an hour polishing them to a gleaming shine with Brasso. The shiny penny was a Guide's weekly contribution. We felt very proud in our uniforms, ties folded and knotted just so, belt buckle and badges polished, socks up, shoes shiny, and we would walk together down to St Augustine's church hall. We learnt first aid, how to tie knots (very handy years later when I bought my boat), how to put up and strike a tent, build a camp-fire, and cook scrambled eggs in a scooped-out orange. One skill I never again put into practice!

We both enjoyed the Saturday afternoon movies. 'Nancy, make sure you look after Margaret,' Mum told her. But once out of sight we'd split up. Nancy was six years older and into flirting with the boys at the back of the theatre. I'd be with a girlfriend or Ronnie and Denny Wilson in the front of the theatre where the real action was — up on the screen. I enjoyed musicals but I loved westerns best — Hopalong Cassidy, Tom Mix, Roy

Rogers and the Indians. I always wanted to be the Indian when we re-enacted the movies in the backyard. I'm sure this was because of the costumes. The Indian maid wore beautiful, white, fringed chamois skins, beaded and trimmed with feathers. That was far more attractive than the white girl's simple check cotton dirndl dress and a bad bonnet!

Late one afternoon, coming out of the picture theatre, I lost my sister in the crowd and was left to walk home alone. Next to the theatre was a tempting little sweet shop where I always bought my favourite apricot nougat bar. I was halfway home, eating it when a man stopped in a car and asked me if I wanted a lift. My mother had told me never to talk to strangers. I knew it was wrong to get in the car but he was very persuasive and somehow talked me into it. I realised I'd done the wrong thing when he leant over and put his hand up my panties. I screamed blue murder. As we sailed past my street I yelled even louder. He panicked, stopped the car and I leapt out, shaking and crying, heart pounding. I felt sick. I ran across the road and turned into our street. My mother, who'd been waiting at the gate, asked, 'Why are you coming from that direction? The theatre's the other way.' She was so sharp. I suppose she had to be with four daughters. I quickly made up a story about walking my friend Beverley home. I couldn't tell her the truth. As it turned out, this wasn't the only time I got into trouble in a car.

My only early sexual experiences had been with girlfriends. I would sleep over at a girlfriend's house and we'd kiss and take turns being Clark Gable. But then a new boy, Jeffrey, moved in over the back fence. His eyes were set too close together, like a mongrel dog. One day he took me into his woodshed and it was: 'You show me yours and I'll show you mine.' I had never even seen my father naked. I just thought, Gee, what a strange looking thing and it was so pink!

By the time I was in my early teens, my father was drinking steadily. He hardly ate and his long frame grew thinner and thinner. The only serious arguments in our house were about money (lack of it), or about Daddy's drinking (way too much of it). He wasn't a nasty drunk, he didn't get loud or abusive. He just became fuzzy and quiet, very quiet. But he held down his job and financially, as my sisters left home to marry, things became a little easier. We took holidays at Victor Harbour in a funny old guesthouse called Linger Longer. A horse-drawn tram brought us out from the mainland across the causeway to Granite Island. I have photographs of Dad, Mum and my sisters with heads popping out of a hole in a rock. That's about all there was to do at Victor Harbour, walk around the island and stick your head out of a hole!

School vacations were spent with my aunt. She wasn't really an aunt but she had met my mother in hospital when they both gave birth to daughters and named them Margaret. She was married to a sheep and wheat farmer. I loved their farm in Happy Valley. We would ride the big wheat harvesters, round up the sheep for shearing, and climb the tall mulberry tree. Supposedly we were collecting leaves for our silkworms, but we would come down with lips, tongues and fingers stained purple from our indulgence. Aunty would cook huge meals for the shearers — six chickens at a time and trays and trays of bread and herb stuffing. At last enough stuffing! I was in heaven.

When I was fourteen Nancy married Lewis Paterson, who rode a huge motorbike. I loved going for a ride but I'd hang on like grim death, excited but nervous. I was thrilled when Nancy asked me to be one of her bridesmaids. She chose the style and fabric for my dress. It was silver-grey satin and I thought it was the most beautiful dress in the world. Keith Rainsford was the photographer who took her wedding shots.

Shortly after he asked my mother if I could do a modelling job for Shephard's Jewellery. He took a head shot of me wearing a 'too tight' perm with my hand up to my face sporting a diamond ring. The photo appeared on the front page of the *Adelaide Advertiser* and was followed, I'm afraid, by the usual adolescent showing off.

At this time I started to lobby my parents to let me leave school. Once I succeeded life really changed. Now Saturday afternoons were spent at my girlfriend Judy Holmes' getting ready for the evening's dance. Putting our hair in curlers, painting our nails, then turning the radio up full blast and singing along to all the hits, playing bongos on up-turned saucepans. It drove the neighbours mad. Judy's mother took herself off to the races.

My first job was as a sales assistant at Birks Chemist. It was fine until a man asked for condoms. I couldn't find them on the shelf; I didn't even know what they were. This was a 'fill-in' job until I could get an apprenticeship in hairdressing; my mother's idea. Nancy was a hairdresser, it was respectable. Fortunately an apprenticeship soon came up in a little salon in Gawler Place, in the centre of Adelaide, where Nancy had trained. I can't say I enjoyed scrubbing people's grimy hair. When I accidentally dropped and broke a glass perming dish and the boss docked the cost out of my meagre wage, I was out of there. Mother was not amused.

Judy worked in the office of the Alaska Icecream Company, where a position was vacant in accounts. Ignoring my lack of skill with figures I applied and got the job. I worked a great clunky machine, recording sales: so many blocks of icecream, the amount of vanilla, chocolate, strawberry. I made terrible errors. Pat, who ran the department, must have despaired but she was kind to me and would patiently explain how to delete the wrong entry and record the right one. I muddled along. Judy and I rode the tram together to and from work, knitting bunny wool sweaters, the fluff flying all over the businessmen's blue suits. We gossiped, planned our weekends. And staff were given a free block of icecream to take home every Friday night, so we had a great time.

The Alaska Icecream Company chose me to be their entrant, 'Miss Alaska', in a beachgirl competition at Glenelg. A street parade was held on the day of the judging and I rode on top of the Alaska delivery truck, tossing little tubs of icecream known as Dandies at the crowd. It was a wonder I didn't knock someone out. Nancy had lent me her best swimsuit for the judging. It was dark blue satin with a zip fastening, which had a habit of inching its way down. It would inch, I would hitch. This did nothing for my confidence. But I came second in the quest and my photo was printed in the local papers.

One night, at a dance at the Palais Royal, I met Johnny Gredula, the resident singer — a six-foot tall, gorgeous Hungarian. All the girls were mad about him. He would croon Nat King Cole numbers and I'd go weak at the knees. A big mirror ball spun around in the ceiling, reflecting its magical light. Nancy had given me my first dance dress, a 'ballerina' it was called, strapless, pale blue embroidered organza. I was ecstatic. I looked so grown up. One night during a music break Johnny Gredula, in his glamorous white jacket, made a beeline for me and asked me out to dinner. I thought all my dreams had come true. My girlfriends were tight-lipped with jealousy. We went to what was considered a very trendy little nightclub. I was so impressed. Halfway through dinner he said, 'I'm taking you home. Now!'

'What's the matter?' I asked.

'You're not interested in me,' he sulked. 'You're looking all around the room.'

It was true. I had been looking around to see who was looking at me! Little Margaret Trigar out with the gorgeous Johnny Gredula! I was devastated. It was my introduction to that mysterious, maddening thing called the male ego.

Back at the Palais, into my life came a man called Sam. He was Italian, in his thirties and known around town. Sam was a rather successful builder and he drove the biggest navy-blue Buick I had ever seen. And he obviously had a 'thing' about young girls. He would pick me up at the dance and drive me home. The first few times he tried to have sex with me I was terrified and flustered. I'd say, 'No, I can't' or 'No, I won't.' He would reply, 'Well, you're going to have to get used to it.' When we finally did it, it was horrible and painful. The two or three times I gave in to his pressure I didn't have any real sexual pleasure.

Although Sam was shorter than me and quite ugly, I was flattered by his interest in me. Probably I thought he was rich as he had all the trappings. He was older, sophisticated and unmarried, and all the girls in town thought he was the greatest because he was a flashy Italian and drove a flashy car. Once he took me to see some of his friends, a married couple, and we stayed for dinner. She served up an Italian meal and I had never tasted food like it. I thought, Wow! How long has this been around? Could you actually cook chicken that tastes like this? We went to glamorous hotels for dinner, including the posh South Australian Hotel and the ornate dining room of the Oriental. Not long after Sam and I first had sex in the car I began to feel very sick in the mornings.

My mother was so canny. After I had lost my virginity in the Buick, I was bleeding so I had washed my knickers and stuck them over a little rack on the back verandah to dry, then went to bed feeling frightened and ashamed. The next morning Mum looked me straight in the eye and said, 'Why did you wash your pants?' I fibbed but I knew that she was suspicious. Mother had always warned me that pregnancy before marriage would ruin your life. I had seen girls having to leave school for this reason and I thought they were doomed. I asked my girlfriends what I should do and they gave me the address of a doctor on North Terrace. I was terrified and felt very alone. After my visit to the doctor I stumbled out into the street bawling my eyes out having been assured I was pregnant. That night I told Nancy. She didn't think I should get married at fifteen. I agreed with her, and the last thing my struggling family needed was an illegitimate child.

Sam organised the abortion. He took me to a little street off Anzac Highway, to a perfectly ordinary house where the door was answered by a very normal-looking neat lady in a black dress. I had no idea what she was going to do to me. Sam went out to the kitchen while she took me into the bedroom. I had some liquid pumped into me; the pain was excruciating. Afterwards the woman said, 'If you have any problems this is my number, you ring me.' I went home and in the middle of the night the pain woke me. It was unbearable. The woman had shown me how I should stand back from the wall and push my tummy into it. That's how I was standing, perspiration pouring, filled with fear, when my mother came in. I told her what I'd done. She rang the woman who came at about six o'clock in the morning and stayed with me for an hour or so until it was all over. My mother was pacing and crying, while I thought I was going to die. Dad went to work as usual. Did he know? I stayed in bed all day. 'You see what happens and how you can ruin your life,' my mother said. I had the horror of it as well as the shame and my mother's tears. God, what had I done to her? Guilt on guilt.

I kept on seeing Sam for a while but there was certainly no sex. Once he came to the house and I walked in and sat on his lap. My father went berserk: 'What are you doing? This is how you got yourself in trouble in the first place.' Suddenly I realised he knew. It was amazing that we could live in such a small house and go through something like that and yet it was not talked about. Hushed up and hidden. I broke off with Sam.

Charles,
Marriage
&
Babies

I RETURNED to work at the Alaska Icecream Company and back to Saturday night dances at the Palais, going with girl-friends. It was there I met Ric Hoskings, a tall brash sort of a lad who worked as a car salesman and drove smart little sports cars. I went out with him a few times, always with a gang of friends, and then he asked me to his twenty-first birthday party. Ric's parents lived in a small apartment and he wanted a big party. An older bachelor friend in the car business, Charles Tabberer, offered him the use of his large house in North Adelaide for the celebration.

I was sitting on a low stool, chatting to friends, when Ric came up and said, 'Have you met Charles Tabberer? This is his house.' Charles and I talked for most of the evening. He later said that he walked into the room, having returned from a dinner date, saw my shoulders — I was wearing my blue, strapless organza dress — and insisted on an introduction.

Charles was a good-looking man, with a strong build and an aristocratic, if prominent nose and moustache. He had thick, floppy, straight blond hair with a side part, like an English schoolboy. In fact his whole style was rather English: tweed jackets, corduroy trousers, check Viyella shirts and his old school tie. He had been educated at Shore, a private boys' college in Sydney. We started going out: dinners, dancing, movies. Occasionally he'd cook simple meals at home.

Gradually I met his friends, mostly married couples much older than me, but they were kind and welcomed me into their set. Although, I suspect amongst the fellas there was a bit of nudge, nudge, wink, wink, 'You dirty old devil, cradle snatching, what?' I often felt inadequate as they were all quite sophisticated. However, I was on a steep learning curve and I learnt fast. Soon I was able to keep up with their conversation, enjoy the witty jibes and even comprehend the double entendres. I suppose I had enrolled in the Charles Graham Vousden Tabberer Finishing School, and it didn't take me long to graduate! Charles was clearly 'grooming' his girl. 'Darling, it's everything, not everythink,' he told me. I didn't speak badly, Mother had always corrected us at home. We never said 'aint' or 'I done', which was how many of my school friends spoke. At one stage Nancy and I had taken elocution lessons. 'How now brown cow.'

Charles had been married and divorced. There were no children by the union, but he failed to mention an illegitimate daughter by a previous relationship. While this would not have made any difference to me, he may have thought it might influence my family.

His parents were divorced. His father, an Englishman, had run off with an opera star leaving his mother, Jane, while she was holidaying in Australia. She came from a well-known Tasmanian family who made their money in retail. Jane joined the Communist Party (a fact I kept from my father for some time), and visited Russia and China. She later wrote a book on her experiences. Charles had one sister, Marguerita. I always felt there was a coolness in his family relationships.

After we had been dating for about six months Charles announced he was going to ask my parents for their permission for us to marry. I don't remember him ever actually asking me, but I went along with it. I liked being with him. I enjoyed the life he'd introduced me to, his style, his friends, and he drove a fantastic white Chevrolet convertible. (Always a sucker for a flash car. Or was it just a reaction to riding in the buggy with Gifty farting on my neck?)

My parents were marginally concerned about the eighteen-year age difference, but by then they were both worn out. I had been trouble. They probably thought, let someone else take responsibility for her. Charles was respectful, financially able to care for me. I would be 'marrying well'. We became engaged.

That was a wonderful summer. On weekends we'd go boating; Charles had a passion for speedboat racing. One day during a race we flipped. I felt the *Tempest* come out of a corner, hit a wash, lift off, turn in midair and slam down. I was sucked into the murky river. The only thing I could think, as my life jacket drew me to the surface, was, stay down, Margaret. Stay down. We'd been at the front of the field and I knew the other boats in the race were following, and could easily carve a big chunk out of me. Charles was in a panic when I finally surfaced, fearful that I'd been knocked unconscious.

He was an excellent tennis player and a member of the Keswick and Wayville Tennis Club, where the rule was 'Members and spouses only' in the clubhouse. The clubhouse, incidentally, was no great shakes; just a cement-block building with some old formica tables, uncomfortable chairs and a bar at one end. After I had gone there a few times and sat outside (with Charles bringing me my lemonade), he asked if his fiancée could use the clubhouse. This was met with whispers and huddled meetings, and I couldn't fathom what all the fuss was about. Finally the verdict came back — 'No.' It seems Charles had taken a previous girlfriend to the club and also said they were engaged. The committee was not about to be duped again. I didn't want to go into their crummy clubhouse anyway, although after our marriage I was allowed in.

In winter Charles played golf and I used to walk the round with him. He played in the beautiful Adelaide Hills at the Mt Osmond Golf Club, where my father had previously worked. The first time we lunched in the rather grand old clubhouse I was terrified someone would step up and say, 'Aren't you our groundsman's daughter?' (Oh Molly, there's that 'not good enough' feeling again.) The Saturday night dinner dances held at the club were some of the happiest of times I spent with Charles and his friends, the Pozzas, the Batchelors and the Fosters.

Italian-born Hugh Pozza was Adelaide's leading tailor, and his wife Mavis was the prettiest of women, always beautifully groomed. Naughty Gordon Foster was a canny businessman with a deliciously wicked sense of humour. He did a perfect take-off of Hugh's broken English. It always got a laugh — the loudest of all was from Hughie. Gordon's wife Betty was warm and gentle to me, and she readily embraced me into their circle. Bill Batchelor was a tall, elegant, blond man with a robust moustache. He was in real estate. Quiet, pipe-smoking Bill sat on the sidelines, observing all, I thought. He may have been quiet because his dynamic wife, Font, had such a lively personality. She was to become one of my best friends — a sort of Aunty Mame. She steered me through those early social occasions. It was she who was to name my second child Amanda, a name she adored after seeing Noel Coward's *Private Lives*. We were regulars at the club and had great fun together. We'd dine, dance and laugh at Gordon Foster's endless supply of jokes. I didn't always get the punchline, but there was no way I was going to admit it.

I had told Charles about Sam, although I don't think I told him about the abortion. I was very scared about sex, but eventually I trusted him. He was older, wiser, responsible and I knew he would look after me. After all, he was thirty-five. I was still very naive about birth control. My mother had never discussed sex with me, and Nancy only the basics. In my teens I believed it was the man's responsibility. How dopey can you be?

The wedding was planned, Nancy guided my fabric choice, the styling and choosing the right dressmaker. My dress was very simple — white, sheer organza with a delicate lily-of-the-valley print. I wore a short veil caught with a sparkling tiara. Nancy as my matron of honour wore a ballerina length, shell-pink dress in the same fabric and a large picture hat. I thought it was just too, too divine. The ceremony took place at the Parkside Baptist Church in 1953.

The reception was held at my parents' house. My mother, sisters and aunts were largely responsible for the spread. I'm sure Charles kicked in for the drinks. Daddy had given me away and only had a couple before we left for the church, Mother having warned him to 'keep yourself nice'. Poor Alf, I'm sure he couldn't wait to get home to have a drink.

Charles' friends and his mother joined in with my family and friends, and it was a jolly and warm occasion. Ours was a humble house but there was a rich sense of 'family' which Charles didn't have. After our divorce, Charles remarried (again a young girl), fathered another daughter and divorced. Maybe there are patterns in all our lives.

My mother cried when we left the reception. I knew what she was feeling and I cried too. All those years her kids had been her life and here I was, the last, leaving home forever. Dad put his arm around her as they stood at the gate, and I was driven off to a whole new world.

The next day we set out in the white convertible to drive via Sydney to Surfers Paradise in Queensland. It was glorious weather. We drove with the hood down and both became deeply tanned. Charles had given me money to buy my trousseau, so I wore my new clothes and felt very grown up. He took me to the Blue Mountains where he'd cavorted as a youth and showed me the Hydro Majestic Hotel at Medlow Bath where he said the management rang a bell at three o'clock each morning: a cue for everyone to return to their own rooms. We stayed at the Carrington Hotel in Katoomba. Spooky, I thought, with its endless corridors, heavy drapes and bronze lions roaring at you around every corner. But the dining room with its bevelled glass doors and whiter than white starched tablecloths was fabulous. We made a lot of love.

However, it was during our stay in the Blue Mountains that I was introduced to the flip side of Charles' nature. He wanted us to climb to the Three Sisters, an awesome trio of rocks that soar up near the jagged cliff face at the edge of Katoomba. I'd glimpsed them from a distance and frankly had some reservations. But they were a part of Charles' childhood memories and he was determined. When we arrived at the steps leading to them I looked up, horrified. The stairs were steep and narrow. 'No, Charles, please I'm scared of heights. Let's go back,' I said. We argued for a couple of minutes but Charles demanded I pull myself together and stop being stupid. We started to climb. I tried not to look down and clung to the cliff side of the steps, but as other sightseers descended I was forced to the

My parents, Mary (Molly) Ryan and Alfred Trigar, on their wedding day. Aren't they gorgeous? Although their footwear leaves a little to be desired.

My mother, Molly Ryan, at about eighteen years of age. With her olive skin and big, sad, dark-brown eyes, Molly, it was said, never looked 'Australian'.

Me, Margaret May, as a toddler. Even then I had fine, dead-straight hair, the bane of my life. I'm so excited at being in front of the camera that I'm pinching my knee!

Above: The Trigar girls photographed in the late 1940s at my sister Betty's twenty-first birthday party. *From left:* me, Mummy, Nancy, Betty and Joan.

Left: I played basketball as a teenager and was known to be a mean defence goalie. Of course, height helped.

At the age of thirteen I was chosen to represent South Australia in the Combined Churches Physical Education national titles in Ballarat. Here I am, tallest in the team, sporting a terrible perm and wearing my cute costume for one of the song and dance routines.

Me with a girlfriend at the wheel of Charles' boat, the *Tempest*. This was snapped by our friend, the photographer Dick Joyner, and made it into the *Adelaide Advertiser*.

My wedding to Charles Graham Vousden Tabberer at the Parkside Baptist Church, Adelaide, 1953. *From left:* best man, Clive Fricker, my sister and matron of honour, Nancy Paterson, Charles and me. Note my tiara — well, it *was* a bit of a fairytale!

Another Dick Joyner *Adelaide Advertiser* shot, here amongst the winter wattle. I believe Charles was quite chuffed when the newspaper's caption read: 'Mrs Charles Tabberer'.

Christmas 1957, we had just moved into the 'soulless' new house at Glengowrie. Brooke (aged two), Charles, Amanda (aged nine months) and me. (Dick Joyner)

With Charles at my twenty-first birthday party, held at the Glengowrie house. (Dick Joyner)

When I first started modelling in Adelaide in late 1957, Ross Luck, the advertising manager for David Jones, 'claimed me for DJs'. Here I am modelling at an in-store promotion for British Cotton. (Courtesy *Adelaide Advertiser*)

outside. I started to shake and sweat. 'Please, take me back. I can't do this.'

'Stop it, Margaret, just do as I say.' By now he was very angry with me. I couldn't control my shaking legs and every step increased my fear. I was almost crawling on all fours. People behind asked to pass. Charles grew angrier and angrier. We eventually made it to the top. My blouse was wringing wet with my sweat, my chest felt constricted, I could hardly breathe. I burst into tears of relief.

There was very little conversation in the car on the way back to the hotel. I couldn't believe that he could be so callous. I kept hearing his angry words, 'Just do as I say.' Damn you, Charles. Damn you! At dinner that night he gave me a pompous lecture on facing one's fear. He also said for the first time, 'There can only be one captain of the ship.' It was a phrase he was to use again and again throughout our relationship. I only half heard him. I sat there thinking, if you love someone is this how you treat them? And, my God, he sounds like a headmaster; this is like being back at school. And remember, I hated school.

Was that love at seventeen? How can I reach back over forty years and tell you how I really felt? Surely memories are distorted, if only by the passage of time and the experiences since lived. Charles was a father figure for me. And after the shame and pain I had known with Sam, I needed Charles to make me feel safe and secure.

In Sydney we stayed in the heart of Kings Cross. I'd never seen anything like it — the lights, the noise, the people and how they dressed, the so-called shady ladies, their pimps, the night-clubs. How sophisticated was this? At a restaurant we had curried prawns for dinner. At two in the morning I was in the bathroom heaving my heart out. Charles banged on the locked door and yelled out to me. He thought I was dying, but there was no way I was going to let him in. Not until everything was pristine. I cleaned the bath, showered and staggered out exhausted. Charles was furious with me but only out of concern. The next day we drove on to Queensland. Surfers was a small town in those days. The Surfers Paradise Hotel, where we stayed, was probably the largest building in town, all three storeys of it. In its garden was a private zoo. We strolled out to see the animals and were confronted with two very large, red-bummed baboons caught in an indecent act. I was extremely embarrassed. Ever the Baptist!

We spent several days lying on the beach, surfing, going to bed in the afternoon, making love, then dressing and going out to dinner. Charles was teaching me a lot about making love and I was a keen student. All the old guilt about sex vanished. I was a married woman; anything and everything was possible.

The honeymoon over it was back to Adelaide to set up house. Toorak Gardens was one of *the* suburbs in Adelaide — an assortment of lovely old houses with picture-book gardens set in soft tree-lined streets. (The rabbito man certainly didn't call here.) Charles had leased a large Tudor-style house from a sweet elderly couple who were moving to something smaller. I remember the living room had a very large crack down one wall. Just before we married, Adelaide had experienced a severe earthquake. I was at my parents' home in bed when it struck in the early hours of the morning. Suddenly my mother flew into my room: 'It's an earthquake, earthquake! Get into bed between Daddy and me. If we are going to go, we'll all go together.' Go where together? Finally the rocking stopped, the noise stopped. It was very still. A horse neighed in distress. We sat up in bed and through the window, under the street light, we saw the milkman's horse, down on all fours, the buggy shafts still attached. Dad went out to help. That's how the crack came to be running down the wall of my new home. We moved in. I bought fabric and with the help of my sisters sewed curtains and a bedspread for the master bedroom.

Gradually I came to grips with running a household. I didn't have a cleaning lady as all our friends did, but I'd labour away and my kitchen floor shone. I wanted our house to look as pristine as theirs. I struggled in the kitchen. Mum's cooking was hardly inspiring but I'd been exposed to good food in restaurants, at the club and in the homes of Charles' friends. I mastered a few recipes. And I knew the difference between a table looking exceptional and a table looking ordinary. I observed and I learnt. Charles was fussy about his clothes. I perfected the art of ironing a shirt. Jane Tabberer taught me how to stack a linen press: bottom sheet folded between top sheet; place the folded edges to the front raw edges to the back. To this day my linen press is a 'Janie' design. I was like a big sponge absorbing everything.

Charles would work Saturday morning, play sport in the afternoon, and my Saturday had to be organised around his lunch. And lunch was always his favourite: sausages and eggs. He would phone me as he left his car yard, Glandore Motors; on would go the sausages. Then the crunch of car tyres on the gravel drive was my cue to pop on the eggs, covered with a plate so they would be cooked to perfection by the time he'd changed into his tennis or golf gear. I stayed home and cooked that same lunch Saturday after Saturday. It never occurred to me to say, 'I'm not going to be here, you'll have to cook it yourself.' Wives didn't talk like that in the 1950s.

During this time we met an Adelaide press photographer, Dick Joyner. He seemed to be everywhere: at social functions, balls, theatre nights, even at sports meetings. He took my photograph sitting on top of Charles' boat, wearing a shirt, shorts and a sailor's peaked cap. It made it into the newspaper.

Some time later, when the first winter wattle appeared, he asked me to pose again, in amongst the blossoms. It also made it into the paper. Charles didn't mind. He was quite chuffed when the caption read: 'Mrs Charles Tabberer.' Perhaps being photographed planted an idea in my mind.

I wasn't quite ready to fall pregnant nine months after we married, but Charles was keen. He mentioned the issue of his age and we stopped taking precautions. Very soon I was throwing up and feeling vile. Forget morning sickness, I was having twenty-four hour sickness. I even had to get up in the middle of the night. Everybody else got pregnant and fatter, I got pregnant and thinner. I hated it. I'd prepare dinner and not be able to eat. My mother was concerned. I tried the old family formula, eating a dry biscuit before I got out of bed. The doctor gave me pills. Nothing worked. I was washed out. Then suddenly, at about five and a half months, it stopped and I blossomed. I felt fantastic, looked fantastic and grew bigger and bigger.

The day before the birth I cleaned the entire house: scrubbed the floors, washed, ironed, cleaned the silver. When my sister Betty rang I told her about my day. 'The baby will be born tomorrow,' she said. I was already ten days overdue. I thought it was just never going to happen. Five o'clock the next morning the contractions started. I realised then that I hadn't really thought about this bit, I'd been so occupied fitting out the nursery and buying pretty things for the baby. This was crunch time and I wasn't prepared. 'I want my Mummy.' Charles drove me to the hospital.

It was to be a long day. Brooke was born at three-thirty in the afternoon, on 14 November 1955. My body felt as though it had been physically assaulted. I was extremely uncomfortable for about four days, but I loved the little bundle they kept bringing me. I had copious milk, the family was thrilled and Charles? Charles was over the moon.

I think my mother felt a great sense of relief. I would stop being a larrikin — I had a husband, a baby, a house. I settled into a new routine, and she and my sisters were wonderful and guided me gently through those first scary weeks of motherhood. There were days and nights when I thought, does it ever stop? You put it in one end and it comes out the other. Charles made it very clear he had no intention of changing a nappy, ever, or getting up to the baby in the night. 'I have to work and this is your job.' I didn't dare say, 'Well, I clean the house, shop, cook, wash, iron. Isn't that a job too?' Isn't parenting a job for two?

Charles had bought me my first car and efficiently taught me to drive. It was a little 1935 Chevrolet coupe with a dicky seat in the back. I'd collect Mum and we would lunch with my sisters at least once a fortnight, taking it in turns to host the lunch. If it rained whoever was in the dicky seat would simply put up an umbrella and I'd drive a bit slower. I adored that little car. It gave me my first real taste of freedom.

I had just got my figure back, had mothering down to some sort of order and was taking golf lessons when I woke one morning with that unmistakable feeling. No, it couldn't be. I was pregnant again. Brooke was six months old. There would be just fifteen months difference between her and her baby sister? Brother?

I went through all the same heave ho I had with my first pregnancy, made harder by the day to day reality of mashing Brooke's vegetables and changing her nappies. But it was all over by the time I was four months pregnant and again I bloomed. If it's a boy, I thought, Charles will have his complete family. On 9 March 1957, Amanda May was born. She was an exceptionally beautiful baby with masses of black hair, an adorable turned-up nose and a mouth drawn by the gods. She made up for the hideously lonely night I'd spent in labour. I'd walked the corridors of the hospital, stood and watched the rain by the orange streetlights and because I knew what was coming, felt nervous, tense and again thought, I want my Mummy. At around six in the morning I swung into action. The doctor had been called but he didn't make it in time. Sister Diamond delivered Amanda. At one stage the nurses had told me to stop pushing, we had to 'wait for the doctor'. 'Wait for the doctor. Are you kidding?' I said. 'I'm having this baby as soon as I can.' And I did.

Brooke by now was a beautiful, chubby little blond bomb who was into everything, despite the fact that she refused to walk. I'd lugged her around on my hip throughout my pregnancy, much to my mother's consternation. 'Put her down, darling, then she will have to walk.' She didn't. That is until a few days after Amanda's birth. Nanna, as my mother was now called by her growing brood of grandchildren, arrived at the hospital, came into my flower-decked room and held the door wide as this dear little girl in a sweet blue and white hand-smocked dress toddled in. Brooke thought the baby was some wonderful new toy.

Charles didn't mind in the least not getting his son. He thought Amanda was gorgeous, but not gorgeous enough to change her nappy or get up when she cried in the night. She was a good baby. I would often check on her; I couldn't believe a new baby could sleep so soundly, especially after Brooke who was such a night owl. I seemed to be constantly tired, and I was 'too thin' according to my mother. But I settled into a new routine. Then Charles announced we were moving. He had leased a brand new house in Glengowrie. While I was happy in the old house and liked the area, I looked forward to a change. Surely a new house would be easier to clean and maintain.

The surroundings, however, were soulless, and if I hadn't had my little car I probably would have gone mad. Ours was one of only a few houses finished in the developing suburb, which was quite remote. Fortunately, it was only a short distance from where Nancy lived, so we saw more and more of each other. She had two little boys, Mark and Scott, who were close in age to my girls. Later she would also have two daughters, Melinda and Christina.

At this time Charles' business was beginning to experience some difficulties. Also, I became restless. It was probably inevitable that sooner rather than later I would need more in my young life than a demanding husband and two little girls. Maybe it was the routine of babies' bottoms and bottles, Charles' sausages and eggs. I don't remember how I came up with the idea of taking a modelling course, perhaps because people often suggested that I should be a model. I loved to read fashion magazines, and I suppose I knew I had the height and the looks. All I needed was the know-how. I discussed the idea with Nancy, who had always been my greatest supporter, and she was encouraging. God knows how I gained Charles' approval. In retrospect I realise that it was not something he would have agreed to easily. Perhaps I had begun to assert myself and he agreed just to keep me quiet. He also paid for my lessons as I had no money of my own. One of the things I hated most was asking him for money; anything more than the housekeeping allowance required some explanation. This might also have acted as a catalyst.

I went to see Jill Dempster (who later became Jill Robb). She was running a modelling school and agency in partnership with a fashion photographer, I think Adelaide's only fashion photographer, Don Mellor. He had an office and studio up a narrow flight of stairs off Rundle Street with a showcase for his photography at street level. I used to walk past that showcase every day on my way to work at both Birks Chemist and later my hairdressing job. I'd often pause to look at the glamorous model shots. Don photographed in his studio during the day, and Jill ran the agency from their shared office. In the evenings the studio would become a classroom where Jill taught. However, as the business grew she employed some of the more mature local models to take classes in makeup, deportment, catwalk, etc. One of these models, Pam Ellis, eventually bought the business when Jill was ready to move on.

Don Mellor wandered through the school from time to time. He was a loose-limbed, untidy sort of a guy. His shirt never seemed to be tucked in and his sleeves were always rolled to different lengths. He smoked incessantly and his thick dark hair had an unruly wave. Later I was to work with him a lot. He was always sweet. No genius but a good old professional.

Jill was gorgeous, with luxurious, long blond hair, a turned-up nose and a neat little figure, and we were about the same age. She was English and had come to Australia as a film continuity girl and settled in Adelaide. She was married to a big, blond, chauvinistic car dealer several years her senior. Sound familiar? Charles and Bob were very alike. I enrolled in her school, and Jill felt certain I had a future in the business. Charles was understanding about my decision. Often he would look after the babies once I had fed them and settled them down for the night, or I'd drop them off to Mummy. Then I would go to my evening classes twice a week for about six weeks.

There was to be a graduation party, and Jill arranged for me to buy a new dress at cost through a fashion agent, Harry Munn. He was a big bear of a man, gentle and fun, and he loved a laugh. I did some work for him eventually, but I didn't have to go through the fashion agencies to get started in modelling. I took off and went straight into store parades and fashion store advertising, thanks to a man called Ross Luck. The night of my graduation, in late 1957, Ross had plucked my name tag off my new navy-blue polkadot sack dress, popped it in his pocket and 'claimed me for David Jones'. Ross was the advertising manager of DJs in Adelaide; a slight, dapper man with a pencil-thin moustache and a charming lisp. His beautiful wife, Ina, wrote a fashion column for the *Adelaide Advertiser*. She was indescribably chic. They had one son, Peter, who grew up to be Peter Luck of television fame.

Ross Luck from day one was as good as his word. He kept me busy for David Jones with a hold that, while not actually contractual, suited us both. Very occasionally I'd do some work for either Myers or John Martins, and Ross didn't approve at all. Jill my teacher had become Jill my agent. And for the first time in my married life I was earning my own money. I'd buy things for my mother and give her a few pounds for babysitting the girls while I worked. It helped us both. I could afford to buy special clothes for the girls, a tie for Charles and new shoes, hosiery or makeup for myself. I liked this financial independence.

Jill also became my best friend, and our older husbands got on well. So our social life now included the Dempsters. Jill and Bob lived in what must have been Adelaide's smallest apartment, at Glenelg. Although it was tiny, Jill had given it style, with yellow and white-striped wallpaper and white cane furniture. Bob's pride and joy was a studded leather bar. Bars were big in those days, but bars had always been big for Bob. Often he would drink too much, fall asleep and wake in the wee hours of the morning, starving. Jill, who had put in a fourteen-hour day at the agency and school, would have to get out of bed, on demand, and cook him steak and chips. Me with sausages and eggs every Saturday, Jill with steak and chips after midnight. Those Adelaide boys had it good, but what they didn't know was that they had two young tigers by the tails.

With the Dempsters we'd go camping, boating and waterskiing on the Murray River. One memorable holiday was spent cruising from Adelaide to Sydney on a P&O liner and driving back together. We were great looking girls with our contrasting blonde/brunette looks and our handsome older husbands, and we had a lot of fun. Jill predicted that modelling would take me out of South Australia and it did. We stayed in touch, and years later when Jill and I were living in Sydney we saw a lot of each other. Our lives were strangely parallel. Her only child, Louise, is my god-daughter and has my second name, May. Louise is as smart as a tack and a carbon copy of how her beautiful mother looked when she helped me turn a corner in my life all those years ago.

I now had a new routine in my life: working. My sisters would come to the parades and the next day take care of the girls so Mummy could see the show too. I'd bring her back to my dressing room to meet the other models and give her a close look at the clothes. She collected all the newspaper cuttings of my advertising shots. For the first time in my life I felt I was doing something right; I was no longer a problem or a disappointment.

Although I knew my mother was proud of my new career, she frequently sounded a warning: 'As long as it doesn't interfere with your husband and children.' I didn't think it would. I was the one who had to put in the extra work. And I certainly wasn't modelling full-time. Sometimes I would do a week of parades at David Jones, amounting to about two hours a day. Then just one day of photography the following week.

I had only been modelling for a short time when I was booked for the big Wool Board parades. The fashion director of the Wool Board, Nan Sanders, was one tough cookie. Her pro-motional campaign announced the Wool Awards as a designers' and manufacturers' competition to find the best wool styling of the year. Winners were paraded in store promotions around Australia and supported with extensive advertising in magazines and press. It was hugely successful for many years until, in an effort to satisfy all wool users in the business, it deteriorated into silliness; almost 'Best lady's wool cardigan with three buttons' and 'Best lady's wool cardigan with one button'. The awards lost their legitimacy.

The Wool Board toured a group of top Melbourne models for the in-store parades, which was how I met Diane Masters, Helen Homewood and Janice Wakely. All would later become my good friends. Diane was extraordinary on the catwalk, extremely tall with long arms, legs and facial features. She had tawny blond hair and the most beautiful hands, always perfectly manicured. But behind those rather daunting good looks was a warm and sometimes wacky girl. She was the first to tell me that I should, 'Go to Melbourne. You would do very, very well.' How nice, I thought and didn't think about it again until a few weeks later when Lillian Wightman, of Le Louvre couture fashion in Melbourne, requested I fly over for her big annual charity parade. Diane had told Lillian about 'this Adelaide girl'. Dear Diane insisted I stay with her. I was thrilled. I was also terrified — I mean, this was big time.

Lillian Wightman and Le Louvre are part of the Australian fashion legend. She was an extraordinary woman with a discerning eye and acerbic tongue. She also understood her clientele; she knew who would buy what and often marked garments 'sold to Mrs so-and-so' even before the woman had seen it. She was rarely wrong. Lillian was a one-off. Her collection was always breathtakingly beautiful. She bought the best of European designers and complemented them with her own designs. I flew to Melbourne full of trepidation. What if she didn't like me? Diane met me at the airport in her little Volkswagen, and I remarked on how hot it was in the car. 'Oh the heating is on, darling. Something's stuck and I can't turn it off.' She drove it like that for years, summer and winter.

Le Louvre was a little gem of a building at the Paris end of Collins Street. My knees were knocking when we arrived. Lillian sat on her chaise on the ground floor surrounded by a cloud of delicate fragrance and endless chiffon scarves, her hair piled into her signature topknot. I was sent upstairs, three perilous narrow flights, to the workroom to be fitted. I'd go up, change into some gorgeous ballgown and teeter back down to get Lillian's approval. 'Walk, dear, let me see you walk,' she'd bark. And I'd walk. 'Think about the gown, dear. Now walk again.' Think about the gown? 'You have to feel the clothes, dear.' Feel the clothes?

A window opened — I realised there was more to modelling than just looking good. The big night came and went in a blur. I tried to remember Lillian's instructions, but it was all so different from the parades at home. Backstage there were hairdressers to fix your hair, milliners to put the hats on, furriers to toss a fox around your neck, jewellers to add diamonds to your ears, dressers to get you in and out of your garments. It was very special. Lillian knew how to put on a parade. My final garment was a strapless, white tulle dress with an enormous full flowing skirt, pheasant's feathers covered the bodice and spread out down the vast skirt. Catwalks in those days were just wide enough to let two girls pass. But the skirt of this dress was wider than the catwalk, and the black-tie audience had placed their champagne glasses on the side of the catwalk. As I walked the glasses were swept aside. If I had one moment of clear recall about the night it was trying not to laugh as the guys made a grab to save their glasses before my pheasant-feather dress claimed them. Lillian was pleased. I thanked her and Diane, and went back to my husband, babies and Adelaide.

Charles was seriously playing golf and had got his handicap down to a respectable nine. We decided to drive to Melbourne and take a golfing holiday with a group of friends, staying at the Victorian Golf Club. The boys played golf all day. We girls drove into Melbourne for lunch and to shop. I bought myself the latest summer sandals. They were called scuffs: a flip-flop affair in sand-coloured leather. Very new and trendy, I thought. We arrived back at the clubhouse in time to lunch with our golfing husbands.

Charles dropped his napkin, bent down to retrieve it and saw my new sandals. 'Margaret, whatever you have on your feet you can go to the room and remove them immediately. That is no way to dress.' I was stunned, embarrassed, tears stung my eyes. I tried to explain how fashionable they were. The others tried to make a joke of it, but Charles wouldn't let it be. I fled upstairs to our room, threw myself on the bed and bawled my eyes out. In retrospect I think I was crying about more than my sandals. For the first time I felt the gap in our ages. Charles was being an old fuddy duddy. He came to the room and I flatly refused to go back to lunch. I was told the boys really got stuck into him, particularly Gordon Foster, who was something of my champion. Gordon was a dapper dresser, he obviously loved clothes, and his wife Betty was always stylishly dressed. Gordon appreciated women, too. He may have been naughty but he was also protective of me.

Charles came back to our room and apologised. It was silly and it blew over. But it was also mean. Strange how a little incident like that can stay in your memory for years and years. I don't believe I've ever forgiven him. I imagine Charles could see the changes taking place in me and he didn't like them.

I'd been a seventeen-year-old bride who said, 'Yes Charles, yes Charles,' and suddenly here I was saying, 'I don't think so, Charles.' And worse, 'No.'

As well as having found a little independence through modelling I was now the mother of two children. You grow up fast when you're a mother. And for the first time in my young life I realised that nothing, absolutely nothing, stays the same. Many times I was to wish it could but the reality is it doesn't. Sometimes this would make me sad. Much, much later in tough times it was all I had to hang onto.

The Start
of a
Career

I HAD become friendly with the agent Harry Munn, whose major account was a very successful label 'Shareen' produced by a crazy Melbourne manufacturer, Simon Schinberg. I once saw Simon wear a gold lamé dinner jacket. Enough said. Simon had appointed a new sales manager, Ralph Dahan. Ralphy, with his dark good looks, beard, French accent and ever-ready laugh, was naughty and fun.

I hadn't done any manufacturers' showings up until this time as Ross Luck and David Jones had kept me busy. On this occasion, however, Jill begged me to do some important showings for Harry as his principals were coming to Adelaide and he wanted to have the top models in his showroom. Flattered and recalling Harry's kindness when I often bought garments wholesale from him, I agreed. At the end of the week I must have gone home full of stories about 'the boys'. Suddenly Charles was concerned. 'Are you sure they don't come into the dressing room?' he asked.

Days later Jill received an urgent call from Ralph in Melbourne. The Wool Board had every top model in town booked for the Wool Awards judging. Could I go over and do his Melbourne showings? Patsy Blucher, another Adelaide model, and I flew over. Showroom work is always a slog, but during that visit it seemed the buyers were particularly bitchy. Older women, probably menopausal, they seemed to hate us on sight and made us try the same garment on again and again. There was no chance of a coffee break or time to take the killing stilettos off for a few minutes before the next appointment. It was exhausting. Simon took great care of his buyers, giving them red roses, boxes of chocolates, the best French champagne, dinners at the most expensive restaurants and more. It was all part of the business. During the week Ralphy said to me, 'You should meet Newton. He will be mad about you.' Newton being Helmut Newton, perhaps the most famous, certainly the most contro-versial fashion photographer working in Australia at the time. Diane Masters had told me the same thing. 'OK,' I said. 'Let's meet Mr Newton.' Not long afterwards Ralph came up to me. 'I've set up a meeting with Helmut,' he said. 'We will see him this afternoon.'

My stomach lurched — after all Newton had something of a fearsome reputation. Of Jewish descent, he was born in Berlin. He had come to Australia and married a strikingly beautiful actress, June Bunnell. Known to be demanding and difficult, Helmut was also the consummate professional, and if you were working for him you bloody well had better be, too. His work had a very different look from the other top Australian photog-raphers. Melbourne's Athol Shmith's work was romantic; he used frail, untouchable girls in strapless evening gowns, urns of full-blown roses, archways and elaborate wrought-iron gates. Sydney's Laurie Le Guy favoured healthy, cute, outdoor girls; they ran, jumped, wore gingham, sailed boats and caught buses. Newton was different. He liked big, tall girls who had knowing looks, newspapers, cigarettes, black limousines, half-hidden men and dark, rain-soaked alleys. His photographs had an edge, a hidden threat. Other models had told me this, and I also knew about his style from my own observations of his photographs in *Vogue* Australia.

Helmut's studio was a series of cramped little rooms at the top of a narrow building in Flinders Lane, the then fashion centre of Melbourne. The place was buzzing with clients, models, secretaries, phones ringing and general chaos. This slight man in baggy trousers took us up to the roof garden 'where it's sane'. I was to be evaluated. I had a dry mouth, I was tense, and Helmut and Ralph proceeded to discuss me. 'She's tall.' 'She's got great legs.' 'I don't know about the hair.' It was as if I wasn't there. Rude little so-and-so, I thought, but I should have known that this was the name of the game.

Helmut then mentioned he was 'into' a swimsuit shoot and debated whether to squeeze me into it as a photographic test. Finally, 'No, I don't think so 'cause I got all the gals booked already.' In the years I knew him I never understood why occasionally he'd lapse into Humphrey Bogart speak! Thank God he didn't include me in the swimwear shoot. I knew I wasn't then, nor ever had been, a swimsuit girl. I had decent boobs and I was thin but two babies had thickened my waist. Although later Newton declared I had the best legs in the world, I knew I wasn't swimsuit material. It was decided that trying to photograph me on this trip would be too hard; I was only in town for another couple of days and Newton had the swimwear campaign to finish shooting. He said he was interested in photographing me, but I left his studio feeling it was a case of 'Don't call us, we'll call you.' I went back to my hotel and found a message to call Ralph urgently. He said Newton had reconsidered and wanted to photograph me immediately. 'Darling, this is a great opportunity, you've got to do it.' And so it was arranged.

Newton's house in East Melbourne was a handsome old bungalow with a modern glass annexe at the back. June Newton was very sweet to me, she sensed I was nervous. I did my makeup and put on a big slouchy felt hat and a soft wool wrap coat that Newton supplied. Surprisingly, the shoot was very quiet and simple. I stood against a wall in the annex and just did as I was told. At most I think he said once or twice, 'Good. Good.' The next day I flew home to Adelaide. Helmut rang and said the unthinkable, 'Your shots are wonderful. Just wonderful.' I was exhilarated. This was from the master, *the* Helmut Newton. And I went off to peel the potatoes for dinner.

We had moved again. Charles had an opportunity to buy a property through the Returned Servicemen's Fund. He'd taken me to see the house and it was horrible. Liver brick with woodwork painted bright yellow and blue, like the colours on a Kraft cheese packet. I christened it the 'Kraft Cheese House'. Charles promised we would have it repainted. We never did. I hated it but I had no say in the matter.

Within days Newton phoned again: 'I need you for three days next week, for a Pierre Cardin brochure. And there's a Michele lipstick campaign coming up. And maybe the week after I'm shooting the Renee Furs collection. Can you come?' And so it started, to Melbourne and back, to and fro. Pack for me, pack the kids, deliver them to my dear parents, stack the fridge for Charles, fly off, work like hell — exciting, heady stuff. Seeing the first images Newton took of me, I thought, my God! Is that really me? They were so different from my Adelaide shots.

And I was learning, always learning. Helmut would show me the contact sheets or the transparencies. 'See this, that's great if you do that. This? This is not so good.' 'I like that look, the right side of your face is your best side.' Or, 'Junie thinks you should alter the eyebrow shape,' and, 'Let's try the hair slicked back.' By now I felt very comfortable with Helmut. He had a great sense of humour, and he loved my Aussiness. I could make him roar with laughter with a 'G'day mate' or 'Jeez, I feel crook.' He latched onto 'crook'; it became a favourite expression. Once, on a truly horrific location, the wind up to gale force, the heat unbearable and the flies driving us insane, I waited for that quiet still moment when he lined up the shot and was just about to shoot the first frame, and I said, 'Jeez, nice day for it.' He doubled over.

Helmut gave me confidence to try things, to be spontaneous, to follow my instincts on a shoot. I knew what he wanted, the mood, what the clothes were about. We developed a sort of communication shorthand and it was fun. Always great fun. As I worked with him I thought, I can really do this. Hoo-bloody-ray! At last I'm really good at something. Very quickly I was earning extraordinary money, although I worked hard for it. Long days and sometimes late-night location shoots. Freezing in summer clothes in the middle of a harsh Melbourne winter and later the reverse. Packing, running for planes, late nights, early mornings. But it was all worth it. I was acknowledged. Helmut was a genius as a photographer, and as a person I had started to adore him.

During this time, Diane Masters took me to the atelier of Hall Ludlow. He was possibly the only original couture designer in Australia and had successfully built a clientele of Australia's rich and famous. When I met him he had just received a commission from the Australian Wool Board to design an Australian wool collection. It was to go on a world tour to promote the great Aussie fibre. Ludlow was so grand he terrified me. A small, beautifully groomed man, he was a dead ringer for Sir Robert Helpmann with his immaculately combed coif of grey hair. He wore exquisite clothes. Years later, when Hall and I had become great friends, he swore that the day I first came to his studio I was wearing a full skirt with stiff petticoats, a picture hat and long white gloves. He was always given to exaggeration! Although I don't deny my dress was more 'Adelaide off the rack' than 'Collins Street couture'.

Hall was born in New Zealand. An orphan, he was forced into farm work at the age of fourteen. He told me he would thaw out his frozen little hands in the warm hay bales and promise himself he would leave the orphanage as soon as he could. At sixteen he struck out on his own. He worked as a waiter, a barman and a host of other jobs before spotting a 'Help wanted' sign in a boutique window. He had been sewing for friends, and although he had no formal training, he applied for the job anyway. The owner of the boutique handed Hall a roll of fabric and gave him just a few hours in which to cut and sew a dress. When it was finished she put the dress in the window and it sold immediately. Hall had the job. He had also taken the first step on his road to becoming a leading fashion designer.

AFTER A few hectic working weeks, it became apparent that Charles and I had to consider our finances as the credit squeeze had seriously affected his business. It made sense for us to move to Melbourne as a family and it would be a better situation for the children. I hated disturbing their routine, expecting them to sleep at home one night, Nanna's the next, then back home. I knew that this was not right. I discussed it at length with Nancy, Mum and Charles. We all knew a big change was inevitable. My agent, Jill, agreed.

Helmut had suggested we move, and he talked it through over the phone with Charles. 'She's going to be a star,' he said.

'She'll make a lot of money.' There was no resistance from Charles. A bigger city, bigger opportunities for both of us. He became enthusiastic. Within a short time we had leased the Kraft Cheese House and found a full-time nanny for the children, a gorgeous, gentle girl, with a Salvation Army upbringing. Then, after lots of tears, hugs and goodbyes to family and friends, we packed two cars and headed off to Melbourne. We spent a few days in a hotel and went house hunting, settling on a large garden apartment, which took up the entire ground floor of a lovely old house in South Yarra. It was decently furnished, had a safe place for the children to play and a kindergarten just around the corner. Perfect.

Then I really began to work with Newton. And my marriage gradually, ever so gradually, moved into a downward spiral. It wasn't Newton's fault, he offered me an opportunity and I grabbed it. Charles had agreed. I was working very hard, the kids and nanny were ticking along, the girls loved their new kindergarten, there were pretty parks to play in. They were happy. I was happy. Charles was not so happy. As hard as he tried, and he did, he just couldn't start up again in business. A silly scheme with a hopeless partner failed and obviously took its toll. I appreciate that it could not have been easy for him. He couldn't get rolling and it appeared I was full steam ahead. I didn't mind paying the rent. I felt sure it was only a temporary state of affairs. It was, however, to become a lifetime responsibility.

I didn't have a Melbourne agent, I didn't need one. I worked with Helmut every day. He would phone in the evening to give me the rundown on what and where we were going to shoot the next day. I'd be at the hairdresser's most mornings by seven and be at the studio an hour later, do my own makeup and be ready. (There were no makeup stylists or hairdressers on the set in those days.)

We mostly worked alone, Helmut would ban clients if he could. The exceptions were fashion artist, Patrick Russell, and account executive, June McCallum, who both worked on the Wool Board advertising account. Patrick went on to become a highly successful fashion photographer and later film director. June became Editor of *Vogue* Australia for a number of years. Another was a top PR woman, Esta Handfield, who had numerous fashion accounts, including Renee Furs. The owners of that company, Bruno and Renee Stern, were an adorable couple. They often used me in their parades, and after one particularly successful showing of their collection they gave me a little sleeveless jacket of black monkey fur, quite radical in design. I wore it for years, over everything from a long black evening dress to jodhpurs and a polo-neck sweater. On one occasion, many years later when I was single again, I had a date with a funny, droll man called David Shmith. I answered the door, he eyed my black monkey fur and said very slowly, 'Now look, Tabs, you have to shave under your arms before I take you anywhere, let alone out to dinner.' I cracked up, and the jacket never ever had the same appeal.

Helmut Newton really changed my life. For the first time I knew what it was to work hard. And for the first time I found immense satisfaction in work. I was also learning more than how to be a good model. When we worked alone I started to contribute to styling the shots. I'd suggest accessories or a 'look' and Helmut was always encouraging and generous. He had also renamed me; I was now 'Maggie'. The first time he called me Maggie I nearly died, to my Adelaide ears it was something my Nanna may have called one of her cows! But from Helmut it was funny, it was different, and soon everyone called me Maggie. The exceptions were Charles and my mother, to them I would always be Margaret. Deep down I think I knew 'Margaret' had gone, I was definitely Maggie now.

Not long after I moved to Melbourne Helmut set up a new studio in the basement of Wool Board House with another photographer, Henry Talbot. It was all very modern and roomy. I was to spend a lot of time there.

The knowledge I gained while working with Newton I use to this day. Later I was to build a business on that 'know-how'. Occasionally I'd work with other photographers, mainly Athol Shmith. 'Winky', as he was lovingly called, was a reed-thin dark man with huge eyes behind thick black-framed glasses. He always wore a dark suit and he smoked non-stop. He had been married to the model Bambi Shmith. After they divorced she married the Queen's cousin, Lord Harewood. I never knew her but she was a legendary beauty, petite with a wonderful little nose and an enviable waistline. She photographed like a dream. Many of her shots were still hanging in Winky's studio, despite her departure.

Helmut hated me working for other photographers or on promotions that he wasn't involved in, such as Myers advertising. Ann Moffet, the publicity manager for Myers, would book me for special designer collections, so both the clothes and the ads were stylish. But all Helmut could say was, 'Why are you doing this shit?'

'Well Helmut,' I'd reply, 'I have two kids, a husband, a nanny and myself to support and rent to pay.' He'd shut up. Clearly he knew I had those responsibilities.

The advantage I had as a model was that I could do both photography and parades. I was booked for all the big shows: Georges of Melbourne (the most stylish of fashion retailers), Myers' European collections, Le Louvre with dear Lil Wightman, and there were big travelling shows for the Australian Wool Board and the British Nylon Spinners, which would bring out stunning European designer collections to illustrate how the fibres and fabrics they marketed in Australia could be used. The top models for the parades were Diane Masters; Helen Homewood, a stunning brunette with a milk-white complexion, a wicked sense of humour and a great ability as a cook; and Janice Wakely, a fine-featured blonde. While the rest of us would take taxis, Janice would catch a tram, she knew how to look after the shillings. Good thing, too, because she later married Eric McIllree, the head of Avis Car Rental, and following his death she has a lot of shillings to look after!

Helen and Janice were also great photographic girls. We often worked together with Helmut, usually on big advertising campaigns. We'd have lunch between shows and invariably the talk would be about their love-lives, who they were seeing, not seeing, sleeping with or not sleeping with. I felt quite different. I was a mother with two daughters, a husband and a nanny. At the end of the day I went home to cook dinner for the family, they went off to restaurants and clubs.

Another Melbourne model was Joan Green, who wore her hair in a rather unusual style. She would pin a padded cone of false hair onto the top of her head then sweep her own hair up over the pile. Once in place she would then spray the whole thing silver-white. It was nothing if not different — very, very different. I was told that she once said no one got a look in with Helmut after 'that Adelaide housewife appeared'. I don't think my presence had anything to do with Helmut declining to give her work. I think it was more a case of his aversion for silvered conic hairstyles. Of course, in the nineties she would have been a hit with the designer Christian Lacroix.

One of the first synthetic fibres to come onto the Australian fashion market was Arnel. The clothes were terrible, but with Helmut's photography, his top model team, good accessories that were usually ten times more expensive than the dress, the photographs were marvellous. We had a ball on those shoots, although group shots are never easy. Helmut would call us by our surnames: 'Homewood, tuck in your bloody hip.' 'Wakely, for God's sake, I can't see the damn garment.' 'Tabberer, ya gotta stay in, it's getting too wide.' And that was on a good day. He could be adorable, or abusive if the elements were against him. 'Shit, I'm just a poor little photographer, how in the hell can I work in this bloody gale?' He could be very funny. He hated 'new' girls pressed to be used by the client. He could reduce them to tears. He'd bark, 'Jesus, she looks dead,' or some such comment, and everyone on the set would become silent. But he rarely let the insult stay. He'd quietly, in his own way, apologise. It was simply that Helmut Newton wanted the best for his client, for the shoot, for himself. He hated compromise. It became infectious.

There was another model, Maggie Hibble, who Helmut liked to partner me with. We were direct opposites: she was blond, I was dark. She had a translucent complexion and could do the best 'cool blonde' look. She was marginally shorter and finer of figure than me. I quickly learnt how to hide my hip behind her, standing just off to one side and tucked in behind. We liked each other. She had just come out of a turbulent romance and was emotionally bruised by the experience, and could be rather nervous. Nevertheless, working close, just the three of us, we had many good laughs. If a trip was coming up Helmut inevitably booked the two Maggies. We were both professional, he knew he could rely on us, no matter how bad the weather or conditions were. The job would be completed without complaint, the shots would be good.

We had begun to work for *Vogue* Australia, so the trips became more frequent. One *Vogue* trip was to the snow country, and having never seen snow I was very excited. Most of the first day was spent trying on the collection of clothes, deciding who looked best in what, and which accessories worked for each garment. Late in the afternoon Helmut thought he might just get in one shoot. He needed the late light to strike the village. The plan was to shoot high up the mountain from the top station with me in the snow lift and the village way below. Way, way below!

By the time we rode up the mountain the weather was turning murky but we ploughed on. I dressed at the top station in a huge hooded white wool poncho, black ski pants and boots. I climbed onto the ski-lift and was slowly backed out from the station. Helmut was on the deck of the top station with his camera set on a tripod. So there I was, with my fear of heights, dangling in mid-air a mile or so above the village. The wind started to build, Helmut clicked away for a few minutes as I changed my head angle. Look left, right, lean left, lean right, the feet this way, then that, smile, don't smile! This was one shoot I wanted to get over and done with — fast. Suddenly Helmut was waving his arms to gain my attention and yelling instructions, his words swept away on the wind. I cupped my hand to my ear to indicate I couldn't hear him. With that he did a little charade which clearly indicated he wanted me to undo the safety belt holding me in. In between gusts of wind I heard, 'It's disturbing the fall of the garment.' Disturbing the fall of the garment. What about saving me from a fatal fall? 'Just do it, Maggie,' I said to myself. And I did.

'Got it,' he yelled, and to my relief I was moving back to the safety of the top station. We rode down the mountain in what the locals would later describe as a 'small gale'. I drank very little in those days but I headed straight for the bar and ordered a double brandy.

The next day was God-given — bright white light, perfect.

We worked quickly and efficiently, mainly double shots with a Sydney model, Wendy List, then a single on me. I found walking in the snow difficult. We did a lot of falling over and a lot of laughing on the way to the location. I had to strip down and dress at the site so the garment would be perfect. Wriggling into a one-piece ski suit standing in the snow was not easy. The *Vogue* assistant was down on her hands and knees pulling on my socks and boots, and our noses were running with the cold. Helmut set up his camera angle from below a smooth rise. I was eased into position on the very tip of the hill, wearing ski suit, cap, goggles, skis and stocks. A ski instructor who was taking care of us showed me how to station my skis, lean in and the correct way to angle the stocks. Helmut worked away: 'Look out to the right.' 'No, back this way a bit.' Then, 'Now, Maggie, really lean into the shot.' 'Good, good.' I always love encouragement. I leant a little further … then too much, I felt my skis move. 'Oh no.' I went careering down the mountain and I heard shouted as I disappeared in a flurry of white snow, 'Don't get the suit wet.' I thumped to a stop against a rather large tree. As they dug me out I said, 'Shit, Helmut, I could have broken my neck.'

'Not you, darling, not my big strong Maggie.' And he laughed that laugh which made me laugh.

IT WAS while we were travelling that we began our affair. Helmut had been wonderful to me, and working with him was stimulating. There was an enormous physical attraction building between us. The opportunity was there, it was possibly the most exciting thing that ever happened to me. We both felt guilty about our partners, and while the attraction was irresistible we knew the affair had to be contained. I was never silly enough to think it could go on. June was Helmut's wife totally, she was

also his great strength, his fiercest critic. We were very discreet
in Melbourne. When we travelled we found time to be together
and I adored him, I absolutely adored him. He said to me once,
'I wonder if your husband understands that you're like a young
horse tethered in a stable. If anyone opens the door, look out.' I
don't know if Helmut opened the door but he may well have
slipped the latch.

One of the most unusual trips Maggie Hibble, Helmut and I
took was for British Nylon Spinners, to New Guinea. We flew
into Port Moresby, where the surrounding country offered some
stunning locations. A small hill village had been chosen for the
shoot and we trekked in under the care of our guide, a tall
Australian who spoke pidgin and had a thorough knowledge of
the local scene and customs.

When we arrived, the village seemed to be deserted. Gradually
though, some children came to watch us, their curiosity having
got the better of them. Hibble and I made friends with them.
An old man lounged in his hammock by a log fire, his eyes never
left us as we were setting up. We changed behind some huts,
both nervous. I had the distinct feeling we were being watched.
At one stage Helmut wanted me to pick up a carved wooden
bowl left on the step of one of the huts. I suggested that this
may not be kosher in local custom, but he insisted. Two seconds
later there was a loud rustle in the bush. I looked up to see the
whole village surrounded by tribesmen. Oh great! And I'm the
one holding the bowl. Our guide stepped forward and a lot
of rapid pidgin was spoken, then the men quietly drifted back
into the bush or went on their way through the village. I've
never been so happy to leave a place as most of them carried
enormous machetes.

We took a different route out from the village and had to cross
a fast-flowing little river. Jokingly I said to the guide, 'Any crocs?'

'Oh yes,' he replied quite cheerily, whereby Helmut paled.

I said, 'OK, scaredy cat, hop on,' and I piggy-backed him across the river, his precious camera held high. Helmut made a great story of it for weeks after.

Just on the outskirts of Port Moresby was a ramshackle village, nothing like the one we had visited earlier with its perfectly thatched huts. Here it was pieces of old iron thrown over rickety timber frames, and thin mangy dogs prowled around piles of rubbish. But the village was situated next to one of the most beautiful beaches I'd ever seen. That was where Newton wanted to shoot. To do so we had to get the head man's permission and that meant going through the village. An indolent group of cheeky teenagers started to annoy us, jumping in front of the camera, touching the car, chiacking around. We all tried to keep our cool but it was more than a little threatening. One girl grew increasingly offensive with her face-pulling and rude gestures, until she finally spat at my feet. I held up my hand close to her face, then very slowly ripped one, two, three long red fingernails off. She let out an almighty howl and ran off with her gang. False nails reapplied, we did the shoot and left.

That night, after we'd retired to our rooms in a little motel set in a fantastic garden I heard a bloodcurdling yell. Without thinking I flew out of bed and opened my door. There pinned to the wall, his face dead white, was Helmut. 'What's the matter?' I screamed. By now other guests, including Hibble, had gathered. There was a loud croak and something enormous took a great leap and disappeared down the hallway. Helmut stammered something about stepping out for air and in the dark treading on the biggest of New Guinea toads. We all went back to bed. A little later he came to my room and we tried not to laugh too loudly about the romantic rendezvous being interrupted by the bare-foot horror of stepping on a big wet toad.

Back in Melbourne, down at the docks, we were shooting a series of photographs for the Wool Board. I was standing in front of a large freighter when an enormous truck, stacked high with bales of wool, pulled in to unload. In a flash, Helmut had persuaded the driver and the dock workers to take a smoko. I was helped up to the top of the truck cabin, then, tucking my pointy-toe stilettos in between the wool bales, step by step I managed to reach the top. Gingerly on hands and knees I inched my way out across the bales to the centre and found the courage to stand up. All this while wearing a big black and white check wool coat and a Jackie Kennedy pillbox hat. I stood up, pointed my arm out in a 'They went that-a-way' attitude. Click, click. Wool bales, wool coat, shipping Aussie wool to the world, all in one shot. 'Fabulous,' Helmut shouted, and I clamoured back down. I'd finally conquered my fear of heights. A good thing too, because time and time again I found myself climbing up, hanging from or leaping off tall structures, or worse. Anything for Newton. He loved that I didn't whinge, that I was game for anything. I surprised myself.

We were at the airport one day, I was decked out in a wool coat, hat and gloves and very high-heeled stiletto shoes. The male model, Patrick, was Helmut's favourite because he was older and had a certain 'lived in' sophistication, unlike the rash of 'beach boy' types who made up the majority of the male model market. Patrick and I were supposed to be the 'glam rich couple' arriving in their own helicopter. We took up a position by the chopper, Newton punched off a couple of shots but somehow it wasn't working so he said, 'Maggie, get up into the chopper and stand on the step. Patrick, reach up to help her, that's better.' Click, click. On the spur of the moment I leapt out into mid-air. 'Fabulous, do it again,' said Newton. I did. Have you ever leapt about three feet to the ground in impossibly high heels? He wouldn't even let me change feet because the coat looked better flying open toward the camera. I must have leapt twenty times before he called, 'Got it.' I hobbled to the car. My foot was killing me. The next day it was the size of a football with a blue-black bruised instep. When I explained this to Helmut over the phone he said, 'Sweetheart, it was worth it, the shots look terrific.' You had to be tough!

When Helmut developed a passion for night photography I thought my days were numbered. Shooting evening gowns in rain-slicked back alleys in the depth of a Melbourne winter is a sure way to catch pneumonia. Helmut would pack a small flask of brandy, and when I turned blue I was allowed a nip. On the coldest nights I'd often arrive home feeling no pain. There was one occasion when we almost got locked up. Helmut had devised a concept for a Pierre Cardin brochure. The French clothes and accessories we were to model were quite extraordinary for their time. Helmut's idea involved a group of guys in dark glasses, slouch hats and trench coats. They would carry machine-guns and would be robbing a Mayne Nickless truck. I was the 'wicked lady' with a neat little hand gun and a big handbag, trailing jewels.

Early one morning we were all assembled down by the Albert Park Lake. We started to shoot — guys, guns, trucks, me. I noticed some rather startled faces peering from cars as they drove past. Suddenly sirens sounded and we were surrounded by four police cars, coming from every direction. They formed a barrier around us and the cops leapt out, guns at the ready. Helmut had to do some very fast talking. The cops had received calls saying a hold-up was taking place. Even when they discovered that the machine-guns were actually wooden props they were not exactly friendly. There was a lot of stern talk about irresponsibility, formal notice, permission, and so on. Helmut turned on the charm. One car was assigned to remain on location with us and the others took off. Back at the studio the bad boy of photography had the staff in stitches and the story grew and grew. A week later when I heard it recycled, we'd actually spent the night in the clink!

Helmut asked once if he could photograph my girls with me for a Wool Board calendar. The photograph shows me sitting in a pretty doorway with my little daughters at my side watching me knit. As I recall they were both very good and their fee went into their bank accounts. On another occasion he wanted to shoot us together in his studio for a British Cotton promotion. I raced out and bought the girls new shoes, black patent leather 'Shirley Temple' jobs. When it came to dressing them Helmut thought the contrast between the black shoes and their pale cotton dresses was too striking. He decided they could wear their old white shoes. On hearing this Amanda let out a bellow and didn't stop for some time. Finally we coaxed her onto the set but she didn't look happy in any of the shots. That was the end of the girls' modelling career. I found it too harrowing and Helmut wasn't exactly good with kids.

AS TIME went on Charles was playing more and more golf. We were arguing. He appeared to have given up trying to start a business. I realised this situation couldn't go on but I was reluctant to force the issue. I loved my work and I knew a confrontation could jeopardise it. In retrospect, I should have seen the inevitable coming. I returned home one night cold and tired. We started to argue. Charles said he wanted us to pack up and go back to Adelaide. That may have been the first time I really stood my ground. I told him there was nothing for us in Adelaide, and as I was the only one working I had to be where the work was. Nothing had changed in Adelaide, the car business, he knew, was still doing it tough. Nevertheless, he was adamant we should go back. Charles realised he was losing his control over me; it must have been threatening. I went to take a shower. The argument continued, enraged he came into the bathroom, ripped back the shower curtain and slapped my behind with all his might — three times. I screamed and shoved him away, grabbed a towel and fled to the bedroom. I'd never been hit by a man before. I'm sure the moment he did it he regretted it. I knew he was frustrated and I knew that he hated my growing up.

When we were first married I had relied on him for everything. This was the new me. I had an opinion, I voiced it, I was earning money, I was independent, I was moving in a pretty sophisticated world. It rubs off. Charles didn't understand the fashion industry. He knew about cars and boats and golf. He wasn't into the fashion crowd — photographers, models — and the arty life they led — the theatre, gallery openings, eating in Italian bistros in Carlton, arguing about anything and everything, and drinking cheap red wine till midnight. That wasn't his scene at all. We had gone out on a few occasions with my fashion gang but Charles obviously hadn't enjoyed himself. I found it easier to stay home and cook dinner for the family. He would have his golfing mates in to play cards.

Over time we made friends with a few couples in the fashion business — Maggie Hibble and her Dutch boyfriend; Helmut's secretary, Jenny Sexton, and her French fiancé, Robaire Rosenberg; Bruno Benini and later his wife Hazel Craig. Bruno was a tall, grey-haired, impossibly handsome Italian photographer. Newton had persuaded him to model for him, so we had worked together. Bruno was gentle, Hazel dynamic, but they were both funny. Over time they were to become my very close friends, however in those days it was just the occasional invitation to come home for dinner.

A cold war developed between Charles and me. We lurched on for a few more weeks but then it became a daily debate, a daily argument. I have blocked the final split out of my mind because it was so dreadful. It involved a huge row, Charles packing and leaving for Adelaide. Everyone was in tears, the children, the nanny, Charles, me. Brooke gave him her teddy bear. It broke my heart. There were lots of calls from my sister Nancy and my mother: neither approved. I felt very isolated. Clearly life had changed. I kept working.

Charles rang me on his way to Adelaide and said, 'I'm coming back.' In a flash I thought about the weeks and weeks of unhappiness, the arguments. From somewhere I found the courage to say, 'No, don't.' I cried, I worried, had I done the wrong thing? He rang from Adelaide and we argued again. The more abusive he became the more convinced I was that separation was the right thing. But I'd wake in the night, sweating, fearful. I'm on my own, I thought, I have the responsibility of my two little daughters, can I do this? I was twenty-four years old.

Eventually the children responded to a new tranquillity in the house. Daddy had gone but so had the arguments. I had hated them hearing our rows, I felt one happy parent had to be better than two fighting ones. I was still shaky about my role as sole parent, but daily I grew in strength.

One day I opened the mail to find an 'invoice' from Charles for the things he had bought for the apartment. This was for a few odds and ends and his children's beds. I couldn't believe it. Another phone call, another row. I suggested he couldn't be serious about the bill. I'd largely kept the family and paid the rent since we had moved to Melbourne. This led to, 'Well, I never wanted to go to Melbourne.'

'Not true, you agreed.' It was endless, and I realised it was also pointless. Charles hadn't supported his children for some time, he was never going to again. Alright, damn it, I will support us by myself. And I did. But it was a frightening prospect at the time.

Not long after the separation I was working with Helmut in a popular city bistro, once again partnered with Patrick. We were shooting at the bar and a waiter passed by carrying a large bottle of soda water. It slipped from his hand, there was a crash, I didn't feel a thing but I glanced down and blood was pumping out of my foot. A piece of glass had severed an artery. There was great panic as the staff tied tea towels around my foot to try to stem the flow of blood. I glanced up to an almost surreal vision, on the tables were steaming bowls of pasta, but the patrons had fled. I was bundled into Helmut's car and driven at breakneck speed to the hospital, fortunately only a couple of blocks away.

A young doctor stitched my foot and said, 'Well, you can go now.'
'How?' I asked.

'Oh it's fine to walk on,' he assured me. I thought that was pretty ambitious, but I gingerly hobbled out of the cubicle and started to walk down a long corridor. I could see Helmut and Patrick at the other end anxiously pacing up and down. I had taken no more than a few steps when I felt a tearing sensation in my foot. I looked down, blood everywhere. Back on the table, more stitches, a night in hospital. I was sent home to bed. Reality bit, I couldn't work.

I spent anxious days facing the fact that this was to be my life, my new responsibility. I had my children, a nanny and myself to support, I couldn't afford to get sick, to not work. Hell, I had to work. I had been booked to wear an entry in the Gown of the Year, in those days the most prestigious design competition in the industry. The designer came to my house for the final fitting. I stood on one leg, my cut foot propped on pillows on the bed. It wasn't easy but we managed. We were both hoping my foot would be alright for the judging scheduled just eight days away.

I did get to the judging, bandaged, but mobile. And I wore the winning Gown of the Year for 1960. Triumphant I went back home to bed. The foot was not healing. They put me back into hospital, operated to clean up the tissue and stitched it up again. I spent three weeks in bed, another two resting. I was getting very low on cash and I spent many anxious nights. If anything, the experience taught me that I had to put some money aside. I had to have a nest egg. It was scary, very scary. Eventually the restaurant paid compensation, and the owners made fun of me for years after. Every time I went into the bistro they would joke and push the waiters away saying, don't go near her. We laughed then. At the time we didn't.

ABOUT TWO and a half years after I had moved to Melbourne, Helmut stunned me by saying that he and June had decided he had to work in Europe. He had gone as far as he could in Australia. He wanted to tackle the big time. They were planning to live in Paris and were leaving in a couple of months.

I was devastated at first but it was obvious Helmut had to lead his own life. I realised he had been my champion but I also knew I would still find work. I had to — I had the responsibility of my children. They were my priority. It was important that I kept a stable home life for them. I believe that kids respond to routine. They need regularity in their lives and discipline — dinner on the table at a certain hour every night, their own beds, their own room, their toys. I really believe in those things; they are comforting, secure. My separation from their father was enough for them to contend with.

As Helmut's departure loomed our workload increased. For

an evening-wear spread for *Vogue* we took off to an artists' colony called Montsalvat in Eltham, outside of Melbourne. Matcham Skipper was the Lord of the Manor, so to speak. I was introduced to this huge bearded man then we went to work. Late in the day Matcham showed us a collection of silver jewellery he had made. One outstanding piece was a bracelet, a big wide silver band with beautiful relief figures. Helmut and Matcham talked and I went to change. Back in the car Helmut handed me a small parcel. It was the bracelet. It sits on my bedside table today and I still treasure it.

WHILE WE were in Sydney in early 1960, on a trip for *Vogue* Australia, Helmut once more changed the pattern of my life. He was frequently at war with the then editor of *Vogue* Australia, a stocky little Englishwoman with gravy stains on her lapels, Rosemary Cooper. She had a thing about hats, the kind of hats Helmut hated. He liked mannish hats, soft, slouchy. She'd produce these po-like numbers, shaped like old-world chamber pots. Helmut would simply not use them in the shots and all hell would break loose. Often Bernard Leser, the Chairman of *Vogue* Australia, had to step in to pour oil on the troubled waters. I liked Bernie, he never treated me just as a model. Our friendship has survived more than thirty-six years. Later, in 1972, Bernard purchased *Vogue* Australia, then in 1989, sold it back to Condé Nast and he held high international positions with them until his retirement in 1997. During this trip the hat issue had caused another big blue. Helmut said, 'Stuff it, let's go out for a slap-up dinner and forget the bloody hats. I'll take you to meet the most handsome man in Sydney. His name is Ettore Prossimo.'

Italian-born Ettore Prossimo, with his partner Nick Frangi, owned and ran the Buonasera Restaurant in the heart of Kings

Cross, just down from the famous El Alamein 'thistle' Fountain. It was one of the first, and for many years considered the best Italian restaurant in Sydney. Not large, it had a warm intimacy behind its big windows and sliding glass doors. You could sit for hours and watch the world go by. In those days the Cross was colourful but without the danger zones established in later years with the advent of illegal drugs and the accompanying crime. Then it was exotic with its artists, writers, models, photographers, musicians, advertising executives, gamblers, playboys and high-priced hookers.

I remember seeing Pross for the first time. In those days he was known as Reb (short for Rebel, I wondered), a nickname bestowed by a previous mistress. He stood behind the bar at the cash register counting the money. I was to learn he loved to count the money. He had a cigarette stuck in one side of his mouth, the smoke spiralled slowly to the ceiling. He was dressed in a well-cut, three-piece dark grey suit with a snow-white shirt and dark tie. He was tall, dark and ridiculously handsome with a perfectly barbered black beard and moustache. Helmut and I arrived, he nodded, a waiter showed us to a front window table. I took in the rustic interior: white bagged walls, tiled floor, red and white check tablecloths, straw-covered Chianti bottles holding candles, piled with wax dribbled from many a long evening. Pross came to the table, we were introduced. He and Helmut knew each other well and there was talk of mutual friends, work and a bit of gossip. He looked at me a lot. He sent us a fine bottle of wine with his compliments, found numerous excuses to come to the table and joined us late in the evening for a Sambuca. As we walked back to our hotel Helmut asked me what I thought of Pross. 'He's handsome, seems nice. But I'm sure he's a terrible playboy.'

'All true,' said Newton.

A week later we were back in Sydney and again dined at the Buonasera. The next day I received a message at the hotel that Pross had called to invite me to dinner. No mention of Helmut. 'You go,' said Helmut. With the exception of dinner with Helmut when we travelled, I hadn't had a date since Charles. Dinner with Pross was flirtatious and when he kissed me good-night in the car tingles shot up my spine. As I walked back into my hotel room the phone rang. It was Helmut. We talked about the evening, he didn't come to my room. It was as if he was handing me on to another protector. He never actually said so, but I had a distinct feeling that was how he saw it. I can't say I felt offended. Helmut, I knew, had great affection for me, if not love, but I also knew I now had a choice in my future. I had grown up a lot since meeting Charles. Helmut was to leave for Paris in a few weeks. We'll see, I thought.

In the next few days, back in Melbourne, red roses started to arrive. Daily I'd walk into Helmut's studio and his secretary, Jenny, would complain, 'I've got them in buckets, I've got them in jars, they're everywhere.' I'd take a cab home toting the roses and transfer them to my buckets, my jars and whatever looked like a vase. At first the cards read: 'Love Reb,' nothing more. Then they became: 'Ti voglio bene, Reb.' We were falling in love. It was to be a turbulent, torrid, passionate, all-consuming love.

The day before Helmut left Australia he took me to lunch at the Menzies Hotel in Melbourne, just up from his studio in Wool Board House. I cried, he was tender, concerned that I was financially alright. He'd write, we'd stay in touch, and all too soon he left. I went on working but I missed him like hell. Oh God, how I missed him. I'd look at my shots and think, Helmut would have done it this way or Helmut would never do it that way. His was a high benchmark and I'd carry it with me for a long, long time. Perhaps I still do. At that time I felt that despite all the personal trauma, marriage failure and heavy responsibility of keeping my family, I had just lived two and a half years of the most exciting time of my life. I still have a lot of love for Helmut Newton. A different love but a lot of it. Just after Helmut left Australia I was named Model of the Year for 1960. It would never have happened without him.

Pross, Love & Loss

WITH HELMUT gone from both my life and my work, Melbourne suddenly lost all its attraction. I continued to go through the motions of modelling but I never stopped comparing the results with my previous Newton shots. And Pross was bombarding me with phone calls, flowers and frequently unannounced visits to Melbourne. I was falling in love with this big, handsome Italian. He was tenacious in his pursuit and made me feel very, very desired. He was sexy, passionate and romantic. He started lobbying me to move to Sydney. He never actually said 'live together', but it was clear that he loved me, genuinely cared for my kids and was prepared to look after us. The move made sense. We were in love and wanted to be together, but there was a lot to do, not the least was informing my mother.

My marriage break-up had distressed her. She begged me frequently to reconsider and go back to Adelaide, and she was very concerned about the girls and me. 'How will you manage?'

she asked again and again. I explained that I had managed, was managing, that I was earning good money and felt confident — despite my secret anxieties — and I could and would continue to do so. I guess her old-fashioned beliefs couldn't accommodate me being alone without a husband to protect me. How could I tell her Charles finally hadn't protected me? It was too painful. Now I had to tell her I had fallen in love with an Italian, and I was going to uproot my family once again to join him in Sydney.

We had a long phone discussion during which I assured her I wasn't 'racing into anything silly'. I wasn't going to actually live with Pross. I really did feel confident about my work prospects in Sydney. The kids would be secure. They would still have a nanny. I hung up the phone and felt like a delinquent teenager. Mothers have a way of making you feel like that, regardless of your age. But having told her, I suddenly felt free. I started packing, organised removalists, made my farewells, and with a new nanny in tow we flew to Sydney in December 1960.

Pross had taken a suite in a small Potts Point hotel for us while he showed me three or four apartments he'd scouted. The first night Amanda, who was just three and a half years old, protested loud and clear about not wanting to sleep in a cot. She was a 'big girl', she informed us. She was used to her bunk bed and didn't want to sleep in a 'baby's bed'. So she turned on a tantrum. We were all tired, nervous and obviously feeling the strain of being in a strange place in a big strange city, and for once I simply couldn't control her. After fifteen minutes of her screaming, at full pitch, with Brooke having joined in the protest, Pross strode manfully into the bedroom and gave Amanda's bottom a tiny smack. He came out and burst into tears, so distressed at what he'd done. She simply snuggled down and went to sleep. My daughters had already wound him around their little fingers. He adored them and in a very short time they adored him too. It was never to change.

The apartment we eventually chose to lease was in Warners Avenue, Bondi, selected because it was close to a school and the beach. Essentials for two small daughters and a working mum. It was the entire top floor of a white Spanish mission style building, furnished in a funny mixture of old pieces, but it was light, airy and comfortable. We settled into our new life with ease. The kids enrolled in school and kindy and spent late afternoons on the beach with their nanny. I returned to modelling, working with Sydney photographers, including Laurie Le Guy and Geoff Lee, and later David Franklin, for magazines such as *Vogue* and *Flair*. Pross continued to live in his Wylde Street apartment in Potts Point, with its chic, black and white decor. It took me some time to learn that a former girlfriend, Sheila Scotter, was responsible for its look. I knew there had been a lot of former girlfriends. Pross was, after all, romantic, Italian and so damn good-looking. He was also generous.

A couple of months before I moved to Sydney, I was passing through on my way to a photographic location. There was a scant thirty minutes between my flights, but Pross met me at the airport and hurried me out to his car. He had a portable record player on the back seat and played me the song 'Petite Fleur' then presented me with a beautifully wrapped gift. It contained a gorgeous gold watch. I'd never owned anything so precious. I was overwhelmed by his act of love and his generosity. We kissed then we ran back through the airport lounge just in time for me to catch my flight.

Pross always worked hard. His restaurant was a success because he was always there. So we didn't really go out in the evenings, although I sometimes went out with friends. But we had Sundays together, and he would swing by the apartment very early each morning. We would have coffee, and sometimes he would drive the kids to school. Then he would go off to the markets or to do his accounts, and I would go to work. We would meet later in the day, or he would take us all to the restaurant for an early dinner. The girls quickly developed rather sophisticated palates, enjoying oysters Kilpatrick or garlic prawns, veal scaloppine and tiramisu. Pross indulged them. I knew he felt bad about leaving his small son, Nicolas, in Italy with his former wife. He obviously missed him more than he cared to admit. He treated my daughters as his own. It was a relationship that lasted until the day he died, because as well as their warm mutual love they were also good friends.

Pross introduced me to his closest friends, Judy and Ian Potts. Judy was a famous and stunning model. She walked a catwalk better than any other in the business and had worked in London for designers such as Molyneux, Hartnell and Amies, while her husband worked at becoming an eminent doctor. When they returned to Australia, Judy led all the major parades for Madame Roche, Sydney's premier fashion house at the time, along with all the other gala fashion shows. We hit it off, and the Potts became my firm, loyal friends.

Judy had a superb figure with an enviably small waist. She wore her hair in a unique, short hairstyle with a sort of duck's bum swish at the back. She cut it herself with nail scissors, which I never believed until I actually saw her do it! And she had a delicious smile with a crazy crooked front tooth. Judy loved to laugh and had a great sense of the ridiculous. Ian was tall, handsome, an elegant dresser and a little droll. Together they made a stunning couple. They also made stunning babies, two snowy-haired boys, Tony and Tim, close in age to my girls. Judy and I spent a lot of time showing off our figures and tans in strapless black swimsuits, playing on Camp Cove beach or Bondi with our four beautiful blond kids.

Our first Christmas in Sydney we went with the Potts to a beach party somewhere near Palm Beach and I met another couple, Georgie and Snow Swift. Snow was a dashing former fighter pilot, who'd swapped cockpits and for a time was Sir Frank Packer's pilot. He'd gone on to become manager of the *Sunday Telegraph* before moving into a new war zone — advertising. Georgie, one of Sydney's most stunningly beautiful women, had met Snow when she was a young columnist with the *Sun* newspaper. She later became Fashion Editor of *Woman's Day* magazine and the national PR manager for David Jones for many years. They have carried their style through the years and are still handsome, beautiful and my close friends.

Over time I built up friendships with others, including Leo and Ann Schofield. Leo was an advertising whiz and a fabulous cook. He could whip up a delicious dinner faster than anyone else I know. Ann, dark, petite and fascinating, ran her antique jewellery business with the same style she practises to this day. From the fashion world there was Hall Ludlow, who popped up from Melbourne regularly. Another designer was Frankie Mitchell, whose salon on New South Head Road near White City always had fabulous window displays. At a party one evening Lady Lloyd Jones, of David Jones, remarked to Frankie, 'I always admire your window displays, Mr Mitchell.' To which he replied, 'And I always admire yours, Lady Lloyd Jones.' There were also Ann and Ross Fraser. Ross was a brilliant jeweller and over the years I collected many of his beautiful pieces, some made specially for me. Ann had a sense of presentation that was unequalled. She created Christmas window displays for their tiny shop, Anina, in Angel Place and later Elizabeth Street in the city, that literally stopped the traffic. And no one, but no one, can wrap a gift like Annie. So gradually I gathered friends and found a new life in Sydney with my wonderful man and my wonderful kids. I stayed in touch with my family in Adelaide, although I don't believe Mother ever stopped worrying about me living in Sin City.

When Hall Ludlow came back from an extensive overseas trip in 1961 he moved to Sydney to set up a salon, and we saw a lot of each other. Judy and I starred in his parades. His clothes were always superb, and he staged the first grand fashion parade in the Art Gallery of New South Wales.

I don't know whether it was all the Italian food I was enjoying, but inch by inch my figure started to change. One day Georges of Melbourne rang and asked me to fly down for fittings for their forthcoming French fashion parades. The clothes, as always, were a very narrow cut, probably equal to our size eight or at most a size ten. After I'd tried on a few garments it was apparent I wasn't as narrow as I used to be, or should have been. The fashion director, dear Ron Lardner, just looked at me and said, 'I'm so sorry, Maggie.' I left the store with a quivering lip and facing the harsh reality that I had better get out of modelling before it got out of me!

Little did I realise at the time that I had entered what was to become a lifelong battle with my weight. It would be a source of great anxiety for me. It would cost me a career in modelling but lead me to a career in a new fashion field. It would be talked about and written about ad nauseam. Eventually I desperately tried every fad diet that came along, ultimately they all failed. But back then I thought my weight gain was just temporary. Now I realise that like all who battle a weight problem, I was clearly in denial.

What was I equipped to do? Modelling was all I knew. I agonised and staggered on for a few months, subjecting myself to a series of ridiculous crash diets, but like the tide the weight crept back. In despair one day, I discussed this with Hally. 'Why don't you come and work for me?' he said. 'I need someone to run the salon and I'll make for you so you can still do the parades.' By then, 1962, I was a size twelve, not a fashionable ten as all models were. It was also the time of the sack dress, a distinct advantage!

Hall made my clothes so I had a fabulous wardrobe, and Pross paid my rent in Bondi and was always turning up with fillets of beef or cartons of fruit and vegetables and Italian wine. Nevertheless, in the past I had made really good money modelling and now I would be on a standard wage. I had to seriously budget. I knew Pross would look after me but I didn't want to ask for money. I had discovered my independence and it was important for me that I manage my own life.

I knew nothing about the accounting side of the business, but I knew about fashion and Hall felt sure I understood women. I gratefully accepted his offer and my life did another U-turn. I loved working with Ludlow. He was incredibly talented and always generous with me, asking my opinion on designs, including me when he selected fabrics. It was another huge learning curve. I also started to sketch the collection for him. I'd always been able to draw but now I was developing a new talent in fashion illustration, although he always laughed and said my sketched hands looked more like 'chooks' feet'. He was right.

We would compile the collection by his description and my sketched interpretations. It was fun, challenging, although, actually getting him to cut the designs was somewhat harder. Hally only worked well one way — right on deadline. His associates would be near screaming point waiting for him to start. But Hall would leave it till the last minute, then work without sleep for hours and hours, occasionally, exhausted, grabbing a nap on the salon floor or cutting table. All part of his creative process. The staff often worked through the night to finish the collection for the launch. I never got used to it. In later years, when I staged large parades, I'm sure the reason I was so manic about finalising everything at least three days in advance was because of those nerve-racking days with Hally.

But there was no one to touch Ludlow when it came to design. He was truly original. During my time in his salon he was approached by Moira Wallis, who was responsible for promoting a fibre called Banlon. Would Hally create an entry for the 1962 Gown of the Year in Melbourne? He did better than that; he designed two gowns. One for Judy Potts, one for me, and for good measure he decided to enter the racewear section as well as the casual section. I wore the winning garment in the racewear section and its design is printed on my brain; I could sketch it for you today. They were wonderful, glamorous dresses, styled to perfection.

We had a suite in the Menzies Hotel, where the judging was held over a couple of days, along with a gala presentation dinner of all the entries. On the first day of judging Hally gave us each a good-luck charm. Mine came from his home country, New Zealand. It was a tiny jade Tiki. 'Just tuck him in your strapless bra,' Hall said. 'He will bring us luck.' As the day dragged on, with calls and recalls to see the judges I was in and out of my gown so many times I lost count. As we moved into the final round Hally said, 'Rub the Tiki for luck, darling.' I reached inside my bra. No Tiki. I searched high and low, if you get what I mean, and I couldn't find it. I was distraught and being my mother's daughter, superstitious. If we lose it will be my fault, I thought. After the final judging call I went to the loo, and there in my knickers I found the little green Tiki. Hally got a great laugh and spent days sending me up about 'no sense, no feeling'.

We didn't win in the gown section but we were placed. I don't think it was because the Tiki was snuggled up in my knickers. And anyway, we had won in the racewear section.

Hally had a passion for nightclubs. He loved to dress up and go out to Chequers, Andre's or Sammy Lee's fabulous Latin Quarter. Later it was the Silver Spade Room at the Chevron. I frequently took calls from these clubs the next day: 'Mr Ludlow asked us to forward his bill. Could you write a cheque, please?' He was outrageously generous, and time and again I had to point out that it was too costly to pay for champagne for the whole chorus line! Often he'd gather Judy and me, dress us to the nines from his collection, and we'd hit the town.

By midnight, after he'd shut his restaurant, Pross always came to collect me and take me home. He wasn't a nightclub boy. At the most he'd drink a Coca-Cola, then get toey and we would leave. It got so that Normie Erskine, the large, loud and funny singer at the Latin Quarter, used to ad lib witty lines about Pross into his songs if Pross arrived during his performance. They were great nights when top performers, including Sammy Davis Jr, Shirley Bassey and Frances Faye, brought the house down. Frances and Hall struck up a friendship. Hall made some wonderful clothes for her. Frances and her gay partner spent a lot of time at the salon having fittings, and we spent many nights at her performances, Frances sitting at the piano, belting out, 'Maggie May loves Hally, Hally loves Frances, Frances loves Judy, what a drag, what a drag!' A mad song where she wove all the locals into the melody and won hearts and followers in one.

Because I always went home with Pross I often wasn't there when other performers would pop into the club in the wee hours and jam with the star, but Judy and Hally frequently came home at dawn. If the budget ran low after an expensive month around the clubs Hally would buy cheap sherry in large flagons for the salon, and we would pour it into his stylish crystal decanters. The clients — the who's who of Sydney and Melbourne society — when offered a sherry never knew that it wasn't 'Spain's finest'.

Hally loved Brooke and Amanda, and he got a great laugh when Amanda for one school concert had to sing, 'If you believe in fairies, fairies believe in you'. He made her a couture fairy dress — outrageously beautiful, with layers and layers of the finest silk tulle on a tiny fitted satin bodice. Embarrassingly perfect against the other little fairies in their wonky homemade jobs.

WHEN MY mother came to visit us, Pross cast his spell. They became great mates. He would tease her mercilessly and she would giggle like a schoolgirl. He was fascinated with Mum's sayings. 'Feel like a cuppa?' she'd ask. (I don't think he'd drunk tea in his entire life.) If he paid her a compliment she would respond with, 'I haven't got any small change,' and he'd throw back his big handsome head and laugh and laugh.

We stayed in Bondi for a little over a year, then Pross took a big house in Bulkara Road, Bellevue Hill and suggested it was time we lived together. I had tried to talk to Charles about a divorce but the phone calls always ended in an argument, and I didn't have the money to pursue it with a solicitor. Charles said that he had been divorced before and didn't intend to be again! He wanted to divorce *me*. I felt wronged, after all he'd chosen to leave me. A technicality I'll admit, but in those days an act that by law had to be considered, and he had never contributed to his daughters' welfare. Finally I didn't care who did the divorcing, I just wanted it over. I suggested he get on with it because, although Pross and I hadn't really discussed marriage,

I assumed the moment I was free we would. After all, we were deeply in love.

Neville Marsh, a well-known Sydney decorator and a friend, had helped Pross with the Bellevue Hill house. It was rather glamorous for its time — seagrass wallpaper, white carpet, white canvas curtains, chocolate-brown corduroy couches. The girls had their own bedroom. There was one for the nanny and another for us. We lived as man and wife, and I thought I was in heaven.

PROSS AND I were at home one evening when my mother called. My father's health had been declining for years then, after being diagnosed with cancer, he had been admitted to hospital. Mother had assured me the radium treatment was proceeding as expected and she would let me know if there was a change. Now it didn't look good. She was teary and I felt her fear come down the line. Without hesitation Pross booked my flight and the next morning I was home in Adelaide.

Mummy and I walked through the grounds of the old Royal Adelaide Hospital. There wasn't a lot to say, I just held her hand tightly. Daddy was in one of the 'temporary' wards, the problem was that temporary had spanned several years. It was a Nissan hut with a long verandah, a tin roof and no cooling system. It was a hot day as only Adelaide can have — that searing dry heat that makes your face frizzle and your temper fray. At the door to the ward Mummy stopped, looked at me with her big, sad, brown eyes and said, 'Darling, I don't want you to get a shock, Daddy's lost a lot of weight. Be prepared for that.' I wasn't.

My tall, gorgeous father was paper thin, his face ravaged with pain and fear. There were blue Biro lines along his jaw, down his neck and onto his chest. 'Where they're zapping me,' he explained later. But as I approached he offered up a bright smile and his long thin arms squeezed me hard in an embrace. We chatted about my girls, my work, everything but his condition until Mummy walked away to talk to the nursing sister. Then he took my hand and pleaded, 'Skeeter, tell them to stop, will you? I don't want this any more.' He pulled his sleeve up to show me the blue-black bruises from the injections. I was stunned. Lost for the right words I kissed his cheek and murmured assurances that I would speak to his doctors; we would find another way. I guess we both knew that wasn't to be. He thanked me for coming and his eyes filled with tears as I walked away. Outside neither Mummy nor I could retain our control.

My father died a few days later, on 18 January 1963. His heart had finally given up the battle. For some years he had suffered from chronic bronchial asthma, had cancer of the throat and jaw and undergone the cruelty of radium treatment which had weakened his heart. He was sixty-six years old.

Our family was devastated, but no one more than my mother. She had loved him deeply through the years: the good times when their children were born, the bad times when their finances were stretched and Daddy had found a friend in the bottle. In the years just before he died, because of his failing health, he had abandoned his drinking and their life was settled and harmonious. At his funeral I couldn't look at my mother. I couldn't trust myself to witness her pain.

BACK HOME in Sydney Pross would take me in his arms when I found myself overcome with grief. He understood the loss — his parents meant a great deal to him.

From the start our relationship had been extremely physical but it was also romantic. We were both spirited so there were wonderful rows but making up made them almost worthwhile. I have no idea what we argued about; silly little things and sometimes jealousies. But they paled into insignificance when about eighteen months after we moved in together I discovered 'the other woman'. I won't name her, although eventually I called her 'Pokey'. She had been Pross' mistress for a few years, a relationship that had continued despite his meeting me, bringing me to Sydney, installing me in Bondi and Bellevue Hill.

Pross had opened a second restaurant in the city. It was never to achieve the success Buonasera enjoyed, but he was ambitious. He worked gruelling hours, which in itself was a strain. How he also managed his double private life was simply inconceivable. Etched in my memory is every detail of that awful night when I called him at the new restaurant. He answered the phone with impatience in his voice, spoke briefly then asked me to hold. There were two lines into the restaurant, I heard him pick up the second phone. At first I couldn't hear but as he raised his voice in anger I clearly heard him say, 'Come on, leave me alone, it's not what you think. I'm not with her, she's a poor woman, she's got two kids. She is living downstairs, she has nowhere to go.'

I believe I stopped breathing for what seemed minutes but must have been only seconds. The realisation that he was speaking about me slowly spread through my brain and my entire being. The shock was instant. Oh God, no. Don't let this be. Please don't let this be! I screamed into the abandoned phone: 'Reb ... Reb ... Rebel, answer me. Answer me!' Eventually he did. 'I heard you, I heard you, you bastard. You lying bastard. Who was that? Who were you talking to? Why were you lying about us?' The row that erupted was hideous. He denied he had been referring to me but had no explanation of what the conversation had been about.

I knew he was lying, my mind fast-tracked back over things that had been alluded to by friends for some time. Veiled suggestions came into focus. I had been a fool. Was this great passionate love a fabrication? There was another woman. How dare he? How could he treat me like this? I immediately rang Judy. Sobbing into the phone I begged her to tell me the truth. Reluctantly she did.

Pross came home and I gave full vent to my feelings. He was distraught, pleading with me to be quiet, not to wake the girls. It was nothing. I was mistaken. Then I said that Judy had told me all. I knew who the woman was, how long they had been together, that he was still seeing her and had been all the time we had been together. He tried to convince me that she was a past lover, they had just remained friends. She had helped him decorate.

In a flash I recalled that some months back things had disappeared from the house — a lamp, ashtrays, a painting. 'What's going on?' I asked.

'Oh, I've lent them to a friend.'

She had suspected that I was not simply a tenant, living downstairs as he claimed. She guessed that Pross and I were involved, and she had protested about me living in a house full of her gifts. So he'd given them back, then reclaimed them when he'd convinced her that it was innocent. In a blinding rage I walked around the living room. 'Did she give you this?' I grabbed a cigarette box and smashed it. 'Did she give you this?' I threw a lamp to the floor. I'd never behaved like that in my life but the rage, passion and fury at his deceit were all-consuming. I was pelting things onto the floor. He was picking up the pieces. Finally I spotted a very large marble ashtray. 'And did that bitch give you this too, Romeo?' I aimed it straight at his head and threw it with all my might. Pross ducked behind a screen at the top of the stairs. It hit the wall and smashed into a thousand pieces.

I stood there sobbing. He came and took me in his arms. I was exhausted. He kissed my face, wiped my tears, begged me to understand. He said she was 'mad', she had threatened to kill herself, it was emotional blackmail, he couldn't get away from her. He'd tried since the day he met me to finish it, but now it was out in the open it was over, he promised. He had finished with her, he wanted me, the girls. He cried floods of tears. Pross was a great crier. He could turn them on to waterfall proportions in an instant. I so wanted to believe him. He was my world. I loved him. I didn't want our life to change. We would start again.

Within weeks I discovered he was still seeing her. One night he said he would be home very late, he had to do stocktaking. He didn't come home, he didn't answer the restaurant phone. In the small hours of morning I was anxiously walking the floor. Finally at dawn I was desperately ringing friends. 'Have you seen him?' I was out of my mind with fear. Had something terrible happened to him? Should I call the police? The hospitals? No. Deep down I knew. I just knew he was with her.

A little later he walked in full of excuses and I told him there could be no more deception, no more lies. I had to know the truth. He said one of her parents had died. She hated to fly so he had taken her to Melbourne on the overnight train and flown back. He claimed it was innocent, an act of friendship. I was devastated. I went through all the motions of everyday life, cutting lunches for the girls, taking them to school, going to work. Hally patiently spent hours that day discussing my situation with me. Like Judy he had known about the other woman for some time.

'Why didn't you tell me, Hally?' I asked.

'Because I thought you might shoot the messenger,' he replied.

A few days later Pokey phoned. 'I think we should have a

discussion,' she commanded. I suggested she come to the house. I suppose I wanted her to see for herself that Pross and I really were living together. She was dark, attractive, older. She was also bossy and confident. She sat in what I thought of as my living room, took a handwritten list from her handbag and arrogantly started to question me: 'Well, where did you think he was on such and such a date?' and 'What did you imagine when he was out of Sydney on such and such a day?' I sat stunned. I don't recall how we finished. I do remember that after she had left I was furious with myself.

How could I allow her to humiliate me? Why in hell hadn't I challenged her? After all Pross was living with me, sleeping with me, caring for my children. What in the bloody hell did *she* think he'd been up to? Did she really believe I was just a tenant? Not bloody likely. Come on Pokey, give me a break. Did I look like a tenant? But of course I hadn't said any of those things. I had no retaliation skills. I had sat in a weepy heap and I hated it. I rang Judy.

'I can't cope with this, Judy, I have to get away from this house. He's lied to me all this time. I need time to think clearly, sort out my life. I have the girls to think of.' And like the wonderful friend she was she said, 'Pack up the kids and come to us.' At the time the Potts were living in a charming but small cottage off Edgecliff Road. I slept on the couch. The kids thought it was a great adventure sleeping in bunks, sharing Tim and Tony's room. Ian, who normally had little patience with the drama of others' lives, was kind and considerate to me and each night administered a sleeping pill to ensure I got some rest. We muddled along for about ten days.

I was deeply concerned for the girls. They adored Pross and were obviously confused about what was happening. Pross was constantly coming around begging me to go home, arguing when Judy stopped him at the door. I firmly told him I needed time to think. He phoned at all hours of the night and day, sent flowers with passionate notes and even telegrams to say, '*Ti voglio bene.*' He kept the pressure up, pleading that he had finally finished with Pokey, promising he would never deceive me again, and the tears flowed. He was so very, very Italian.

I hadn't stopped loving him but I couldn't find it in my heart or head to believe him, to once again put my trust in him. I discussed the situation with Judy and Hally. Judy must have found it difficult to counsel me as she and Pross had been friends for years. But we were close now and she was aware my happiness was at stake and, more importantly, that I had to build a secure future for my girls. She had shown great strength on my behalf, standing her ground when Pross had time and again pounded on her door wanting to see me. Ultimately she knew he had to change. He would have to make a real commitment to the relationship. His double life had to be terminated. Hally, on the other hand, had always got on well with Pross but he felt Pross would never change.

Despite a fragile financial situation I found a small, modern but depressingly plain apartment in Edgecliff. It was all I could afford but it was very close to the Fourth Street School, a demonstration school where I knew my girls would get the best education. I went back to Bellevue Hill to pack. I walked around shoving my things in packing cases, and Pross followed, ripping them out. The removalists arrived. I pointed to a packing case and said, 'Take this out.' Pross shouted, 'No, put it down.' Two big burly removalists lingered by the door, embarrassed and confused. In retrospect it was a very funny scene, worthy of the best soap opera. Or the worst?

Some months before, the girls' nanny, who had come to work for me just before we left Melbourne, failed to collect them from school one afternoon. A teacher had phoned Pross, who picked them up then called me at work. Shaken, I raced home, where we discovered that the nanny had taken both cash and a suitcase, and left a sad little note about 'keeping the baby'. I never saw or heard from her again. I had since managed without a nanny by taking the kids to school on my way to work, with Pross collecting them each afternoon. Finally I found a reliable older woman, Hattie, who taught my girls how to crochet and knit. She would baby-sit when required and Brooke and Amanda grew to love her.

Now I had to look after the girls on my own. When I told my mother what was happening, she jumped on a train and came to Sydney. She was firm with me: 'You've made your bed, Margaret, now you have to lie in it.' But I knew she harboured great concern for us. I assured her I would always find work and had no intention of staying in that apartment for long. I didn't. Hally, because of some home-grown business problems and a lucrative offer to design in Hong Kong, was leaving Australia. He had a small but very attractive apartment in Guilfoyle Avenue, Double Bay. I gathered all my charm and enough dollars for the rent deposit, and on the same day he gave notice I persuaded the agent that I would be the perfect replacement tenant. Hally kindly left me his furnishings. I bought stretcher beds for the kids and I slept on a mattress on the floor for some weeks until I saved enough to buy us each a bed.

The Tabberer girls were really on their own, and we became even closer. A strong bond was forged, probably out of Brooke and Amanda's confusion and my hurt. Although Pross and I were not speaking, he still picked the kids up from school each afternoon and brought them home. He also never relented about getting me back. One night I had the greatest scare of my life. I'd refused his calls all evening, hanging up on hearing his voice and finally taking the phone off the hook. I was asleep under the open window in my first floor apartment when, in the dead of night, a huge figure lurched through the window, falling on top of me and kissing me passionately. Pross, who was not exactly the agile type, had climbed the pergola, hauled himself up a drainpipe and through my window. I shrieked in fright and demanded he leave — by the door. When I told Judy the next morning she convulsed with laughter, and for the first time since the drama had begun I admit I had a good laugh too. Pross — so immaculate in his navy-blue, three-piece suit, so unathletic — scaling a building playing cat man was a pretty funny image.

WITH HALLY gone, my job had gone. My meagre savings were rapidly running out. I knew I had to find alternative work. I didn't want to starve myself with another obscene round of diets and be cranky with the kids just to go back to modelling. Anyway, it was a job with a use-by date. I realised it was time to make a change and build a different career, something with long-term security. No one was going to look after me and my daughters, it was up to me. I went to see my friend Bernard Leser, the head of *Vogue* Australia. During Helmut's battles with the editor at *Vogue*, Bernard and I had formed a warm friendship. He suggested I go into fashion public relations.

'Bernard, I don't know anything about PR.'

'Nonsense,' he said. 'You'll learn and I'll help you.'

He was wonderful. Within days he had packed me off to a meeting at the Dow Chemical Company. The company marketed a metallic fibre called Lurex. But Lurex had become a generic term, and with many cheaper look-alike glitter fibres on the market they needed to protect their fibre and its registered trade name. Bernard had armed me with all the right PR lingo. I rattled on about all the people I knew in the industry and to my surprise I suddenly found a measure of confidence. I did know most of the designers, the fashion editors and writers, and, more importantly, knitters and fabric houses. Modelling had introduced me to that world. I had just never realised those contacts could work for me in a different way. By the time I left the meeting I had the account — a contract for a year working three days a week. I was delirious and I knew this was a great first step. Of course I still had to learn how to 'drive the job' but Bernard proved to be a real friend and provided me with the basic formula. For the rest, I learnt as I went and found great satisfaction in doing so. I had that account for about three years, but by then I had others too.

I set up my little typewriter at a small desk in the living room of my apartment, which I was to use as my office. Pross was still calling by, phoning frequently and sending flowers. He wasn't thrilled with my new-found job. I believe he thought eventually I'd have to call on him for financial help and he would get me back. I was determined that this would not be the case. It was at about this time I met a friend of Hally's, handsome Barry Young, who had a few PR accounts but was subsidising his income selling encyclopedias.

One day he called me, knowing I had just started in the publicity game, and offered me a spot promotion. He would front the account and I would do the leg work. I agreed, even though I had reservations when he explained it was for Andre's nightclub. I knew nothing about the entertainment industry. Barry handled the club's overseas entertainers. 'It will be a cinch,' he said. 'He's a singer called Dick Haymes. He used to be married to Rita Hayworth.' Barry duly handed over press kits with Dick's photograph, airbrushed to perfection, and a list of the Sydney entertainment press. My job was to lock in stories and handle the airport press conference on the star's arrival. The press were kind and after two weeks I had articles placed in all the major papers and journalists committed to interview Dick. Barry was pleased. Two nights later I received a phone call informing me that Haymes had thrown a wobbly. It was hinted he was engaged in a battle royale with the bottle, and would not be appearing at Andre's. I nearly took to the bottle myself. How on earth could I go back to all those columnists?

'Oh Barry, I can't do this,' I whinged.

'Yes you can,' he said, 'and what's more, you have to get publicity for the replacement act. They're called the Treniers. They're an Afro–American group of musicians and singers. They're supposed to be fantastic.'

'Maybe,' I replied, 'but they haven't been married to Rita Hayworth!'

To this day I don't know how I did it, but I apologised to the journos about Mr Haymes and tried my damnedest to sell them the Treniers. There wasn't time to get pre-show press, it would all have to happen at the airport. It was essential that I get the press to cover the arrival. God love 'em! They must have known a greenhorn when they saw one, they all turned up. I settled them into coffee and buns, and went with special permission into Customs to welcome the unknown, unseen Treniers. There were ten of them — all very black and very short. One big happy family: uncles, cousins, fathers and sons. I rounded them up and then like a headmistress led them in single file out of Customs and into the press conference. They were on their own, I thought. In two minutes guitars appeared together with a sax, a trumpet and away they went, doing what they did best. They belted out some harmonies and backchatted the press and each other. Twenty minutes of high octane entertainment.

I delivered them to the hotel, made my follow-up calls to the press, then phoned Barry. I told him I thought it was going to be alright. 'It will be,' he replied. 'I've just spoken to the *Mirror* guy. He told me the sight of Maggie, six-foot-something in her stilettos, leading this gang of little black guys through the airport had the hardened old journos rolling with laughter. They'll give it space, they had such a good time.' True to their word they did and the Treniers became our friends and nightly brought the house down at Andre's. They were even asked to extend their stay. However, I decided fashion PR was more my speed.

A FEW months later the phone went and a voice said, 'Is that Maggie Tabberer?'

'Yes,' I replied.

'This is Harry Dearth.'

'Oh sure, and I'm Minnie Mouse!' I said.

Harry Dearth was a very famous radio star. I had sat on my Dad's lap all those years before, our radio tuned to Harry Dearth's 'Playhouse'. Now the famous man was actually phoning me? Never! He finally convinced me he really was Harry Dearth and was working for the Seven Network. They were about to make a pilot for a new programme called 'Beauty and the Beast', would I be interested in being one of the Beauties? 'Well sure,' I said, 'but it will never go with a corny name like that.' Little did I know!

The remarkable thing was that none of the original panel had any television experience. I suppose we were picked for our looks and then it was up to the individual to sink or swim!

Beauty
and the
Beast

I HAD no idea when I flippantly accepted Harry Dearth's offer that my life was to change so dramatically. Apart from the occasional modelling job I had never been involved in the world of television. Now it would become central to my career for many years, and I would never know what it was to be anonymous again.

It was late 1963 when we filmed the pilot of 'Beauty and the Beast' in Studio A at Channel Seven. The show's format was based around a male 'Beast' and a panel of four female 'Beauties'. The Beast would read a problem letter, written by a member of the public, and the Beauties would play Dorothy Dix with the answers. Graham McPherson was producer, Kevin Burston, the director. The Beast was radio star Eric Baume, a formidable old bugger if ever there was one.

When I knew I was going to work with him I thought I had better tune into his radio show 'This I Believe'. I listened intently.

He ranted, raved and didn't draw breath for a second, but by the time he had finished I felt he hadn't really made much sense. His bombastic presentation sounded great, energetic, committed but it was thin on rationale and, therefore, on credibility. When I came to know him better I realised he was an incredible old fox. One week he'd be all for capital punishment, the next not. He changed his opinion to suit the mood of the populace, and somehow he got away with it.

Also on the panel for the pilot was Sheila Scotter, ex-girlfriend of one Ettore Prossimo — our meeting was marginally cool! — model Ann Michaelitz and Irene Elphert, who I was told was there because she was a friend of Baume's.

On the first day my face twitched with nerves and my mouth dried like the Sahara when it was my turn to answer, but once we got underway my fear evaporated and I had a good time. The network was thrilled with the pilot. When Graham McPherson rang to tell me we were to do a series, he swears I said, 'Hoo-bloody-ray. Now I can buy carpet for the apartment!' The additional income would ease the financial uncertainty for me and my girls.

Irene didn't reappear after the pilot. Sheila Scotter didn't last long either. After a few weeks I was the only pilot survivor. But by then I was in good company with girls who went on to become the staple of the show for a number of years.

Pat Firman was a dark beauty who had previously hosted a programme on Seven called 'Penthouse'. Her mentor was Rupert 'Rags' Henderson, who ran both Fairfax and the Seven Network. He had suggested her to Graham for 'Beauty and the Beast'. Pat's pencil-thin eyebrows and style of dress belonged to the past. While most were wearing bushy eyebrows Pat stuck to her thin 1940s jobs. When the sack dress came into fashion Pat stayed with her full dirndl skirts and boat necklines.

She had her own style and it never changed, regardless of times and trends.

Pat Lovell was petite, blond and bouncy. She was Miss Pat on 'Mr Squiggle', the ABC's kids' programme and was married to the actor Nigel Lovell. They had two children around the same age as my girls. As young women with older husbands or partners we related to one another. And as fate would have it, she too finally brought her kids up alone. Hazel Phillips was a cracker-box redhead. Born in England, she was theatrical and wonderfully eccentric. Her marriage also dissolved, leaving her to raise two sons alone. Hazel thought nothing of popping on a glittery cocktail frock and a feather boa for a show that went to air at noon. She was a real character with the most delicious laugh and a ready sense of humour.

Anne Deveson was a brain. A marvellous, horsy looking girl with a lop-sided toothy grin, she was married to Ellis Blain of ABC radio. Ellis, I thought, was something of an intellectual snob but Annie was his antithesis. Clare Dunne was an actress with milk-white skin, rich auburn hair and a lilting Irish accent. Later there was Freda Irving, another brain and a solicitor, married to our producer, Graham McPherson. There was Diana 'Bubbles' Fisher, 9000-miles-an-hour Bubbles. She was married to Humphrey Fisher, the son of the Archbishop of Canterbury.

Then we had the much-married Dita Cobb. Dita got a face lift, a front-page story about it in the *Daily Mirror* and a job on 'Beauty and the Beast', all at the same time. She had escaped Nazi Germany and was proud of her Jewish ancestry. She was a survivor in more ways than one. Outrageous and scandalous. To prepare for the show all the other girls would go to makeup then slip into a dress. With Dita it was more a case of walking onto an assembly line — thick cake makeup, enough cheek and chin shading to camouflage a tank, double sets of false eyelashes, lavish wigs. During her years on 'Beauty and the Beast' she had practically every body part nipped, tucked or lifted — cheeks, eyes, chins, tits and tummy — and it always made headlines. Frankly, I thought it was a drastic way to get publicity. After a couple of years Ena Harwood joined the panel. She was a grand-mother and widow (a rather merry widow) who by then was Baume's special companion.

'Beauty and the Beast' began in January 1964 and it was a huge success from the start, dominating the ratings around the country. And it changed all our lives. Within a very short time we were known nationally. The show and its Beauties were frequently front-page news: Dita's facelifts, Clare Dunne winning the leading role in the Aussie film *They're a Weird Mob*, my eventual marriage to Ettore Prossimo. It was slightly ridiculous but it did wonders for the ratings. It was also beneficial, I discovered, for my PR work. Being known opened doors that might other-wise have stayed firmly closed. Above all I was making money.

We recorded the five shows over the weekend. Graham had a roster system so the panel members on each show changed, although Hazel and I seemed to do most of the programmes. Judy Potts cared for my girls or they went to a neighbour whose daughter was the same age. They also really enjoyed coming to the studio with me. Pat Lovell and I tried to coordinate these days so her daughter Jenny could play with Brooke and Amanda. They raided the Channel Seven canteen and adored daubing each other's faces in the makeup room.

The problem I initially faced was getting from Double Bay to the Epping studios of Channel Seven. The taxi fare was killing and public transport, impossible. I *had* to buy a car. Margaret McGurkin, a fellow model, was married to a man in the car business. Noel had a funny little car yard with fluttering flags in William Street where a skyscraper stands today. He showed me an old pale grey Simca, which he assured me would go like a rocket. Although it had a few cosmetic problems I didn't care, I just needed reliable wheels. I scraped together the seventy-five pounds and had the new-found freedom of my own car.

As Pat Firman lived at Rose Bay, close to me, I offered to give her a lift to the studio. We developed a routine; she would kick in for some petrol and I'd pick her up and drop her home. The only problem was that the Simca had a tricky front door — it refused to shut securely. I'd had it fixed a couple of times but finally I gave up and bought a length of rope. Pat would hop in then I'd tie the rope from the front door to the back door handle so she wouldn't fall out, and we'd chug all the way to Epping.

Back home Pat always insisted I went in for a drink. Mickey, her mother, would have cheese and bacon on toast ready for us. She would pour us a brandy and dry, and we would tell her about our day. Pat was the centre of Mickey's world. Some years earlier Pat had survived a disastrous marriage to a Dutch flier based in Surabaya. He once tied her to the bed and went off on a mission for three days. Eventually the authorities intervened and flew Pat home on a stretcher. She weighed a mere six and a half stone. It was a traumatic time for her. Mickey and Pat had lived together ever since. Theirs was an incredibly strong bond but I observed a role reversal. Mickey was often the spoilt child and poor Pat the exasperated parent.

Some of the other girls felt that Pat was difficult to get to know. She did have a very reserved and controlled air, but perhaps because I was invited into her more private life I came to know her better. She had enjoyed a certain profile in both the theatre and television. She was a 'star'; Mickey told her so. Pat was determined that was how the world would see her, no matter what the cost to her personal happiness. I often wished

Pat could just relax, but Mickey was a handful. It was a little sad really. On the set Pat would scold Patty Lovell, Hazel Phillips and me for 'laughing too much'. 'We'd get lines,' she said. She even tried to convince us to place a bandaid between our eyebrows when we went to bed each night, supposedly to keep the lines at bay! None of us took it up, and thank God we kept laughing. We all needed to sooner or later.

Away from the studio the Beauties didn't socialise together very often. I'd sometimes see Pat Lovell for lunch. She was adorable and our kids liked each other. She and Anne Deveson were old mates so often Anne came too. Bubbles and her husband lived in an elegant apartment in the eastern suburbs. They had a Sunday night supper tradition where they'd invite interesting people who would sit around drinking bubbly while Humph and Bubbles argued about the best way to cook scrambled eggs for twenty people!

Graham McPherson had cunningly put together a group of women with diverse backgrounds, styles, looks and, of course, opinions. The fact that we were for the most part emotionally crippled in some way didn't bother him a bit. I think he believed that between us we had lived through most experiences. And our answers were as diverse as we were. Hazel would say, 'Don't eat red meat, meditate and try alternative medicines.' Pat Lovell was practical: 'There's an organisation that can help you. It's called so and so.' No one else had ever even heard of it! Anne Deveson favoured the academic answer: 'A university degree or another educational course' was the way to go. Pat Firman took the Christian approach, with 'Talk to your priest' type solutions. And Dita, well Dita was something else. Sock 'em and shock 'em: 'Take a lover, daaarling. Wear red underwear and sleep in black satin sheets, drink champagne and paint your nails blue.' This as an answer to some poor woman locked in the suburbs with five kids and a boozy husband who bashed her up every Saturday night!

I may have been a bit of a ratbag in my style but I took the job seriously and I tried to be rational and responsible. Although I probably said, 'Leave the so-and-so! He's never going to change' more often than, 'You have to try to make this marriage work regardless.' If women were being abused and beaten up I thought it was appalling and I'd say so. The Beast would go berserk at my answers, but our on-air battles only helped the ratings. By then I had got his number and Eric Baume didn't frighten me one bit. One day, though, he did reduce me to tears, and after the show he sought me out and offered an apology. Well, as close to an apology as Baume could get; something like, 'Listen you silly old cow, you know me, it's just to keep the show alive.'

I quickly developed some combative skills when he played dirty tricks such as favouring Ena Harwood when it came to whose turn it was to answer. 'Last' was always best because you had the advantage of adding to what the other girls had said, or better still taking a totally different tack. Normally there was a rotation system so everyone was equal, but when Ena Harwood joined the panel Baume definitely gave her priority. Ena was so bloody predictable I always knew what she would say. It was just maddening that it took her so long to say it! And the Beast, who constantly cut in on everyone else's answers, never interrupted her, so she would waffle on and on. Finally I decided to take action. I'd wait, then just as she finished I'd drop in a fast counter-comment. The director soon realised what I was doing and I would always steal the last camera shot of the segment. Eventually I think Baume twigged. Ena never did but Baume and I formed a sort of truce: you ask the questions in a fair way and I'll stop stealing the camera.

One of the most telling stories about Baume concerns the

time he was invited to speak at the Wagga Wagga RSL Club on the eve of Anzac Day. The producer was being very efficient, hurrying us along during recording breaks because time was tight for Baume. He was to be collected by a car with a police escort in order to get to the airport in time to catch his plane to Wagga Wagga. Now despite all his bravado, I knew Baume was scared of flying in bad weather, and this particular afternoon the weather had turned foul. To cover his fear he adopted his full bluff and bluster mode. At the airport he pushed past a terrified flight attendant waving his ticket and boarded a plane. Sometime later he landed in a remote town a thousand miles from Wagga Wagga. Baume had bullied his way onto the wrong flight. So five hundred old diggers sat down to dinner without their 'star' speaker and Baume had a lonely chop in a terrible motel. Graham McPherson literally cried with laughter as he told this story to Pat and me. Baume was a producer's nightmare: temperamental, irrational and bloody difficult to deal with. Perhaps Graham felt Baume had got his just deserts. But always wary of his temper we never let on we knew the real story.

Letters about troubled lives poured into the programme: bashed wives, alcoholic husbands, delinquent kids, savage in-laws, aggressive neighbours. It was all there, but it took McPherson's skill to select a variety of problems for each show. Like a good recipe it was essential to have the right mix of ingredients.

Soon after 'Beauty and the Beast' started, Graham McPherson went through what he now calls his 'Baptism of Hell'. To be truthful Graham rewrote the majority of letters. They needed editing and sometimes in the interest of the programme he'd combine two or three problems into one letter. One such letter sought our advice on whether a young woman should consider her boyfriend's offer for a trial marriage with a Surfers Paradise holiday. Only Hazel and I agreed it would be a good idea. We didn't actually say try before you buy, but that was the gist of it. McPherson was carpeted by the control board and the network, and three major companies cancelled their sponsorship of the show. Times sure have changed.

Fan mail came by the carton. We all eyed each other's bundles to see who was getting the most. It would be false modesty not to confess that Hazel and I seemed to have the biggest bundles, but at a price sometimes. We'd get three dozen letters saying they loved us, then one nasty one and immediately we'd go to the floor. There was also the odd nutter who would write long rambling, sometimes threatening letters that were very disturbing. Other letters gave us great joy. One woman named her daughter Tabberer after me and we wrote to each other for some years. Another friendship blossomed with a little Down's Syndrome child. Her parents were so grateful to all the Beauties who corresponded with her, and Graham organised for her to come and see the show being taped. She was adorable and loving. It was a feel-good day for all of us.

In those days the network didn't provide any assistance with answering our considerable mail. We each had to deal with our own. It was time consuming but most of us felt it was certainly part of the job. I often spent long evenings answering mine, but that and being a guest speaker at various clubs around the country built a following.

When 'Beauty and the Beast' started we each had a private dressing room, but eventually we opted to move into one big communal room. That way we could coordinate our wardrobes. If someone was wearing hot pink they wouldn't want to be seated next to another panellist wearing bright red. We also liked the time to gossip. And yes, maybe bitch a bit. Actually there wasn't a lot of that; most of the girls got on well. I do remember a delicate time when Pat Firman objected to Dita's girlfriend sitting around the dressing room while we were getting changed. Dita had entered her 'gay period'. She never made any bones about it. She had tried fellas, she said, and it didn't work. Her friend wore full masculine drag: tweed sports coat, grey flannel trousers, shirts and ties. If anyone was smoking she was first to whip out her gold Dunhill and light up their cigarette.

Dressing for five shows a week was close to a nightmare. At first we each found it a struggle, because wardrobe allowances just didn't exist. As the show became famous it was possible to buy clothes wholesale. I had a marvellous milliner who whipped me up pillbox hats so I could just pull back my hair, wear my different hats and recycle the same little black dress and jacket again and again. Eventually, Valerie Lawson of La Boutique in Double Bay made most of my clothes at a generous discount.

Val Smith was head makeup artist at Channel Seven, her right-hand was Josie Knowland. How they coped with all those women was beyond me, although they said we were easier than Rex Mossop, who insisted a makeup artist stay on to paint his cauliflower ears with pancake for his late-night sports commentary each weekend. The makeup room at the network was painted a dreadful poo brown and a bilious green. The girls wore drab beige uniforms. One day we were moaning about how depressing it all was when the girls explained that they had, time and again, tried to get management to paint the room and give them new uniforms without success. 'I'll try,' I said. But after numerous calls to the production manager, Geoff Healy, I wasn't getting anywhere either. He just avoided me. One day I rang and his secretary said, 'Oh I'm sorry, you've just missed him. He's leaving the station.' I grabbed the makeup girls. 'One of you cover the front door, another cover the back and I'll take the stairs.' It worked. Eventually the room was painted a delicate shell white and the girls got attractive new uniforms. Something of a triumph.

Some other Beauties came and went. I remained friends with Di Richey, a stunning brunette with a wicked sense of humour. She was Australian but had lived in London for many years. Back home on an extended holiday she joined the panel and made a great contribution. She was married to Wing Commander Paul Richey, England's number one war ace. Over the years I frequently visited them in London, where they had a wide circle of interesting friends. I was staying with them one night when Paul answered the phone and after a brief conversation said, 'Yes, see you in a few minutes.' It seems his friend John Paul Getty, who was given to clipping out newspaper articles for Paul, wanted to bring something over. Paul Getty, as he was known, was reputed to be the richest man in the world. He was also highly eccentric. Di's husband said, 'You answer the door, Maggie.' Both hooting with laughter, I guess they anticipated Mr Getty's reaction. The bell rang and I dashed to the door, flung it open and said, 'Mr Getty, how nice to meet you. I'm Maggie Tabberer. Do come in for a drink.' This tiny, strange wizened man gave a yelp and leapt three feet in the air before thrusting an envelope in my hand and fleeing into the night. I never could attract millionaires!

Another memorable Beauty was the super bright Coral Lansbury, an attractive academic. She was only with the programme for a short time before she moved to America, but she made her mark. Her little son would occasionally come to see the show being taped. Today he heads the Australian Republican movement. I dined with him recently, but I didn't mention 'Beauty and the Beast'. Given the serious tone of the conversation whizzing around the table it hardly seemed appropriate, but I've since wondered if Malcolm Turnbull remembers visiting Channel Seven with his mother, and going off to the canteen with Brooke and Amanda to stuff his face on cream buns.

As the show grew in strength we started to travel every five or six weeks to the other states to record. Along with the Beast, our producer would take two or three of the regular Beauties, then add local girls to appear on the show. It provided good publicity in each state and boosted the ratings, because the locals loved to tune in to see their own.

It was while we were on one of our interstate recording sessions of the show that I met Bernard King. A warm, witty man, he kindly invited me to accompany him to the opening night of a musical in Brisbane. I can't recall its name but I do remember I wore a hairpiece piled high in a topknot and long false fingernails. Vile, admittedly, but very much of the time. Anyway, in the middle of the first half of the show my head started to itch. Finally I had to give it a good scratch and — you guessed it — down came the hand minus one false fingernail. I quietly tried to retrieve it but simply couldn't find the damn thing. I whispered to Bernard about my predicament and he laughed so loud we were firmly shushed by other patrons. At interval we staggered out in fits of laughter, found a quiet corner, and Bernard duly dove into the topknot and retrieved my false nail, which being self-adhesive, I simply popped back on my finger. As we resumed out seats, Bernard said out of the side of his mouth, 'Don't scratch, no matter what!'

Years and years later, after I'd bought my first farm and the purchase received some publicity, a damp bundle was delivered to my office. I opened it to find fifty hydrangea cuttings and a note from Bernard: 'These come from my garden to yours with love.' Bernard had a sensational garden at his Brisbane home. It meant a great deal to me to start my farm garden with his cuttings. His act of generosity, considering our paths had not crossed for many years, I think, says it all about the man.

ONE DAY, during 1965, I was at home when the phone rang. 'Zel Rabin calling, Editor of the Sydney *Daily Mirror*.' Oh God, no, I thought. My divorce was imminent and in a flash I could see the headlines: 'Beauty's Bedroom Boredom.' The *Mirror* in those days was given to worse. However, a droll voice came on the line and Mr Rabin asked if I would come and see him. He had an idea for me to write a fashion column. I just about died. I thought it best to come clean.

'Look, Mr Rabin, I can't spell and I don't even know where the commas are supposed to go.'

'If you can write like you talk,' he replied, 'we have a deal. Come and see me tomorrow, three-thirty.' I hung up in a daze. It seems Zel, home with a cold, had been watching 'Beauty and the Beast'. He knew of my fashion background and he was out to build a new fashion profile for the *Mirror*. Grace Bros, then a big retail power, was advertising with his paper and Zel wanted to consolidate the association.

My knees were knocking as I was shown to the Editor's office at Rupert Murdoch's News Limited in Kippax Street, Sydney. Seated behind this huge desk was a small man. 'Mr Rabin?'

'Call me Zel,' he said. I liked him immediately but I was so damned nervous in that foreign environment.

He offered what seemed a handsome sum of money for a weekly, double-page fashion column. He'd even thought of a name: 'Maggie Says.' We sat and nutted out a format then he suggested I go away and write a column and we'd talk again. He was obviously confident it would work because he called in his star columnist, Ron Saw, and instructed him to write a piece to 'welcome Maggie to the *Mirror*'. I was overawed meeting Saw. An avid reader of his witty column, I couldn't believe this big, shambling, warm man was the razor wit behind that page. The three of us chatted, Ron drank what I thought was tea or coffee from a mug with 'Saw' written in red nail varnish. Zel had a similar mug. He topped it up from a bottle in his desk's top drawer. Mind you, the last edition had been put to bed. Rabin was the consummate professional. Later Zel and I got to know each other very well, before he died tragically young of cancer. By then I truly admired him, but he was a sad man whose marriage had dissolved. He saw little of his child and was tortured by the separation.

I was building a business around me: 'Beauty and the Beast', my PR company and now the column. The Women's Editor at the *Daily Mirror* was Lyndal Thompson. I was diligent about meeting my deadline but if I was running even marginally late she let me know about it. She was great. She rarely questioned what I was planning for my pages and she wrote snappy headlines. The column took off, I stayed with the paper for sixteen years and my association with Grace Bros delivered a profitable account to my PR company.

Meanwhile, 'Beauty and the Beast' went from thirty minutes to an hour a day and the ratings soared. Women all around Australia sat down to their sando lunch or fed their babies or did the ironing and watched the show. Years after the programme had finished women would come up to me and say, 'I had lunch with you for six years.' And much later drop dead gorgeous young blokes would step up and say, 'My mum adores you. She never missed your show.' I got more concerned when they started to step up and say, 'My grandmother ...!' On a more serious note, the truth was that for the first time a national television programme was addressing women's problems; real-life problems that inflicted pain, hardship and misery. Just the fact that these issues were aired and discussed helped many women who had previously felt isolated and very alone. It was healthy debate. Best of all, it helped to show women that there were alternatives. They could have choices.

In February 1966, Eric fell ill. He took time off and Stuart Wagstaff stepped into his role. Stuart was the antithesis of Baume, all urbane charm and sharp wit. He didn't yell, he just cut you down to size, with humour. I adored working with Waggers. You needed to be alert. I found myself developing new skills in our verbal combats and I liked that enormously. He was great fun with a million amusing stories to tell from his theatrical days. We are friends today, and it seems he is always there to help me when I'm in crisis.

Waggers and I got on so well it showed on camera and was misinterpreted. Both viewers and the media thought we were an item. We weren't, but it used to make us laugh, particularly when I had a fling with an Adelaide musician while we were down there taping the show. 'If they only knew, my dear,' Waggers would tease me. His humour kept us going, especially when we were bone-tired from a long day in the studio and had to hang around airports waiting for a late flight.

For years and years we did the Perth Telethon. Brian Treasure was the General Manager of the station in Western Australia, and he and his wife Jocelyn were both generous hosts and great fun when we were there. We became good friends over time. The Telethon was a live, twenty-four hour show with a cast of thousands. The floor was managed by a guy called Max Bostock, who made the programme run like clockwork. We met a wide range of people. I remember a gorgeous blond kid, cheeky as all hell, called Johnny Farnham belting out his first hit, 'Sadie the Cleaning Lady'. There were acts of every variety: overseas and national stars, singers, dancers, jugglers, comedy routines, children's groups and, of course, the crippled kids who came into the studio with their parents to tell their stories. Pat Firman and I spent a lot of time fighting off tears, moved by the plight of these children and their families. But we also spent a lot of time laughing.

The Telethon made you fly by the seat of your pants. In between acts a panel of four people read out the list of donations that had come in. Mr and Mrs So-and-so from …? We often stuffed up the pronunciation of the local suburbs, but no one cared. There was always a lot of witty nonsense going on too. One year Waggers, Graham Kennedy and, I think, Bobby Limb, because of a dare by a viewer who promised a substantial donation, had stripped down to their undies. Just then somebody announced that the Premier, Sir Charles Court, was on his way into the studio. Watching the guys in a panic trying to get dressed was one of the funniest things I'd seen. It was this nonsense that made the Perth Telethon. Not only was it the most successful telethon in Australia, but per capita the most successful in the world. And it's still going strong. After twenty-four hours we would all be red-eyed with fatigue but there was a great sense of achievement when that final tally of donation dollars went up. It always exceeded the target.

One year Waggers and I were chosen to be introduced to Princess Margaret, who was in Perth to visit a hospital named in her honour. The organisers thought it would be 'nice' if instead of being part of the formal line-up, we would meet her privately in the hospital. 'Casually discovered,' was the phrase used. We were stationed in a bare little laboratory, and Waggers and I got the giggles as I said, 'Oh sure, this looks casual. Have a look at us.' Waggers was in an immaculate dark suit. I wore a black linen suit, a huge black picture hat and my favourite specs of the time, enormous Sophia Loren dark frames with tinted lenses. What on earth we were supposed to be doing in that laboratory was beyond us. Some little guy kept popping in saying, 'Five minutes.' Then, 'Three minutes.' Then, 'Almost heeere.' I must say, the Princess looked a bit alarmed when she was ushered into this tiny room and confronted by two towering, overdressed

207 & the Beast 117

people. Waggers, who is never lost for words, stuttered and stammered, trying to explain our role in the Telethon. I managed a few words, I have no idea what. The Princess looked fazed, said, 'Eeouu Rahrley,' and she was gone, but not before the formal snap had been taken. Waggers thought it was so funny he had it blown up and hung it on his loo wall. It shows a diminutive Princess Margaret along with two giants, behind us an electric cord snakes its way along a bench and appears to go straight into the Princess' handbag. 'A plugged-in Princess,' was Waggers' favourite line.

About a year after Waggers joined the show Eric Baume died. His health had steadily declined but he was said to be in good spirits. He and Ena had flown back from Perth to Sydney the evening before. There was some speculation as to whether she was still with him when he died or if she had left. I hope she was with him. Baume and I had our battles but I'd like to think he didn't die alone.

I stayed with 'Beauty and the Beast' for six happy years. A tragedy in my life saw me take a long overseas holiday and by the time I returned to Australia I had a different agenda, but I'll never forget those years. 'Beauty and the Beast' was good to me. It made me a household name. The rewards were lucrative commercial contracts. I'm eternally grateful to all those I worked with and learnt from. We worked hard but, gee, we had a hell of a lot of fun.

Maggie
Tabberer
Associates

WHILE I was carving my television career in that first year of 'Beauty and the Beast' I was also building the PR business, dating other men and still fending off a persistent Pross. He intimidated several of my dates by following us in his car or phoning constantly if they were at my apartment. I didn't have any deep relationships but I was sexually active, and he knew this and hated it. Years later he told friends this was my way of punishing him, and I guess that's pretty accurate. There was a handsome grazier from Tasmania, a wealthy Sydney businessman with a piercing wit, a television newsreader, a Swedish diplomat and a European astrophysicist, in Australia to send a rocket up from Woomera. No puns please! Nothing lasted long and it wasn't how I wanted to live my life. In my heart I knew I was searching for something that really had only existed with Pross. Despite my claim that the relationship was over, I knew that chapter in my life wasn't yet closed.

My promotion and publicity company, Maggie Tabberer Associates, became serious when I was offered a second fibre account. Cashmillon was a high-bulk fibre, and while it was quite different from Lurex, it involved the same promotional drive into the same territory. So it fitted perfectly into what I was already doing for Lurex. With this contract secured I could afford to employ a secretary and move into an office — two big rooms on the first floor of a small building in a Double Bay lane — which I furnished with second-hand desks and chairs.

Shortly after I moved in, Tony Garland, a friend who was with a large advertising agency, came to see me. Tony thought we should join forces, and we did for a while but it didn't work. We had different agendas. We remained friends, but once again I was looking for help. Jill Robb, my old Adelaide mate, was working as a promotional director for the Smith Family. She recommended an English girl who had worked with her there, Jan Osterley. Jan had worked for Courtaulds, the fabric giant, in London, and had a sound knowledge of the fibre and fabric territory I was working in. Six months after she came to work for me, in 1966, we formed a partnership. This must have suited both of us, because it lasted almost twenty years. In 1969 Jan married fashion agent John Geary. They met through Maggie Tabberer Associates, as John was the agent for the 'Maglia' fashion label, a client of ours.

In the very early days of MTA, I was introduced to the photographer Alan Nye. Alsie, as we all came to call him, was an original. English-born, he'd earnt his stripes as a newspaper photographer in London, before trying his luck Down Under. With a combination of raw ambition and talent, he quickly established himself in this country. The years he'd spent developing his own black and white prints for the London newspaper eventually secured him his most important client, Grace Bros, because few, if any, could print like Alsie. The quality was exceptional and his prints reproduced magnificently. John Simpson, Grace Bros' advertising guru, endured a turbulent and volatile working relationship with the eccentric photographer. 'The bloody difficulty is to actually get the prints out of him to meet our deadline,' he said again and again. Nevertheless, Simpson knew that the results made all this anguish worthwhile. Alsie's print quality and his compelling photographic style were a vital component of Grace Bros' image for many years.

Alsie battled deadlines and his own personal devils the entire time I knew him. He would only deliver a print order on time if he was broke and chasing a quick cheque. One of our first jobs together was shot in some remote sandhills. We had struggled quite a distance to the right location, in awful weather, lugging garments, accessories, equipment and urging the models along. Tony Garland was still my business partner then, and Alsie had not taken to him. I believe this was reciprocated. Once on location Tony started to brief Alsie on the shoot. Tony had insisted on directing the photography as he'd brought the job to the agency and knew the client. I, for once, took a back seat and decided they would have to sort out their apparent difficulties.

Alsie stood aggressively with his hands on his hips, his tummy outlined by his big floppy T-shirt, his skinny little legs sticking out of baggy shorts and his long hair flying in the breeze. His ever-present cigar was clamped firmly between his gritted teeth. Tony went to great lengths to explain in the finest detail how he saw the shot. Alsie said not a word, then he started to load his camera, took a roll of film from its box and very deliberately unfolded the accompanying instruction pamphlet. He read it for a long time, then he squinted to the sky and studied the weather for what seemed minutes. The silence was uncomfortable and Tony was looking alarmed. Then Alsie, deadpan, said, 'Hey, Mags, what do you reckon? Is it sunny/dull or cloudy/bright?' Shortly after this Tony left the shoot and we got on with it.

Alsie and I worked together for about fifteen years. In this time our relationship was peppered with huge rows, colourful verbal exchanges, reconciliations and some very funny social times. Alsie was a skilled cook. His attention to cleanliness in his house and particularly in his kitchen left a lot to be desired. I marvelled that over the years no one ever became ill because of this. But Alsie, who lived in one of Paddington's smallest cottages, in surely one of its smallest lanes, had a knack of dimming the lights, planting candles and flowers all over the house, lighting the wood fire, setting a big table and then gathering some of Sydney's most interesting, colourful and influential people around it. He would feed them royally, pour non-stop good quality wines and champagne, and argue, abuse and generally get stuck into half his guests. If they left in a huff he'd start on the others, then sit back, laughing his head off at the ensuing melee.

You never knew who you'd meet at Alsie's dinner parties, although regulars were fashion editors, clients, models, society dames. I recall Clyde Packer's regal arrival in a long white caftan, smoking a big cigar, with Lyndal Moore, a stunning model of the time, hanging off his arm. He and Alsie had a funny friendship. They loved to debate everything from politics to who had the best tits in town! Alsie was eccentric, an egomaniac, a brilliant photographer, an intelligent ally and even brighter opponent. He was selfish one moment and outrageously generous the next.

When Brooke fell from a horse and broke her leg rather badly the night before I was to go into hospital for surgery, Alsie took on the 'Mother role'. Each evening he drove all the way from the eastern suburbs to Mona Vale Hospital, taking her special goodies: smoked salmon, delicious pâtés and fresh prawns. 'Because,' he said, 'this bloody hospital tucker will kill you.'

Then he'd swing by St Luke's Hospital and deliver more food to me. Alsie could also be cruel. His character assassinations of those he fell out with (which was just about every fashion editor in town) were legendary.

His accounts were always in disarray until Pam Saunderson, who had run Pat Woodley's model agency after giving up modelling herself, came to the rescue. This was the only time his office ran smoothly. Pam's calm brought some sanity to his business affairs for a while, but it couldn't have been easy for her. Alsie's theory was, 'When you're moving from one disaster to another the trick is to just keep moving.' And he did.

He and I had some terrible arguments but, funnily enough, rarely while we were shooting. He shot the photos for my *Daily Mirror* column for over ten years and he shot practically all our work for Maggie Tabberer Associates — until I found it was just impossible to deal with him. Alsie had an assistant called Garry; a tall, beautiful young man from the country. One day they had both driven their cars into a service station for petrol. Garry was walking between his van and the front of Alsie's big old Bentley, when somehow the Bentley slipped into gear and lunged forward. Garry was sandwiched between the two vehicles. His injuries were extensive and he spent almost a year in St Vincent's Hospital intensive care unit. Alsie was inconsolable. He visited Garry in hospital every day. Eventually Garry recovered but Alsie never did.

He became more and more irrational, and gradually clients found it just too difficult to deal with him. They stopped calling, the work dropped away, his powers diminished, invitations were refused. Alsie looked to other ways to dull his pain, which only made his moods worse. Eventually Jan and I decided the agency could not be held to ransom by his unreliability. It was a messy scene when I told him of our decision. I hated it but knew it had to happen and we all thought he just might pull himself together. But he slipped into another world, a wilderness, for almost ten years. He walked naked through Paddington carrying a candelabra and a large Bible. He abused old friends and strangers. The police came to know him well. He was constantly in and out of care. Then he seemed to just fade away.

No one knew where he was; I hadn't seen or heard of him for a long, long time. Then one day a mutual friend rang to say Alsie had taken his own life. He had left instructions for a particular tape to be played at his funeral. No one bothered to check it beforehand, but as his coffin slipped into the fire Tina Turner came on full blast singing, 'What's Love Got To Do With It'. The congregation broke up. Alsie had the last laugh. Bloody little genius. Bloody little monster. I loved a lot of Alsie.

LATE ONE afternoon Pross contacted me, pleading for me to see him. His son Nicolas was coming to Australia and he wanted me to meet him. I imagine it was because of Pross' generous and loving relationship with my girls that I felt I had to meet his son. Nicolas arrived on my birthday, 11 December. Pross had prepared a special dinner and the girls and I drove up to Bellevue Hill. It was a road we were to travel again and again over the next three years.

Nicolas had his father's handsome looks, big brown eyes behind his glasses, olive skin, and whippet lean. He was just sixteen years old and he and my girls got along immediately. And so the cold war was broken. I refused to move back in with Pross but the girls' room was still as we had left it, and we often stayed over for the night. I kept my Double Bay apartment; I'd vowed I wouldn't be dependent on a man again. We would go up the hill, have dinner, Pross and I would make love, have an argument and then the girls and I would go down the hill.

Days later the whole business would be repeated. Ours was a turbulent, passionate, electric relationship. We must have driven our friends mad.

I don't think my independence sat easily with Pross. He was very European in his outlook, particularly about women and money. But to be truthful he was always proud of my achievements and never jealous of the attention they brought. Even though I was working hard it didn't stop our social life. The Potts had introduced me to the Fallons. Jo and Desiree lived in a huge handsome mansion, called Loch Maree, in Vaucluse. Jo had been a society photographer, and he still dabbled in photography but his life was largely funded, I believe, from his interest in his mother's hotels. She was by then quite old but as sharp as a tack. She lived with them, and I sometimes saw her shadowy Mrs Danvers of *Rebecca* figure at the window, looking down at her son and his guests. I had the sense that perhaps she did not approve.

Jo lived with great style, he knew the who's who of Sydney, of Australia and from around the world. He gathered the infamous and famous, or others who were just interesting, around his table and staged the most amazing dinner parties. At one I met the formidable anthropologist, Margaret Mead. I was so intimidated I don't think I uttered a word. I was more at ease with Mexican-born Alfredo Bouret, a fashion artist who had sketched for the great designers such as Balenciaga. He and Lex Aitken, an Australian interior designer, were visiting from London. Eventually Alfredo brought his 'Mexicana Bazaar' label to Australia, employed my agency to handle his publicity and we began a friendship that remains today.

Desiree was a fantastic cook. The Fallons employed a Spanish couple to help in the house and garden, but nevertheless these dinner parties were always an incredible amount of work for

Desiree. Jo never failed to thank me because I'd slip away from the table and endeavour to help behind the scenes. He would place huge ceramic bowls brimming with crushed ice and stacked with four or five different vintage champagnes on the sandstone balustrade of the verandah. It was all very glamorous, rather like wandering into the *Great Gatsby*. Jo and Desiree exposed me to a style of entertaining I'd never before experienced. Their generosity was immense. As well as offering beautiful food and wine, they took care with the presentation of the table: big glasses, big plates, huge platters, fine linen and fresh flowers. Jo's influence is still seen in the way I set my table today.

Jo once bought a vat of red wine and set up a bottling party in the garden. Pross was syphoning the wine from the vat into bottles, which he passed to me. My job was to top the bottles to the right level before Dr Ian Potts corked them. If they were too low I topped them with wine from a jug. If they were too high, well why waste it? I took a nip. After a couple of hours I needed to lie down before I fell down.

Loch Maree's garden ran right to the harbour. There was a pool and a small pool house where the girls and I often stayed over at the weekends. Desiree's daughter, Felicity, was the same age as Brooke and Amanda. With the Potts boys, Tony and Tim, they had a great time in that pool and garden.

Some time before, Jo had befriended a young naval officer, Prince Philip, when his ship had visited Sydney. Prince Philip would row over to Loch Maree, and a fine old time would be had by all. I loved Jo but for all his sophistication he was still impressed by 'names' and often left his visitors' books open to Philip's signature and always propped his Christmas card in a prominent place.

One hot summer's night about twenty guests sat down for yet another of the Fallons' famous dinners on the lawns in front of their house. I was seated at the end of a long table between Sir Charles Moses, then head of the ABC, and the art dealer Rudy Komon. I was laughing at one of Rudy's stories when I leant back and the canvas director's chair I was sitting in over-balanced and toppled back into the rose garden. The guests were afforded a close-up view of my black knickers, and I had no way of righting myself or the chair. Sir Charles and Rudy sprang to my aid and hauled me out of the roses. Many years later, dining in a Melbourne restaurant, the waiter brought a bottle of French champagne to my table with Rudy's card. He had written on the back, 'I remember the rose garden!' I caught the twinkle in his eye from across the restaurant and thought, no you don't, you old scamp, you remember the knickers!

The late sixties were a whirl. Jan and I took on staff and moved to bigger premises on New South Head Road, Double Bay. I would sit at my desk under a window that afforded me a great view out over the Double Bay shopping strip, writing my column for the *Daily Mirror*. I had injected it with a bit of fun by including a weekly fashion 'boo boo' and fashion honours, often picking them by simply looking out the window as I typed. One woman told me she would deliberately cross the road and sneak along under my window rather than be seen; she so feared being named boo boo of the week! 'Boo boo' became the most read item on the page, and because I never named names I was constantly asked, 'Who was it?' 'Who was it?' I never told.

One day at the office there was a sudden screech of tyres followed by a deafening crash. I raced into the street. About five doors down my friend, the designer Chris Jacovides, had his new shop. A car travelling into New South Head Road had leapt across the road and crashed straight through his window into the shop. I arrived on the scene and screamed Chris' name. He wasn't there but his assistant was lying beneath the car. The staff in the workroom couldn't get down because the lower part of the staircase had been obliterated. Two passers-by were attending to the driver. I crawled over the rubble to help the assistant, who was in agony. Her hand was deeply gashed at the wrist, and there was a lot of blood. I knelt beside her and kept telling her she was going to be alright. I applied pressure to her wrist and she painfully spat a couple of teeth into the palm of my other hand. Police, ambulance and tow trucks arrived. Later I tottered on very shaky pins back to my office. I clearly remember thinking, life is so fragile it can be snatched, damaged and changed in a single moment.

It was during this period that I had a call one day from the *Sun* newspaper, the *Mirror's* direct competitor. They wanted to steal me and offered double the dollars I was getting. I really didn't want to leave the *Daily Mirror*. I liked the people I worked with and I felt a deep loyalty to the late Zel Rabin, after all he'd discovered me. But I couldn't ignore the dollars. I phoned the new Editor of the *Daily Mirror*, made an appointment, then later in the day Mr Murdoch's secretary rang to say the boss would see me himself. With my heart pounding and my mouth dry with nerves I was shown into Rupert Murdoch's office. I had never met him before, although I had been working for him now for a couple of years. I explained the situation, growing bolder and braver as I went. Finally, when I paused, he looked at me and said, 'Well Maggie, I guess we will have to meet their offer.' To this day I don't know where my courage came from but I looked back and said firmly, 'No, Mr Murdoch, I believe you have to beat it.' He stared at me deeply, gave a wry smile and said, 'OK, let's make it so-and-so.' I walked to the carpark on air, drove away and then let out, 'Yippee!'

Shortly after that I received a phone call from Harry M. Miller. I knew he was the high-profile agent to the stars. I just couldn't imagine why he was calling me. We met and he said he felt I had a bigger future than just 'Beauty and the Beast'. There were commercial television opportunities we should be looking at. I've lost count of the commercial contracts Harry has since written for me over the thirty-something years he's acted as my agent. We've flown a lot of missions together and both survived the odd bad time.

As my television profile grew my kids were subjected to a certain amount of teasing and jealousies at school. But they never complained and indeed I really didn't know about this until most of the battles had been settled. Only years later did they confess that there were times when this treatment was hard to handle. Although once, when a school concert was looming, I was asked by two solemn-faced little girls if I could 'dress like the other mothers'! When they reached high school, they weren't past selling 'Mummy's autograph' until I twigged as to why I was being asked to sign so many pieces of paper. I then put a stop to their little enterprise. It wasn't perhaps a normal childhood for Brooke and Amanda, but they learnt to be independent and responsible. I'm convinced that watching me carve a career instilled in them the belief that there wasn't anything they couldn't do if they wanted it badly enough and, above all, if they were prepared to work hard.

As a family it was difficult to find time to holiday together. I was locked into recording the show or office commitments. But when we could, we would join the Potts in an old house in the Blue Mountains or a beach shack somewhere. The girls' greatest joy was going to a riding school just out of Sydney. They adored the woman who ran it despite the fact that she made them toe the line and take their turn at mucking out the stables, scrubbing the loo and making the bunks. Although it sometimes stretched the budget I was determined they would have this time at riding school. It was a healthy outdoor life that taught them more than just how to ride a horse.

Pross would drive us up to deposit the girls for their holiday. He would turn the ignition off and tell them the car had broken down. They would scream and yell and laugh. 'Pappi, no Pappi, pleeease.' And after a while he'd start the car. He played this trick on the kids time and time again, and they always reacted the same way. One day when they were giving a demonstration ride to the parents, the kids came down the paddock at a gentle trot, turned and stopped their horses on command. When it was Brooke's turn she took off like a bat out of hell and flew down the field, blond hair flying, and screeched to a halt like Wild Bill Hickok. I felt more than a little uneasy about her behaviour. Years later, when she fell from a horse galloping down a country road and broke her leg, I wondered if my beautiful child wasn't really a bit of a larrikin at heart. Maybe it's in the genes.

WHILE I was working at Network Seven I met Ronnie Fraser. He was recording the 'Mavis Bramston Show'. Let me tell you about my friend. Recently I found a video of my first 'This Is Your Life'. Twenty years on I was rolling with laughter at the fashion, the hairstyles, the makeup. It was very amusing but then suddenly there was my dear friend Ronnie, and I cried. Not for Ronnie, who never grew old, but for all of us who loved him. I'm still furious with him for dying on us. My God, he was a funny man. He loved living as he loved a good laugh, and he did both in abundance.

One day at Channel Seven I was walking along the corridor having come from the makeup room when a voice shouted from behind, 'When you're finished with that frock, Maggie Tabberer, I'll have it.' I spun around and there he was, long, lanky, tanned, with enormous expressive eyes and a great big gap-toothed grin. We were friends, just like that. I was to learn he could disarm and charm anyone in an instant.

Ronnie had 'divorced' himself from his father and stepmother when he was just a teenager and had moved in with his favourite aunt, Nita. She told me it had been a gradual but obviously well-planned ruse. He would come to stay for the weekend, slowly moving his possessions into her house, visit after visit, until one day he just didn't go back home. He adored her. She more than adored him. They shared a wicked, sharp sense of humour and even sharper tongues. They lived together for many years until Nita, in her nineties, was hospitalised. Ronnie visited her every day until she died, and a little light seemed to leave him when she did. She was his severest critic. Ronnie was fearless at taking risks on stage or in writing a script, and she would tell him when he'd 'gone too far' or 'just wasn't good enough'. They would have a blue, but he always listened to her and he'd change the script or performance accordingly.

Nita was always well-groomed. Ronnie would wheel her off to the hairdresser twice a week, had the manicurist call regularly, and took her shopping or often simply went out and bought her a new dress. She wore her long, rather gnarled nails with a bright lolly-pink polish and constantly smoked her beloved Sobranie cigarettes — blue, pink, turquoise and black with gold tips. She called them her 'balls and parties'.

She had been a successful milliner in her younger years, had married for a minute — 'A disaster, darling, a disaster!' — and then lived a colourful single woman's life with married woman's experience, she would say. She loved the 'gee gees' and went to the races wearing her eccentric hats. When she grew old she would set herself up each Saturday, racing form on the lap, 'balls and parties' cigarettes at hand, maybe a whisky and soda, and almost an open line to her bookie. I suspect she won more than she lost.

From the day we met, Ronnie and I saw each other at least twice a week, and we took holidays together. Pross had a great affection for Ronnie and it was mutual. Ronnie would send Pross up with the perfect take-off of his Italian accent. He'd come charging through the house yelling, 'Good da da day, Daddy.' He always called Pross 'Daddy', which was what my girls called him. Daddy or Pappi. He greeted me in a rather more unusual manner. 'Gooday, you mongrel.' Not all my other friends appreciated this display of affection!

When he decided to have a hair transplant. I cautioned, 'Are you sure?'

'Nothing to it, girl. You go in in the morning, they operate in the arvo and you're out the next day. Be there about six pm, I want a G&T. Don't forget the ice and lemon, and I'd like smoked salmon and bickies,' he instructed.

The head nurse gave me a rather suspicious look as, ice and bottles clinking in my basket, she showed me to Ronnie's room. I pushed the door ajar. Pitch black. 'Ronnie.' Nothing. 'Ronnie,' louder. Still nothing. 'Ronnie.' 'Arrr, arrr,' he groaned. I switched on the light. He was lying there moaning, his pillow saturated in blood. I pounded on the call bell and told the sour-faced nurse that my best friend was bleeding to death and she better do something about it. Fast! She did. New dressing to his head, fresh linen on the bed. I held his hand and finally the painkillers worked. His doctor arrived, and he and I drank the G&Ts and ate the salmon. It took days for Ronnie to forgive me. 'That's gratitude,' I told him. 'I saved your bloody life!'

Later that week he said, 'Come on, girl, let's get out of town for a few days. I can't be seen with these pasties [as he called his bandages] sewn onto my head. A mate will lend me his house at Surfers. We can fly to Brisbane and you can drive me down.'

'Oh alright,' I said. And spent the rest of the day rearranging my working life in order to get away. Another call from Ronnie: 'Look, girl, I have to hide this head. Be a love and whiz over to the Squire shop and buy me one of those soft denim caps. Make it really big, I've got to get it over these pasties.'

So I went to Tony Yeldham's shop and tried on a dozen caps until I found one that came down over my nose. 'Perfect fit, Tony,' I said. Tony looked amazed as I gathered my change and walked out grinning.

We flew to Brisbane, hired a car and set off down the freeway south to Surfers. At a set of traffic lights a huge Mack truck driven by an Arnold Schwarzenegger look-alike drew up alongside us. 'Behave, Ronnie,' I cautioned, noticing a wicked gleam in his eye. At the next set of lights the Mack and Arnold were still there. My irrepressible friend couldn't help himself. He flashed a huge grin at the driver and shouted, 'Want to kiss a famous TV star?' I hit the gas.

After all that, the hair transplant only partly worked. Ronnie took it in his stride. 'Gave you a good story or two,' he quipped.

Ronnie and Nita had lived in an apartment in the grand old Astor on Macquarie Street for many years. It was elegantly furnished but Ronnie's bedroom at the rear was dark and gloomy, and he grew to hate it. 'Think we'll move, girl,' he announced one day. Nita wasn't as keen on the idea. She loved the Astor. He promised her he would find something wonderful and I would make sure her room looked sensational. Ronnie bought a light, airy apartment in a new building in Edgecliff with splendid harbour views. Friends took Nita to stay with them while Ronnie finished packing. My job was to be at the new apartment the next morning to let the removalists in and to whip Nita's room into shape so all would be ready when she came that night.

Ronnie rang very early and said he'd been up half the night finishing the packing and was exhausted. 'I'll have to take a little pep pill,' he said, 'to get through the day.' He duly rummaged around in the packing boxes and found some pills. He then despatched the furnishings with the removalists and arrived at the new apartment where I was waiting with a picnic lunch and a thermos of coffee. He came loping down the hall and I noticed he almost ricocheted off the wall. 'You alright?' I asked. As he tried to answer me, he could hardly keep his eyes open. 'Ronnie, are you OK?' I said, alarmed now.

'Don't know,' he slurred.

'Ronnie, what's happened to you?'

'I took a couple of pills to wake me up and I juth feel so, so tired.' He was sliding down the wall and onto the carpet.

'Show me the bloody pills, Ronnie.' I searched in his coat pocket, found the packet and recognised in an instant they were sleeping pills. Oh great, I thought. By the time the removalists arrived, Ronnie was out like a light. They carried his bed in and then carried Ronnie onto the bed, and I shoved the house into order. He came to three hours later and we ate the picnic lunch and had Nita's room ready for her arrival. They lived happily in that apartment for many years.

Late one afternoon, while driving down William Street, famous for its 'working girls', Ronnie pulled alongside me, yahooing from his car. At the next set of lights, where a gaggle of ABC staffers were crossing, he waved a clutch of notes at me yelling, 'OK, I'll make it fifty dollars. Now how about it?'

Once when we were flying into Vanuatu, the turbulence was horrific. I'm not a courageous flier at the best of times so this was very frightening. We bucketed all over the sky and made three attempts to land before the pilot informed us he was going to give it one more try the only way possible — with the aid of a radio beam! 'Oh, shit. I'm never going to see my kids again Ronnie.' I clutched his arm.

'Yeah, but who do you think will get top billing in the head-lines? Will it say, "Killed in air disaster, Ronnie Fraser and Maggie Tabberer" or "Maggie Tabberer and Ronnie Fraser"?'

'Are you crazy?' I screamed. 'You can't be serious!' He gave me a huge grin and I felt the tension ease as I broke into laughter. The plane hit the deck, the passengers erupted in applause and my mad, adorable friend gave me a big hug and kiss, and laughed and laughed.

While holidaying in Hong Kong, a most stylish friend, Gerald Godfrey, who deals in fine arts and antiques, invited Ronnie and me to a special dinner at a Chinese friend's house; an amazing glamorous monolith that projected out over Hong Kong Harbour. The glass floor of the dining room afforded guests a rather disconcerting view of the water crashing onto the rocks below. But if the house was glamorous the guests were even more so. The host's wife was a delicately beautiful woman dressed top to toe in Valentino. There was a stunning young American actress, an immaculately groomed and bejewelled older woman with a strikingly handsome Indian escort in a white Nehru suit and hot-pink turban, and a few others. We sat down to dinner at an enormous round table with the sea below and the lights of Hong Kong glittering on the skyline. Ronnie was seated opposite me. He looked around the table. I looked around the table. We looked at each other, both obviously thinking, how in hell did we get here? This is too fabulous. Suddenly Ronnie piped up, 'Hands up who's wearing Hush Puppies.' It was so Ronnie, so mad, so off the wall. I just collapsed with laughter. The other guests looked rather stunned. 'Please, what is a Hush Puppy?' said the handsome Indian. I didn't have a hope of explaining that one.

Then at crowded Hong Kong Airport, Ronnie cleared a path to the check-in counter by limping, dribbling, putting an idiot look on his face and clutching at me shouting, 'Mum. Mum. Mum.' Once we were through the check-in he wiped his chin, grew tall and straight, and in his most urbane manner said, 'Come along, my dear,' and ushered an embarrassed me through a rather stunned crowd.

One summer Ronnie had the bright idea that we should share a holiday flat at Palm Beach. I'd have it one weekend, he would have it the next. We found an old place in Sunrise Road. Its best feature was a long verandah that afforded a view of the beach, otherwise it was pretty unattractive. But it was cheap, had three bedrooms and was comfortably, if somewhat eccentrically furnished. I'll never forget the owner showing us over the place. In the living room were clumps of bright orange cushions. In the bathroom, bright orange tiles. We eyed each other. Into the kitchen, every knick-knack bright orange. 'How clever to carry the one colour through,' said Ronnie. The owner beamed appreciatively and I had difficulty keeping a straight face!

Of course when it was Ronnie's turn to stay in the house he always invited the girls and me. When it was my turn I always invited him. We shared the rent and a lot of good laughs, early morning swims and some hellishly good parties. Ronnie found a bronze bust of a Swedish philosopher in a junk shop; a stern old guy with a bald pate. He placed it on the verandah post and dressed him every weekend — sun hat, sunglasses, one of my bras, a cigarette taped to his mouth. 'Fred' was a hoot and the life of every party. When we gave up the house two years later I inherited him. Today 'Fred' stands on the verandah at Greenville, with a pot of white roses to protect his bald head.

Just after I'd won the 1970 Gold Logie for Best Female Television Personality (now there's an inflated title) Ronnie called to ask if he could borrow my 'Logie dress'. He was going to 'do me' on the 'Mavis Bramston Show'! 'Well really, Ronnie, that's a bit rich.' But as usual he could talk me into anything.

'Look,' he said, 'you've arrived if we do you on "Bramston". Stop carrying on and deliver the dress, and don't forget to chuck in that hairpiece.'

'OK,' I said, 'but the shoes won't fit. Nah ne nah nah.'

A couple of weeks later Australia met 'Maggie Blabberer' — or was it 'Daggie Mabberer'? — who went on to win the Gold Logie, plus best lighting, production, direction, staging, sound and I think cut lunch. And 'she' hogged the microphone and gave interminable acceptance speeches, shoving every other winner and the compere out of the way. I called him the next morning. 'Ronnie, are you trying to tell me something?'

He just laughed and said, 'Can I keep the frock?'

'No bloody way,' I replied.

RONNIE'S CAREER had its shares of highs and lows. At one point he gave up the theatre and sold menswear. But the lure of the lights was too much and he bounced back bigger than ever with the advent of television and theatre restaurants. At his best 'The Mavis Bramston Show' for the Seven Network and shows at the Phillip Street Theatre, Bull and Bush, and the Silver Spade Room at the Chevron were memorable. Occasionally he'd find himself in a bomb. He was always philosophical but I sensed toward the end he missed the big hits and hated the prospect of facing his older years.

Late one night the phone rang, it was Bubbles Fisher. She had gone to collect Ronnie earlier that evening for a theatre date. When he didn't answer the door she tried phoning and eventually, alarmed (Ronnie would never forget a date), she called the police. They broke into the apartment and found him on his bed. If he was going out in the evening Ronnie loved an afternoon nap. He'd just forgotten to wake up from this one.

The next day I rang his apartment to speak to his sister who was arriving from Adelaide. I dialled the number and his unmistakable voice said, 'This is a machine, not me because I'm — '

'Dead,' I shouted. 'You silly, silly bugger, you're dead.' And I burst into tears.

In the following days and weeks I cried a lot. I missed our daily phone chats, our laughs, our friendship. In his will Ronnie left me a very beautiful Donald Friend painting of two Balinese boys. Years earlier on a holiday in Bali together, we had spent time with Donald in his glorious house by the sea, drinking enormous pink gins by candlelight, the houseboys bringing us delicious goodies to eat while I listened to those two scallywags reminiscing about their early years in Sydney. Not a day passes when I see that painting hanging in my dining room that I don't think about my mad, gap-toothed, gorgeously funny friend. And I miss him like hell. I always will.

Marriage, a Birth, a Death

MY PRIVATE life in late 1966 was an emotional roller-coaster, but gradually there was a change in Pross. I had defied his pleas to move back into the big house. I never actually said, 'Unless you marry me,' but he knew that I needed a true commitment. I was moving around the country a lot for the business and for 'Beauty and the Beast', and Pross thought that could prove dangerous. In fact he knew it had on an occasion or two. There were many attractive men in my business.

I know now that Pross made a conscious decision to get me pregnant. He had always taken responsibility for practising our birth control, but one night he didn't. I was shocked and then furious. 'Hell, didn't I have a say in this?' But even before I knew for sure I was pregnant he proposed, and I felt an inexplicable joy. In January 1967 he had taken the girls and me for a drive to Palm Beach. The kids were swimming and Pross and I were sitting on the sand. He took both my hands in his and said,

'Maggie, will you marry me?' I can't really describe how I felt. We'd had this turbulent, passionate love story running for seven years and I had so many sound reasons to doubt its future success, but I didn't hesitate for a second. We would be a family. It would work. Pross, me, Nicolas, Brooke, Amanda and a new baby. Our baby. The girls were overjoyed. They wrapped themselves around Pross' neck and covered him with giggles and kisses. And we started to plan a wedding.

I had an upcoming business trip to Hong Kong where I would be visiting my old friend Hall Ludlow. We spoke by phone and he agreed to make the bridal party dresses. Judy Potts was to be my matron of honour and Brooke and Amanda bridesmaids. Our good friend Gianni Michele Picardi, who ran Alitalia in Australia, would be best man. I flew to Hong Kong armed with measurements, and Hall duly turned out gorgeously simple dresses for Judy and the girls. But he went a little wild when it came to mine. It was very much of the time but was it me? Short, white, empire line (so far so good), but then the entire thing, save the small sleeveless bodice, was covered with hand-made silk chiffon and organza petals. It was an extraordinarily beautiful dress. It just wasn't the style of thing I usually wore. However, there was no time for uncertainty. We added a skull cap of the same fabric, caught with a clutch of matching petals. When I looked at myself I tried not to think I looked like an upside-down pineapple that had just had a lobotomy!

Ted Noffs of the Wayside Chapel consented to marry us. We planned to have the reception at home in Bellevue Hill. There was naturally a lot of publicity about the wedding and I remember Graham McPherson warning me that the 'viewers would be out in force'. But nothing could have prepared me for the scene at the Wayside Chapel at Kings Cross on the day of the wedding, 28 February 1967. As the car turned off Macleay Street we came to a forced stop — the street was packed solid with people. It took fifteen minutes to reach the chapel and another ten to get inside. There were shouts of 'Good luck, Maggie' and 'Look this way, Maggie' as they snapped off photographs. It was very touching but I felt weak at the knees by the time we got inside, and very emotional during the service. Once outside it was again a crush to make it to the car. Pross was stunned, and his only comment as we drove away was a very dramatic, *'Madonna!'*

We had a ball at our wedding reception. As we both had work commitments, we decided to follow it with a few days on the Hawkesbury River in a cruiser. Now as I've said before, Pross was not an athletic man but he assured me it was a cinch to handle a Halvorsen cruiser. We drove up the day after the wedding and set off.

Late in the afternoon we wound our way off the main river into a picturesque little estuary. As we chugged along some people fishing on the bank waved frantically. How friendly, I thought, and we waved back. We dropped anchor, poured a drink and watched the sun set. Then, ever so slowly, as the tide moved out, the boat started to heel over and there was considerable creaking and groaning. We were aground. Pross said we'd be fine, we just had to wait for the tide to turn then we'd float off. I tried to cook steaks that night but it was difficult standing at a forty-five degree angle holding the griller uphill! After dinner Pross got out the charts and, with the smoke spiralling from his ever-present cigarette, studied them diligently for about an hour, then announced that due to moon, tide and God, if we didn't get out that night, we'd be stuck there for three months.

Around midnight the boat creaked and groaned a bit more and slowly righted itself. Pross started the engines, we churned up a couple of tons of mud and slowly eased out. It was a pitch dark night, so I took the boathook and with a white tea towel tied to each end so he could see my signals, I stood like Boadicea on the bow and directed him. Port. Starboard. No Port. Out and back into the main river where we secured the boat and relieved, fell into an exhausted sleep. Some honeymoon!

The following morning we headed back to the marina where we spent the next two days. Judy and Ian Potts joined us for a lunch where Pross regaled them with details of our adventure. The more they laughed the bigger the story grew. Pross was a great storyteller; his arms would wave around, his feet planted apart, the ash from his cigarette flying in the breeze.

THROUGHOUT MY pregnancy I continued to work at MTA, 'Beauty and the Beast', and to write my weekly *Mirror* column. I went through three months of chundering, but after that I felt wonderfully healthy. Pross was very caring and excited about the baby. I'd lie in bed, my swollen tummy tucked into the small of his back. He'd feel the baby kick and we'd talk about names. It was probably the most tranquil and harmonious period of our entire relationship, but at times I felt an odd fear clutch me. I was so happy, so contented. Was it all too good to be true? It was only a fleeting feeling but insidious and later, sadly, I would recall it again and again.

'Beauty and the Beast' viewers bombarded me with beautiful gifts. This baby would have a layette beyond description: wonderful knits and hand-embroidered gowns, booties by the dozens and baby blankets by the mile. I was staggered by people's love and generosity. Writing thank-you notes kept me busy, but I was determined each kindness should be acknowledged.

Suddenly my weight ballooned and a month before the baby was due Dr Malcolm Coppleson, my gynaecologist, insisted I go into hospital. I was devastated, hospital had bad vibes for me. In the previous six years I'd had four bladder operations. I used to wail, 'Everyone else has Christmas and I have an operation,' because that was the only time of the year I could take time off. The show was in recess and I could get away from the business.

Malcolm did not hide from me the fact that my condition was less than ideal. Pross and I were both anxious so I didn't argue. I moved into a pleasant private room at St Luke's Hospital. My darling mother came up from Adelaide and took over managing the house, Pross and the girls. They visited me daily and mates came by, but it was a month of stress and boredom.

One morning I woke feeling uncomfortable and strange. By mid-morning Malcolm was by my side. He said he was going to take the baby by Caesarean section. He didn't want my labour to undo all his good work on my last successful bladder operation. Great, I thought, I won't have to go through all that grunt and groan business. Pross and Mummy came by to kiss me. We were all in a state of high excitement, the baby was finally going to arrive. Pross held my hand all the way to the theatre.

There were complications during the operation. Seems I have a major artery where it shouldn't be. I lost a lot of blood, although the baby was delivered quickly and safely. The anaesthetist had to bring me out fast and I had a traumatic experience. I heard what I thought was the voice of God saying, 'Do you remember this, and this and this?' And I had flashes of me living other lives. As I write this, all these years later, it sounds incredible and stupid but it wasn't, it was so real. I gained consciousness with a feeling of dread. The voice had been angry and I was freaked. But then they put this big beautiful baby boy in my arms and Pross was by my side, crying with joy.

On my way back to my room the staff trundled me into an elevator. As I'm so tall my feet were overhanging the trolley and the elevator doors wouldn't shut. The nurse said, 'Just pull your feet up, dear.' A blaze of pain shot through my belly. It was my first indication that a Caesar is no bag of laughs. The girls and Nicolas came the next day to meet their baby brother. He was very beautiful; a handsome ten pounds. The paediatrician pronounced him 'perfect'. I had it all — my man, my girls and now my son. But the crazy thoughts persisted. I couldn't sleep. Had I lived those other lives? I discussed it with Malcolm. He told me that they had thought they were going to lose me, I had lost an enormous amount of blood and they had quite a battle to stabilise my condition. They brought me out of the anaesthetic as close to consciousness as they could, and what I'd heard was not the angry voice of God but an anxious surgical team. But even after this logical explanation I was uneasy. My mind kept replaying the voice and the images.

We allowed only my paper, the *Daily Mirror*, to photograph Francesco, or Francescino as we now called him. They ran a big, front-page headline, 'Meet Francesco', and there he was in his little white singlet. I was inundated with flowers, gifts and his layette grew and grew. There were buckets of mail to the hospital. The nurses used to joke about getting a hernia carrying it all to my room. One morning I opened a horror letter. Some sick individual had clipped my baby's photograph from the paper and written the most vile, disgusting things all over it. I was shaken and sickened by the act. Pross found me in tears and immediately had all the mail directed to my office where my secretary dealt with it.

After about six days my condition worsened and my doctor decided on a blood transfusion. This was a long and boring process. I hate needles at the best of times, but lying for several hours with a transfusion needle in my arm didn't help my mental state. The nurses had just changed onto what I think was the third bottle when my teeth started to clatter and I shook all over and went into shock. It seems there was something incompatible in that particular bottle of blood. I felt panicky. It was quite late at night but Malcolm arrived to once again calm my fears. After a second transfusion I finally started to feel more normal. I was breastfeeding Francescino and he was blooming. He was a hungry, robust, gorgeous baby.

On the tenth day I woke early. My milk was really flowing and my breasts were swollen and sore, and my nightgown wet with the overflow. I waited for a nurse to bring Francescino. I heard the crying of babies and the busy patter of nurses' feet. I waited and waited, growing mildly angry. What were they doing? I'm flooding here! Where is my baby? I punched the call button. There was no response. I tried again. Still no response. By now I was getting agitated. Again I buzzed. Eventually a young nurse put her head in the door and said, 'I'll be back in a minute,' and fled. She hadn't looked at me. Slowly I felt a strange wave of fear flow from my head down through my body. It was weird and I knew something was wrong. Something was awfully wrong. Then I started to scream, 'Nurse. Nurse.' Finally I thought, damn it, I'm going to go and see what's happening. I threw back the bed covers and eased up to a sitting position. A wave of dizziness hit me. I had just planted my feet on the floor when the same young nurse came into the room. 'Why haven't you brought my baby to me?'

'There, there,' she said. 'Just lie down. We'll be with you in a minute.' She still didn't look at me but in a flash she had plunged an injection into my arm.

'What are you doing? What's that for?'

'The doctor has just ordered it. He'll be along in a minute,' she replied.

Now with a sudden certainty I knew something was horribly wrong. The door opened and Malcolm came in. He looked shocking — grey faced, exhausted. He sat on my bed, held my hand and said, 'Darling Maggie.' I screamed and screamed.

'What's the matter? Oh God, Malcolm what's the matter?'

He said, very quietly and simply, 'The baby's gone, Maggie.'

I heard myself shout. 'Someone's done something to him. Who? What?' Then I heard a bloodcurdling scream from the corridor, like an animal in agony. It was Pross. He ran into the room like a madman. He threw himself on the bed and wrapped me in his arms.

'Oh, darling. Oh, darling,' he sobbed.

I shouted through my tears, 'No. No. No.' And I remember thinking, it's never going to be the same again. Never — and it never was.

IN THE bleak early hours of that morning I thought of the abortion I had had all those years before. My Baptist background came to the fore. Was this God's punishment?

It was a cot death. They knew little about the cause. He had been a perfectly healthy baby one day and gone the next. I couldn't go to the funeral. I was heavily sedated, wafting in and out of another world, consumed with grief. I vaguely recall my mother and Pross being there, but the one thing that stuck in my mind was my friend Dr Ian Potts. Pottsy was a cool customer, a little cynical and not given to shows of emotion. But he stood at the end of my bed, we talked and the tears streamed down his cheeks. I was deeply touched. I had befriended two wonderful nursing sisters in my month-long stay. They moved in and for days one or the other was by my side around the clock. It was more than good nursing, it was an act of great kindness.

After several days it was decided to move me from the maternity section to the main hospital. Hearing the babies crying each feed time was too hard for me. As I was gradually weaned off the drugs I found I couldn't sleep. I was terrified.

I thought I too was going to die. I kept reliving the entire experience, what happened during my baby's delivery, the awful letter, my guilt. What would become of my girls and Pross if something happened to me? For days I was convinced some maniac had come into the hospital and murdered my son. Again my health faltered and there were grave concerns for me. I stayed in the hospital for another two weeks, then went home.

My baby's layette, the cot, all the lovely things I'd prepared had disappeared. I went berserk. Although the decision to remove them had been well intended, it was too fast. I guess I needed to travel a different path with my grief. My mother stayed on. It was months before I realised how stoic she had been. After all, as well as losing a grandson, she had nearly lost me, and the pain of watching me so emotionally savaged could not have been easy. But at the time all I knew was me — my pain, my anguish, my grief. I couldn't get out of bed. I had no will to resume life. I cried all day and hardly slept.

Ten days later my mother came into my room and said the unbelievable. I will never forget her words. 'Darling, you had better think about what you're going to give your husband and your children for dinner this evening, because I'm going home today. It's time you moved on. You'll grieve for your son for a long time but you have to consider who's here. You have two children and a husband and stepson to consider, and now you'd better get up and get dressed.' I just couldn't believe that my beloved mother was going to desert me. Not now.

I said, 'Mummy don't. Please don't go. I need you, you can't leave me like this.'

She said, ever so quietly, 'Darling, it's for the best.'

Months later she told me it was the hardest thing she had ever had to do in her life. Eventually I realised that she was right. I knew Pross was in pain and my girls were unusually

One of the first shots of me by the famous fashion photographer Helmut Newton. This was taken at his house in East Melbourne. Helmut phoned the next day to say the shots were 'just wonderful' and I moved into a new world. (Copyright H. Newton)

An early photo shoot with Newton. I'm wearing hideously long false fingernails, the stately Melbourne Town Hall is in the background, and Helmut leaves a little of the balcony wall in the frame. It gives the illusion of stealing the shot. So evocative, so Newton. (Copyright H. Newton)

An intimate moment. I was putting on my makeup for a job at Newton's studio when he came into the room and fired off a roll. (Copyright H. Newton)

from
Paris
to
you

Left: Wearing Pierre Cardin designs for Lucas Australia. I must have jumped out of that bloody helicopter twenty times before Newton had his perfect shot. If you look at the height of my stilettos and the distance I had to jump you'll understand why my foot was black and blue the next day. (Copyright H. Newton)

Right: One of my favourite Newton shots, taken for Renee Furs, Melbourne. I did my own hair and makeup; in those days makeup and hair stylists on location just didn't exist. (Copyright H. Newton)

Below: Winning the 1960 Gown of the Year for A.R. Darlington Pty Ltd in a gown designed by Flora Jeanne — a fine white linen dress topped with a heavy guipure lace tunic.

The
GOWN
of

the
YEAR
1960

Worn by:
A. R. Darlington
& Co. Pty. Ltd.

Designer: Flora Jeanne
Mannequin: Margaret Tabberer

Modelling with my daughters for British Cotton. Helmut decided the new black shoes I'd bought the girls especially for the shot were too stark. When Amanda was told she had to wear her old white ones, she bawled the studio down. (Copyright H. Newton)

Snapped by Athol Shmith on our arrival at Melbourne Airport for the 1962 Gown of the Year. *From left:* Diane Masters, Moira Wallis, Hall Ludlow, Judy Potts and me. Both Judy and I are wearing Ludlow designs.

Above: High above the snow during a Newton shoot for *Vogue* Australia. Note the sign on the left: 'Caution Keep Safety Belt Closed'. But the belt was ruining the fall of the garment so it had to go. Helmut never let a little thing like safety get in the way of a good shot! (Copyright H. Newton)

Left: A David Franklin publicity shot for Hall Ludlow's spectacular parade at the Art Gallery of New South Wales. I'm wearing a pale lilac silk shantung cocktail dress designed by Ludlow.

Above: Young love. Ettore and me at the Buonasera, his restaurant in Kings Cross, Sydney, 1963.

Right: Twenty years on. Wasn't he a handsome devil? (Greg Barrett)

The year was 1967 and we named the wedding day. The girls are wearing their pale pink faille dresses sewn by my best friend Barbara Turnbull out of an old pair of curtains. Shades of Scarlet O'Hara. *From left:* Brooke, Pross, Nicolas (rear), me, Amanda (front). (Courtesy Australian Consolidated Press)

Our wedding at the Wayside Chapel, Kings Cross. To our amazement, the street was jammed with well-wishers — all 'Beauty and the Beast' fans. My friend Dr Ian Potts gave me away and the Reverend Ted Noffs officiated. As we drove off Pross exclaimed, *'Madonna!'* I still don't know if he was referring to the crowds or what he'd done! Here we are at our reception with friends at our home in Bellevue Hill. *From left:* Tony Potts, the late Neville Marsh (rear), Hazel Benini, Amanda (front), Janice Wakely (rear), Pross, me, Bruno Benini, Judy Potts (front).

quiet. It was a traumatic experience for two little girls. They were sad-eyed and solemn. Nicolas, who by now was working and living in his own apartment close by, visited daily. Uneasy, he would tiptoe into my room, kiss my cheek and disappear. For some weeks he drove his father to and from the restaurant, he was so concerned. My pain dominated my life. It was months before I slept through a night without waking in fear. Pross was sad and quiet, and probably lonely. My grief was all-consuming but gradually I moved back into a routine, operating on a memory bank. Some days I thought I'd never make it but I did. Somehow I did.

Graham McPherson, my producer, rang and urged me to go back to work. I went back to the office for a week or two but spent a lot of time in tears in the loo. I felt emotionally fragile, but my health had improved and I guess deep down I knew that work could prove a panacea. I was pretty hopeless on 'Beauty and the Beast'. Any question to do with babies or a death would set me off. The girls on the panel, Waggers and Graham were great. My favourite cameraman, Doug Hanson, nursed me through recording sessions. He'd just give me a special look around his camera or move in after I'd been in tears and say something like, 'Come on, sweetheart, you'll ruin that beautiful eye makeup.' Collectively they were amazing and supportive.

Probably the hardest part was coping with well-intentioned people on the street. They would come up, clutch my arm and say how sorry they were. Such shows of genuine sympathy usually saw me in tears. Also, there was endless mail. Every woman who had lost a child through cot death wrote to me about her experience. They were encouraging, kind letters: 'The pain will pass'; 'Life must go on.' But they dragged me down and answering those letters was excruciating. I felt that I couldn't cope with their grief. I was still trying to survive my own. Much of the time

I was numb. We never sought counselling, which was probably a mistake. Unlike today, crisis counselling was not generally offered and anyway, I was my mother's daughter. Like her, I just hung on when things went wrong. Be strong, get through by yourself. I didn't know any other way. I didn't know how to ask for help.

When I started to write this book Brooke offered to do some research for me, interview my old friends in Adelaide and Melbourne. Pross, who by then was living in Italy, was in Sydney for a few weeks and she taped an interview with him. He said he 'loved me deeply'. He was sad and regretful about our break-up. He called himself a fool for his behaviour but then added, 'If Francescino had lived it would all have been different. Maggie and I would still be together.' That's the second part of the tragedy because I know it's true. We never dealt with our loss and it destroyed our marriage. There was no question of our trying to have another child because of my health problems in the later stages of my pregnancy and my previous bladder surgery. We had made a collective decision to have my tubes tied. I believe now both Pross and I felt a burden of guilt about our decision to deny ourselves a second chance. Francesco was born on 5 September 1968 and died on the 15th. All these years later there are days I still find difficult to get through.

I plugged on with my work although I felt detached from reality like a shadow of myself, or a negative that hadn't been put in the right solution to develop. I was given to fits of dark depression. Pross had discussed this with my doctor, who finally advised, 'Take her away. Go for a long holiday.' The following June we set sail on the *Galileo Galilei* for Italy.

We had connecting first class cabins with the girls. We spent the first two weeks violently seasick as we ploughed through the turbulent winter sea off the Great Australian Bight. The Suez Canal was closed so our route took us around Africa, where eventually the sea calmed and the sun came out. We all took on deep tans and the kids had a wonderful time with the other children on board. For a special fancy dress party I made them Carmen Miranda dresses out of colourful crepe paper. The Captain took a liking to our family and we frequently dined at his table. Pross, resplendent in a white sheet and cardboard crown, played King Neptune with Italian gusto as we crossed the Equator. Just off the coast of Africa the crew went on strike. We pulled into Las Palmas in the Canary Islands and were stuck for three days. We had to make our own beds and the shipping line supplied buses to take us to various restaurants for meals.

One day we decided to explore the island. Decorative horse-drawn carts were the popular form of transport. I will never forget the scene: Pross negotiating a price with the driver. Deal done, the girls clambered up into the two-wheeled cart, then Pross. When I stepped on board the horse went up in the air, still harnessed to the cart shafts, its feet frantically waving in space and a panicky driver screaming, in Spanish, instructions for us all to move forward. It was a family joke for years and I bore the brunt. Well, I wasn't exactly thin but my line of defence remained solid. 'It was our collective weight, not just mine,' I'd argue.

FOR A time Pross and I found one another again. He was wonderful, gentle and caring. My grief had diminished to a dull roar but I was still emotionally fragile. We had a silly tiff one afternoon, and as I was dressing for dinner he returned to the cabin and gave me a small gold compact caught with a lapis lazuli clip. It wasn't the value of the gift that touched me as much as his gesture of apology. Pross had never been big on apologising.

As we approached our destination, Catania in Sicily, where Pross' parents had retired, I grew anxious. I was the second wife.

I had just lost their grandson. I was a mess. Even making up my mind what to wear for the arrival became a ridiculously big deal. Then I blew it by choosing a simple white wool dress. Everyone in Sicily, I mean everyone, wears black or at least dark tan, and there was I, weaving my way through the dense sombre crowd on the dock, standing out like a bloody Christmas tree in this bright white dress. It didn't help that I was also double the average Sicilian's height.

Pross' parents were sweet, although they spoke very little English and my Italian was limited. But we managed. Their old country house was a cool haven from the incredible heat. I remember Papa Prossimo taking me by the hand, leading me through a garden of gnarled fruit trees and into the cool dark of the stone well house. There we sat on an old bench, drank big glasses of water drawn fresh from the well and ate sweet white peaches picked from his trees.

We only stayed a week. Pross found Sicily claustrophobic. He didn't want to hurt his parents' feelings so he sent himself a telegram saying he was required on a business matter in Rome, a deception that didn't sit easily with me. We flew out the next day in a small plane. It was a turbulent flight and all my death fears surfaced. I was a gibbering mess by the end of it, but once in Rome we met old friends and had a wonderful time. The girls were taken by Pross' closest friend, Commander Crucioli, Head Pilot for Alitalia, to Ascoli Piceno on the Adriatic Coast to holiday with his family. Pross and I drove all through Italy, eating, drinking and sightseeing. He had booked us into the most glamorous hotels and I responded to the spoiling. We had never before had a holiday together and he made it very special.

Finally we joined the Crucioli family and returned to Rome. We took a side trip to Capri where we swam in the Blue Grotto and my girls bargained like troupers with a jeweller to buy silver rings. We stayed the night at the splendid Quisisana Hotel, still my favourite Capri hotel. I then flew to London for a few days by myself, visiting Di and Paul Richey, then rejoined my family and we returned home to Australia.

Looking back, Pross and I were both better for the trip but as a couple, sadly, we would never be the same again. I did feel stronger. I looked tanned and healthy, if rounded out by all the great Italian food, and I was resolute I would now be strong and happy. In the wee hours of the morning sometimes it wasn't all that easy, but step by step, as with all tragedies in life, you survive and then you grow again out of some deep-seated necessity. I knew hard work would be my salvation, so I sought a new challenge.

The
Maggie
Show

EVEN BEFORE I left to go overseas I'd thought it was time to move on from 'Beauty and the Beast'. I had a rare meeting with Jim Oswin, head of the Seven Network, and although I didn't have a definite concept to propose, I pointed out that I'd earnt my stripes with Seven. As well as my years on 'Beauty and the Beast', I had filmed numerous pilots with Waggers for the network. None had actually got up, but they had provided me with considerable experience. Now I wanted to do something different. I wanted my own show. Jim promised he would think about it. So to ensure he didn't forget, from every port of call — city, town and village — we visited on the trip, I bombarded him with postcards simply saying, 'Think Maggie.'

When I returned I went back to see him. Jim was a serious sort of guy, but he opened his top drawer, which was overflowing with my cards, laughed and said, 'Well, I guess we will have to give you your own show!'

Scott Mitchell was a new young producer with the network. A solicitor, he thought television would be more fun than law and was probably right. He was given the task of developing a 'Maggie' format. Scott and a friend, Peter McDonald, who worked as a floor manager at Seven, sat around his kitchen table for a few nights and came up with a format. This was run past Seven's General Manager, Geoff Healy, then Jim Oswin. At our first meeting I added a couple of ideas. One was to show how to turn disposal store buys into a fashion look. We used this for the pilot and I was told that particular idea appealed to old Rags Henderson, although he generally thought I was too loud. Well, I wasn't Pat Firman!

Shortly after, Michael Pate joined the network. Michael was an Australian who had found fame in Hollywood, largely by playing American Indians in westerns. His brief was to develop new programmes and he came on board the 'Maggie' show as executive producer. Estelle Myers, a diminutive figure with a fast brain and an even faster tongue, joined as researcher, and the team was complete. Estelle was a dynamic woman whose enthusiasm at times was hard to suppress. She'd be telling to me about 'just one more point' for the next interview as we went into countdown. Maddening but commendable. She would photograph me on the set with every guest, have the shots developed, and the next week they would be sent out to the guests with a short note from me saying, 'Thank you for being on the show.' It was Estelle's idea and it worked magic. Everyone likes to be thanked.

We commenced recording early in 1969, and as Mike said, 'We hit the ground running.' I liked working with Mike, he had an easy manner, a ready laugh and despite his vast experience in the business, was open to suggestions. I suppose 'Maggie' was basically a chat show but the major difference was its pace.

Previous shows, such as Del Cartwright's programme, were leisurely, a slow wander through afternoon television. The 'Maggie' show was fast. No one had a chance to get bored with an item, and if they weren't interested we would soon move on to the next segment. Initially there were a few complaints that it was too fast. But viewers quickly discovered that the show provided tremendous variety.

Another important difference was the look of the set. I had been quite vocal about this. I hated those conventional chat show sets: the phoney living rooms with overstuffed couches, or studies with fake bookcases, dreadful headless statues, too many objects and enormous flower arrangements. Instead we had pale carpet over both the floor and a simple series of stacked backdrops. It provided a soft, textured look. There was a very modern plain desk and even simpler, stylish chairs with only one object — an abstract sculpture — on the desk. The set was fresh and it certainly looked different.

My hairdresser, Xenon, created a series of incredibly mad hairstyles and David Franklin, a friend and photographer I had been working with, shot me in each style for the show's credits. Tommy Tycho, the network's musical director, composed the 'Maggie' theme, which was terrific. Very quickly we were winning our spot and the ratings flourished, helped by an energetic publicity team at Seven.

Eventually Hazel Phillips went to Channel Ten and Dita Cobb went to Channel Nine, and both had their own chat shows. It was strange being up against old mates, but it never affected our friendship.

The 'Maggie' show covered everything: people, places, food, fashion, social and political issues. We quickly became the show everyone wanted to be seen on, so we attracted the big names. Not hard really, most people are out to sell something — a cause, a book, a show, a product. But I'd like to think we did it well. Peter Wyngard, who had a series on BBC, not only came onto the programme, he became a friend. Peter was a dashing dresser, a real dandy. He wore his considerable shirt cuffs out and turned back over his coat sleeves! John Farnham was a regular to entertain us. So was Kamahl. Margaret Fulton came by to 'do food', followed by every top chef in Australia. Ronnie Arnold, the American-born choreographer, taught me how to tap dance on the show. Ray Charles played and sang for us. A very smooth Count Zegna, of the Italian fashion house, charmed everyone, as did Count De Salle, the head of Dior Cosmetics. He came on to tell us about Dior but talked mainly about his vineyard in Champagne in France. The tiny bespectacled Edith Head, legendary Hollywood costume designer, dished out the dirt on some of Hollywood's most temperamental women, such as Bette Davis, who didn't give a fig about how a garment looked as long as it had pockets and a skirt that swished. Admiral Grace Cooper, who developed the Honeywell Univac Computer, was extremely impressive. One of the most disturbing interviews was with Gordon Liddy of Watergate fame. He was a sinister-looking man with 'dead' eyes, plastered-down black hair and a thick black moustache. He also wore black jackboots. They said it all.

As a national show, screening five days a week, it was important to cover the national scene, so we went interstate every few weeks, recording in Melbourne, Perth, Brisbane, Adelaide. We had two days in the Sydney studio each week. We'd record three shows the first day, two the next, then hold production and publicity meetings for half a day. It was fast and furious.

Scott had my dressing room built on the floor of the studio. Each week the crew assembled it — dressing table, chairs, a couch, a clothes rack, full-length mirror and even a Persian carpet —

and discreetly tucked aside a bottle of brandy, some ice and dry ginger for nervous guests and, I'll confess, my occasional bad day. It was the only time I ever drank before a television show and I never have since. Too dicey. Having the dressing room close at hand meant I could change in a flash and be back on the set to tape the next show. If we had any technical hitches I had a comfortable place to escape, and if there was a real disaster I could sneak a brandy and dry!

Harriett Hubard Ayer was a high-profile cosmetic company. Their advertising account executive was a pretty redhead called Rosemary Penman. She came up with the idea that I would do live editorials on the 'Maggie' show about their products. Easy? No! Bloody difficult. Rosemary would arrive at the studio sometimes after I'd started recording. Scott would be pressuring for us to get on with it. We would position the various skin-care products in a row on the desk, and I'd try to take in Rosemary's hurried instructions about the highlights and the benefits of each one. This all had to be ad libbed on the programme. If I had time I'd scribble little notes and tuck them under the jars of creams out of camera range. Then I'd take a deep breath and wham bam, just do it, sometimes speeding through twelve products. Keeping the client happy and Scott on time in the studio was taxing at first, but eventually I could talk under water about Harriett Hubard Ayer. I began to use the products, and that increased my knowledge, commitment and, probably, credibility. It was a very successful arrangement for all of us.

Sometimes we were hit by the odd disaster. I'll never forget the English guy who came on to promote his unbreakable plates. He waxed on about their quality, manufacturing technique and design, and then to illustrate he put a plate on the floor and jumped on it. Naturally it didn't break. I then closed the show and as the credits rolled, on the spur of the moment I thought it would be fun if I jumped on his stack of plates. I did. Crunch. They shattered into a thousand pieces. The crew dissolved at the look of horror on my face frozen full screen by a quick director and an alert cameraman. The plate man just put his head in his hands and cried. Well, you can't win 'em all.

We planned the stories to give us a good mix: one serious, one fun, one controversial, one visual and one about a star, which was always a good publicity hook. I don't believe I suffered from nerves, except for the first week of recording. After that I just enjoyed the challenges. There were enough of those to keep me busy. Like the time I was to interview a visiting Eskimo sculptor only to discover in the countdown to the segment that he didn't speak English. However, he'd brought along his tools and a block of soapstone. So, chatting away like a maniac, I somehow got him to sculpt a small walrus. The camera moved in close, capturing his worn hands working so skilfully, and later when Scott added a moving piece of music, it was good television.

Every international star who visited Australia came on the 'Maggie' show. Generally they were great contributors but occasionally one proved disappointing. Murray Amsterdam, a diminutive, fast-talking American comic came onto the set and totally ignored my first question. He simply launched into a long dialogue of one-liners. They were funny, but I would have liked to have learnt something about the man behind the comic. The more I tried to intervene, the more determined he became to do his act. Given a wind-up signal I paused, looked into the camera and closed the segment with, 'You have just watched the Murray Amsterdam Show!' Another who left a lot to be desired was Roger Moore, the dishy English actor who played both the Saint and James Bond. The makeup room was all a-twitter on his arrival. He charmed everyone, but after introducing him with a clip of his film highlights I turned and asked the first question. There was a long pause. I mean a long, long pause, then very slowly, in his perfect English drawl interspersed with lengthy aaarrruums, Roger replied. He took forever. I panicked. We'd allocated three minutes and he'd just taken two to answer the first question. Disastrous.

A better experience was when Mike Pate secured an exclusive interview for me with the artist Norman Lindsay. He was celebrating his ninetieth birthday, so we bought a large chocolate cake and we drove up to his famous old house at Springwood. The interview was filmed with Norman sitting at his kitchen table rolling a fag with his beautiful if gnarled hands. The cameraman held on those hands for some time while Norman and I talked. Norman, for all his innocent elf-like appearance, still had a wicked glint in his eye. Before we left he wrote me a little note. It said, 'To a beautiful lady who I would have liked to have painted when I could paint well enough to capture her beauty.' Signed, 'Norman Lindsay.' Won me. Later, on his death, someone at Seven remembered that interview and called me. Did I have the tape? No it must still be at the studio. It was, but it was buried as in-fill with another zillion taped productions under the carpark. Someone's madness! Later Norman's granddaughter, Helen, worked at Maggie Tabberer Associates for a time.

When the first big ratings period saw us win our spot around Australia and gather considerable headlines in the TV magazines and newspapers, Lady Mary Fairfax sent to the studio a huge, five-foot-high and five-foot-wide floral heart of daisies with a blue silk sash saying, 'Congratulations Maggie!' It took two guys to carry it onto the set as she had instructed. It was an over-the-top gesture but I was extremely flattered. The crew said it was the only time they ever saw me blush.

During this time, Tommy Leonetti, an American-born singer, came to Australia to host a tonight programme, which was

eventually called 'The Tommy Leonetti Show'. I liked Tommy.
He was of Italian parentage and he was sweet. He just couldn't
put two lines together. Awful jokes did the rounds of the studio
about his need for a cue card even to say, 'Hi, I'm Tommy
Leonetti.' One day he stopped me in the corridor of Seven and
said he'd like me to appear on his show. 'Doing what?' I asked.

'Well, singing a number,' he said.

'You better hear me first, Tommy,' I warned him. Later that
day I went into the rehearsal studio where Tommy Tycho was
working with the band. We fooled around, I sang a few bars,
then a few more and the next thing I knew I was doing not one
but three numbers. In the first, I was dressed like 'Me Jane' in a
long animal-print dress split to the top of one leg. I wore an
enormous tousled wig and swung into the set on a rope, singing
I can't remember what! For my second number, 'Hey, Hey Windy
Day', wardrobe made me a pink chiffon handkerchief dress. I
strolled to and fro across the set with the chorus behind me. A
large fan just off the set blew a light breeze that gradually grew
to a howling gale, and as it did the pink handkerchiefs on my
dress floated off, one, two, three, ten … twenty … fifty! It was
very funny. In a more serious mood I had the gall to sing that
famous Peggy Lee number, 'Is That All There Is?' in a stunning
long white dress trimmed with yards of marabou feathers! You
know what? I got great reviews.

Meanwhile, the publicity business, MTA, was bowling along
and having a national television show didn't do any harm. Jan
and I had been employed by British Leyland to launch two new
cars. We worked with the Leyland PR manager, Evan Green,
who was also a well-known motoring journalist. The cars had
good Aussie names: the Kimberley and Tasman. So we appro-
priately staged a bush picnic, barbecue lunch for the motoring
journalists in the Lane Cove National Park where they could

test drive the cars. A bush band thumped out old ballads, and despite the fact that the beast being barbecued took two hours longer to cook than anticipated by the caterers it was a great success.

The Managing Director of British Leyland was a super guy called Robert Johnston. Impressed with our promotion, he called me one day and said, 'I've had a thought. Can you come and see me?' His idea was that I could design the interior and colour for one of their cars, a new hatchback. It would be the Maggie car and would be used as a promotional gimmick. *Woman's Day* ran a four-page spread about it and we launched the car on the 'Maggie' show. I had it painted bright lime green. Well, lime green was a big fashion colour at the time! And there certainly weren't any other lime green cars around. The interior was all white: white leather upholstery, white carpet, white dash. I then had Harry Gelber, a client who manufactured Frenchknit swimwear and stretch carseat covers, make seat covers using some exciting swimsuit fabrics: a black and white houndstooth, black and white zebra print, plain lime green towelling and a hot-pink floral. It was crazy but it won national press and national television coverage, and I adored buzzing around in it. You could certainly see me coming.

Many years later I met Robert again. By then we were both involved with the Melanoma Foundation. I was patron and Robert was a tireless and generous sponsor and foundation director. Sadly, he was also a victim of melanoma. Despite his rapidly failing health, Robert was determined to keep to his schedule. He was on business in the United States when he lost the fight. I didn't see a lot of him over the years but he made a deep impression on me. He was special and, in the old-fashioned sense, a true gentleman.

WHILE I was working on the 'Maggie' show I became concerned about my mother. She was rattling around in our old family home. It was too big and the garden had become too demanding. I talked it over with Pross and I flew to Adelaide. I'd contacted a friend, Bill Batchelor, who worked in real estate. He had a new small townhouse complex quite close to where my sister Betty lived. Mother adored it. Within twenty-four hours I had bought it for her. I handed her the keys and said, 'Darling, it's yours. All you have to do is move in.' To the amazement of my sisters she sold all her furniture and bought brand-new pieces. She had pale carpet laid and started a new life. She never stopped telling me how wonderful it was and how appreciative she was. I wonder if I told her how much joy it gave me to see her so invigorated and happy. I hope I did.

It was a time of change for us too. Pross had only leased the big house in Bellevue Hill. I felt we should be buying. I guess I nagged a bit but eventually he gave me the all clear to look for a house. I found a modern townhouse in Trelawney Street, Woollahra. It was more compact but had three bedrooms, modern facilities and a double garage. Eventually I carpeted the garage and turned it into a den for the girls. This was more in self-defence than generosity. They were now young teenagers and their music was slowly driving me mad. Putting a floor between them and us saved arguments and gave both generations some peace. Mind you, every now and then I still stood at the top of the stairs leading to their den and screamed at full bore, 'Turn it dooown.'

A few years later, Brooke, just seventeen, came to me and told me she wanted to move out into her own apartment. I looked at my strong-willed daughter and thought, I either go with this or I'll lose her. I decided to cooperate. I went to the linen press and set aside towels and sheets. Then down to the kitchen, pots, pans, plates, knives, forks. I thought by illustrating what it took to set up house she might, just might have second thoughts. But she didn't. Brooke and I were about to set a course for the next few years of her life. She would find an apartment. I would take one look, reel with horror and spend the next few days ripping up old carpet, scrubbing floorboards, painting walls white and moving her in. Again and again I did it until finally I said, 'Enough. You're on your own.' By then she was capable and most importantly we kept our friendship. Pross missed her but she always came home at the weekend and we'd dine at least once or twice a week. So I was able to keep an eye on her.

In 1970, after a year of the 'Maggie' show, our team took off for the Logie Awards in Melbourne. Gossip had it that I would be a winner, and I certainly hoped so. It was a thrill to hear my name called for a Bronze Logie, a state award, but nothing prepared me for the announcement that followed. I won Gold. I have absolutely no recollection of what I said in my acceptance speech. I was numb. It was a huge thrill. Pross was very proud but his only comment was a shrug of his shoulders and, 'Why not? You're the best.' It was high praise coming from him.

That same year I was awarded the Cobb & Co TV Woman of the Year. Cobb & Co was a fragrance company which sponsored awards to high achievers in various fields. My mother was so proud. I'd been such a ratbag of a kid. I think she was always slightly surprised that I had done well.

Halfway through 1971, Seven dropped a bombshell on my head from a very great height. Bruce Gyngell, the first man to appear on Australian television and who had gone on to hold a senior management position with the Nine Network, had just joined Seven. I was informed he had 'sold' my timeslot to a leading sponsor for a new quiz programme to be hosted by Tony Barber. I was outraged and I let everyone know it, but no amount of argument about viewer loyalty to my timeslot and the fact that the show was still rating could alter the financial coup that Bruce had pulled off for the network. I was offered a late morning timeslot.

Depressed, I left the station and went home to think about it. Coming to a decision wasn't easy. We were aware 'Maggie' viewers ate their lunch while they watched the show. So many had written to say it was the break in their day. Morning television in those days was the great grey zone. Women didn't have time — mornings meant housework or shopping. It was clear that a time change would see our ratings suffer. Then what? Has Maggie lost her touch? I decided a quick death would be preferable to a long illness. It took all my nerve to say, 'No thank you.' We had a slap-up last programme, a good party and a tearful farewell to the team. It took me several years to like Bruce Gyngell again, even though he was only doing his job.

The network offered me a first class air ticket around the world as a 'Goodbye and thank you'. Like an idiot I took it and flew off. By the time I got back to Australia the other networks had locked in their programming for the following year.

Harry Miller, however, had negotiated several lucrative television commercials. Maggie Tabberer Associates was still growing and my *Daily Mirror* fashion pages were still popular. I had enough to keep me busy and provide good financial reward. I had been on television for ten years. Time for a break, I consoled myself. I didn't anticipate it would be twenty years before I worked regularly on another television show. Some break!

After I had been off air for six months, I won my second Gold Logie. It seemed that although the 'Maggie' show wasn't on the small screen, it was still in the viewers' minds and hearts. I felt both sad and triumphant.

Bugger Bruce Gyngell! Bugger Channel Seven!

IT WAS during 1971 that I found us a new house in The Mews, Albert Street, Edgecliff. It belonged to photographer David Franklin, who mentioned he was planning to sell. I persuaded Pross to come and see it with me. Spacious, light filled, secure, it was tucked away at the back of an interestingly designed complex, protected from street noise. We bought it and Lex Aitken, my decorator friend, helped me decorate it. I loved The Mews.

It was a wonderful house to entertain in and I did, constantly — big lunches and dinners often set in the garden. I enjoyed cooking and I loved having family and friends around. Often the table would be set for ten or twelve; on special occasions such as birthdays or Christmas it could be eighteen or twenty.

Despite my work commitments and my busy social life, I always travelled overseas at least once a year; memorable trips to Britain, Europe and the USA. But one of the most exciting was when I took my second trip to Mexico to visit my friend Alfredo Bouret and his family. Alfredo was by then resident in London but his fashion business, Mexicana Bazaar, frequently took him home, so we arranged to holiday together. I was excited because the first trip seven years before still held magical memories. Mexico is a passionate country, its people, colours, music, architecture and arts all hold a strong fascination for me. I arrived the day after Christmas to discover Mexico City draped in a million fairy lights — a delicate glittering spider web spun over the entire city.

On New Year's Eve Alfredo took me to dine by candlelight at a sixteenth-century monastery. We watched a huge moon rise over the lake and I marvelled at the grandeur of the setting. Later we watched the *son et lumière* at the pyramids of Teotihuacan. Early in January we drove to Taxco, the silver centre of Mexico, where I bought silver serving plates and small silver items as gifts. I loved taking them out of their tiny cotton bags and admiring the delicacy of the craft. When Alfredo teased me with stories of banditos on the mountain roads, I tucked my stash beneath the front seat of the car. On the way back to Mexico City we stopped in a small inn, the garden a blaze of pink hibiscus. We took a sunset drink out by the pool, where colourful peacocks strutted their stuff. The waiter had just handed me a long cocktail, elaborately decorated, with a bright green mint and a big red cherry on a toothpick when one of the peacocks took a gulp at the cherry. We watched horrified as the toothpick, side on, travelled with some difficulty according to the look on the bird's face, slowly down his long skinny neck. The next morning when I paid my bill I fully expected to see a charge for one dead peacock!

In Puerto Vallarta we spent sunny days on the beach, taking long lunches at the tiny beach restaurants. I'd observed a gaggle of small boys selling rides on a paraglider. Those who were game would be strapped into a parachute harness which in turn was attached by a long rope to a sleek speedboat. The parachute would be faced out to sea to catch the breeze, then the little boys would lift it. The boat would move slowly out while the parachute ballooned and the traveller would effortlessly fly up and away. It looked so tempting. After three days I finally stoked up my courage and said to Alfredo, 'I'm going to fly.' His mouth dropped open and he grabbed the camera to record my brave solo.

'Are you sure you want to do this, Maggie?'

For the first few minutes I was airborne I was only aware of a loud thumping in my ears, then I realised it was my heart pounding. Gradually the beauty of what I was seeing took over and it was sheer bliss; the sea a myriad of wonderful blues and greens, the sand Persil white, a rainbow of boats in the harbour. The next minute I was screaming over the top of a large cruise ship, there was the pool, the decks, the smokestack. The smokestack!

I sailed right over its cavernous hole. All too soon I heard the boys on the beach whistle, and as instructed I hauled on one of the parachute ropes to spill the air from the chute. Then slowly, I came to a perfect two-legged landing on the beach. I must have been the oldest and probably the biggest customer they'd had. It doubled their business, many a robust American tourist trotted along to take a ride after my trip. For the next couple of days the kids were so grateful they kept offering me free rides, but I didn't want to stretch my luck.

One night in Puerto Vallarta the hotel management woke Alfredo to tell him to call Pross. Alfredo knew it had to be bad news. He duly spoke with Pross and he said he would tell me the next morning, he didn't want to wake me. The following morning Alfredo's sombre face at my door told me something was amiss. 'What Alfredo? What's wrong?'

'Maggie, there's been a fire at your house.'

'A fire? Oh my God, Alfredo — Pross, the girls, are they OK?'

'Yes, yes,' he assured me. 'Everyone is safe but the house has been damaged rather badly.'

I flew to the phone and called Pross. He had arrived home to find the house ablaze. The fire had started in the top floor but we never really knew the cause. At first he wanted me to come straight home, but after numerous calls we realised there was little I could do. My friend Barbara Turnbull had been wonderful and helped Pross, Brooke and Amanda move out of The Mews. A friend was overseas, so they could stay in his house. The rebuilding would have to be done before I could redecorate.

Barbara urged me to stay. Amanda had planned to come over and meet me in Los Angeles, and she really needed a holiday. We went through with our plans. I met Amanda at the Beverley Wiltshire Hotel. I walked into her room as she undid her case and I said, 'What's that strange smell?' She burst into tears. The few clothes she had salvaged from the fire still had that unmistakable odour, despite being dry-cleaned twice. 'Come on, baby,' I said. 'Let's go shopping.'

Back home Pross had the rebuilding well under way. The insurance fell short of all the replacement costs but together we rebuilt our home and The Mews looked better than ever. For the next few years, however, every time I opened the doors of the linen press, there was that unmistakable whiff of fire.

MY MOTHER had been enormously proud of my first Logie win. She would phone to tell me what the neighbours had said and how the butcher sent me his regards and Mrs So-and-So sent her love. She was living a happy life in her new home and still travelling by bus to visit my sisters each week. As soon as she walked in the door she would tell them when she planned to leave. 'I'll have to leave by two forty-five, I want to catch the three o'clock bus.' Then she would pitch in and do the ironing or a load of washing. The only time she sat down was to have a quick lunch. She loved to feel as though she was useful. There was no need for a timetable in her life but she had lived with such a strict routine that she couldn't discard that discipline. We would tease her about it and laugh, and she always finished up laughing too.

In March 1971, I was home one evening planning to watch the box and have an early night. Pross had left for the restaurant only an hour before when I heard his key in the door. As he walked in, I glanced up, took one look at his face and knew he was about to give me bad news. 'Maggie,' he paused, put his hand over his eyes and I felt it was minutes before he could go on. I felt frightened yet strangely still. 'Maggie,' he began again. He put his arms around me and I felt him shaking. 'Darling, Nanna, she's ... she's gone. Nancy found her late this afternoon.

She wanted me to tell you. She didn't want to tell you over the phone.'

I broke down and sobbed. I'd received a letter from my mother that very day, her funny scrawl was always difficult to read, but she had boasted about the check-up she'd had only the week before. Her doctor had assured her she was in perfect health, apart from a bit of 'Arthur I teris' as she always called it.

Pross held me for a long time. When I regained some control I went to the phone and called Nancy. She said she had wondered why Mummy hadn't called her, they spoke every day. By mid-afternoon she had phoned her numerous times and there was no answer. She spoke to our sisters, Joan and Betty. They hadn't heard from Mummy either. By late afternoon she was really concerned. Mother's habits were so much a part of her, she always told at least one of my sisters what her plans were. Then Mother's neighbour phoned Nancy. She hadn't heard Mummy moving about her apartment as she always did. She was concerned. Nancy's husband, Lewis, had just come home from work and they immediately drove to her townhouse. Nancy had a key so they let themselves in, calling to her. Lewis went ahead. Nancy said she had a feeling of dread, she knew something was horribly wrong. Then Lewis called, 'She's here, dear. Don't come in.' But of course Nancy did. Mummy was on the floor, still in her nightgown. It's surmised that she woke sometime early in the morning, felt nauseous and had gone to the bathroom. She collapsed there and died alone.

As Nancy told me the story we both cried. Neither of us could bear the thought of her dying with no one to comfort her. I couldn't help thinking how frightened she must have felt. I found that the most difficult. Later her doctor assured us it would have been very quick as she died of a brain haemorrhage. But I'm left with a fear of dying alone. No one should die alone and certainly not my beloved Molly Trigar. I flew to Adelaide the next day.

My sisters had asked if I wanted to go to the funeral parlour to see her. We had been told her face was badly bruised from the fall. I had thought about it during the flight and made up my mind that I would not see her. I recalled at various family funerals Mummy had always thought the viewing of the body unnecessary. 'I don't want anyone to see me, I want to be remembered as I was,' she had said a dozen times, adamantly. I felt this was her wish and I would honour it.

I don't remember much about the funeral. I moved into automatic pilot. I almost lost control when my young nephews walked up to carry their grandmother's casket from the church. Two of them so young, trying bravely to fight back their tears. Molly had had a close relationship with all her grandchildren. She helped raise them, baby-sat for their parents and invited the children to stay during school holidays. It wasn't easy for those boys.

Our mother had always enjoyed her Church. When she moved to the townhouse she joined the local Church of Christ congregation. She figured the Baptists wouldn't really mind. They had welcomed her warmly, she had made new friends and rarely missed Sunday service. Now we were saying our goodbyes at that church. She was buried alongside my father at the Centennial Park Cemetery. I held Nancy's hand, we were both in tears. A small, beautiful wreath of flowers was placed at the foot of her coffin. Mother had had troublesome feet, painful bunions. She hated her feet. I whispered to Nancy, 'Well, darling, Molly's feet are looking the best they ever have tucked under that pretty wreath.' And we had a little giggle. I'm sure Molly would have too.

The next day my sisters insisted I accompany them to Mummy's townhouse. They felt strongly that we should sort her things out together. Over the years one of the great joys I had was buying gifts for my mother. When I was overseas I always brought her home something special: a pearl and gold ring from Hong Kong, a gold clip from Italy. In between I'd find things for her — a velvet dressing-gown, some pretty nightgowns — things I knew she would never buy for herself. She had always had to be so careful with money but even later, in more comfortable circumstances, Molly never spoilt herself. Her children and grandchildren, yes, but never herself.

We started to sort out her things. My sisters said I should take the jewellery I had given Mother for my girls. We found a large folder containing newspaper and magazine clippings of my modelling days. Against every shot, written in Mummy's spidery writing was, 'Margaret'. The world might have called me Maggie but to my mother I was always 'Margaret'.

She had a fierce pride. When I was named Model of the Year in 1960, the *Adelaide News* ran a front-page story with a huge picture. The headline read: 'Adelaide Girl, Rags to Riches.' The following morning Mummy took the tram to town, went to News Corporation, and demanded to see the editor. She told him in no uncertain terms that we may have been poor but I was never in 'rags'. And she shook her umbrella at him as she insisted he print an apology. He didn't but Mother said she felt better for 'giving him a piece of my mind'.

I didn't want to go through her things, it was too painful. We opened the bottom drawer of her bureau and there were my gifts. The beautiful velvet dressing-gown, the nightgowns, each tenderly laid out in tissue paper with my greeting cards stuck to the top. I burst into tears. These were gifts I wanted her to enjoy. Things for her to wear and love, and she never had. 'Why?' I cried to Nancy. 'Why didn't she wear them?'

Nancy said, 'Darling, she got so much pleasure out of showing them off to her friends. She would say, "This is what Margaret has sent me" and lay out the goodies for them to admire.' Nancy tried to comfort me but I can't tell you how it broke my heart. Much later when I'd had time to think about it, I realised that there was still a lot of little Molly Ryan in my mother. The 'nice' things were too good for her to wear, whereas I knew there was nothing good enough for her.

In times of crisis I still talk to her. I remember her strength, her courage and her love. It always helps. Lately on my walks at Greenville I've thought of her a lot, probably because of this book. I don't know that she would approve of everything I've revealed here. I rather think I can hear her saying, 'My goodness, Margaret, what will the neighbours think?'

Life's a
Parade

A T MAGGIE Tabberer Associates, Jan and I now had a
variety of major accounts covering the fashion and beauty
scene. They included designer labels, sportswear, swimwear,
hosiery, jeans, handbags, cosmetics and hair-care products. In
addition to our publicity campaigns, we had achieved a good
reputation for designing and staging excellent promotions. In
the days when a tired old chicken leg in an indifferent pub was
the common press lunch, we had several house rules for special
promotions: choose a different location from the norm; bring in
a top chef and spare no expense on great food and wine; give
media guests an attractive gift of the client's products; and, keep
the press release tight, light, bright and correct. Also, have more
photographs than you think you'll need on hand, and always
follow up. Guests should go away well wined, dined and happy,
having enjoyed themselves. And it worked.

There was one exception. In the early days of the agency we
were working on a knitting fibre. It was generally used in the
lower end of the knitwear business. The merchandise was pretty

ordinary and it took all our skills to photograph it and make it look stylish, then pull it together for the promotional parade staged for the fashion trade and the press. I was to be on stage presenting the parade, introducing the different sections with a brief description of the fibre and its qualities; all of which had been approved by the client. Lights! music! action! I strode on stage, introduced the collection and the first section. On came the girls. It looked great. There was a nice buzz to the room. Three sections into the parade I knew we were going well. The crowd was responding.

I had started on the next introduction when a figure rose up out of the audience and waving his hand, called, 'Just hold it a minute.' He headed for the stage. I paused, horrified, made an attempt to continue but the client was walking up the stairs and called out, 'Maggie, just hold it a minute. I'd like to say a few words.' The music ground to a halt. The models, confused, stopped mid-step. The client took the microphone from my hand and proceeded to give the most boring ten-minute speech about the technicalities of knitting his bloody fibre. I smiled while I fumed. When he left the stage I nodded to the lighting director, the lead model and the musicians. Somehow we cranked up and got the show back on the road, but I'd lost the crowd and couldn't help thinking I'd like to lose the client. From that day on, Jan and I had another promotions rule, a golden rule: control the client — no boring, long speeches, ever. Ever. Ever.

MAYBE IT was my early gymnastic training and dance classes that led me to see fashion shows in a new way. We had always staged well-polished shows, but I wanted to take them a step further. I wanted to produce bigger, better, more intricately choreographed parades. Where two models on the catwalk had been standard I wanted groups of five, then ten, then twenty, then twenty-five! I saw collections in themes. We began to use props, backdrops, slides or film clips. We established contacts with the best shoe and hat makers. We developed a close working relationship with an exciting new talent, Roger Foley, a lighting and sound whiz who worked under the name 'LSD Fogg'. Roger was wonderful. He'd run with an idea and build on it.

Our only difference during the many splendid shows we did together was to do with timing. In the early days, because we could rarely get into the hotel ballroom until the previous night's function was cleared, I'd say, 'Midnight set up, Roger, I want rehearsals at seven am.' But Roger and his team, who would work all night setting up staging and lighting, would think seven o'clock-ish. After a few battles we sorted it out.

Jan was brilliant at costing these productions to the cent, a skill that earnt respect from our clients. No one likes budget blowouts. Generally we were fortunate to have clients who appreciated that a show of such high quality was going to be expensive. The creative side was my responsibility, and it always started with the clothes. Once I'd seen the collection I could shape my thoughts about the location, the staging and the theme of the show.

After selecting the garments and putting them in sections I'd talk to Roger about the sound. 'These garments are very moody. Sort of dark. I need a haunting sound.' 'These designs are very fresh. Young. They need a bit of bounce. Something up tempo.' Or, 'This evening wear is very sophisticated. Here I need a big, dramatic sound.' Then we'd work our way through dozens of tracks to find the right one for each section. I'd know how many minutes I needed in each section and Roger would do clever things to extend the tracks to meet my requirements. He'd make tapes for me and I'd go home, lock myself away from the office and phone for a couple of days, and choreograph the shows. I'd play the music over and over, and visualise the presentation in my head.

I worked with large charts on which I drew the choreography, giving each girl a number and identifying each group by A, B, C, D. Then I'd step it out on my living-room floor, counting and re-counting to the music. Listening for fanfares or pauses in the music where there was an opportunity to insert some additional movement. My cleaning lady sprang me one day, striding around counting, loud music blaring. I'm sure she thought I'd gone absolutely barmy!

This new format developed over time and gradually improved as we put together a team of models who were the best in the business. Beautiful girls who were also bright. Sometimes the models had to learn ten different routines in one day, but I found ways to make it easier; for example, if I took the choreography of one section, which might be slow paced, and used it at a faster speed in a different part of the show no one could pick it. Saving rehearsal time this way meant we could spend more time setting a complex finale or opening to the show.

If a rehearsal was running rough I'd relentlessly press on until Jan would beg me to stop and let the girls grab a sandwich. 'Maggie, they will pass out if you don't give them a break.' I felt like Captain Bligh, but I would be so intent on perfecting the show I'd forget about eating.

No girl ran late for my shows. Or let's put it this way, no girl ran late more than once. They were great and I'd tell them they were great. At the start of every rehearsal I'd line them up and give them a pep talk: 'You're here because you're the best in the modelling business. I'm here because I'm the best at staging parades. Together we are going to put on one hell of a good show. But I need you to listen carefully. Think. Concentrate. And above all, focus. Now let's get on with it.' Models would kill to be included. It was considered really something to do an MTA parade.

The most exceptional shows we produced were for favoured clients Weiss and Zampatti, plus the Australian Fashion Industry awards, known as the Lyrebird Awards. These had been born out of long discussions at the Fashion Industries Conference. This was an industry struggling to find its own identity and to consolidate its talent. While a proportion of the trade still knocked off styles from overseas, we now had a host of young designers who brought a new energy to the business: names such as Prue Acton, Trent Nathan, Geoff Bade, Ken Pirrie.

Maggie Tabberer Associates was contracted to produce the Lyrebird Awards from 1971 to 1974. We organised a judging panel which included retailers and fashion magazine editors. We grouped garments into various sections, such as sportswear, day wear, evening wear. Then we designed the presentation. The first year we chose the Southern Cross Hotel in Melbourne as the venue, and put the parade together like a stage show. I was to compere, which became one of my roles for some years. The parade was broadcast in black and white on the Seven Network, my network at the time.

One award went to Prue Acton. So we came up with the idea of dressing twelve girls in identical Acton outfits and putting them all in curly blond wigs as Acton wore her hair. Voila! Twelve Prue Actons. Harry Miller came to me later and said, 'That was clever. Where in the world did you find all those girls who look like Prue Acton?' Err, what was that Harry?

The next year the awards were held at the Sebel Town House in Sydney, with various television personalities presenting them. It was a heart-stopping production as it went live to air, now in colour. Everyone considered it to be very successful, but I still didn't think we were showing enough fashion.

In 1974 we moved in a new direction. Peter Thompson, brother of actor Jack and a filmmaker, had been a friend of mine for some time. I'd discussed with him how we could make fashion look more interesting on television. I felt the parade format didn't show viewers the details and textures of the clothes and didn't sell the lifestyle of the garments. So we decided instead to film the fashion nominations in various spots around Sydney. The camera could then capture the illusive magic of the clothes in close-up shots and show them to their best advantage in interesting real-life locations. We filmed city fashion in Macquarie Street in peak hour traffic, the models striding along the footpath, doing what real girls do. For the children's wear we filmed kids playing ball in a park as real kids do.

We invited the urbane and charming British broadcaster David Frost to present the awards at a simple cocktail party at the Sydney Opera House, which Peter filmed. He then put the two together for the telecast. It was a new and refreshing look.

The awards were demanding, they took weeks of preparation, and we had to please the various factions and stroke many egos. Exhausting. While it was flattering to be asked to continue after 1974, Jan and I decided our energy could be better spent on our more lucrative accounts. It was a hard decision but it seemed time to take a break. So we walked away from fashion awards for a few years.

For their own parades, top designers, including Mark and Geoffrey, Maria Finlay, Carla Zampatti and Peter Weiss, were all prepared to roll with us, and budgets were frequently stretched to accommodate the design. In 1980, for Carla Zampatti, we built a huge catwalk in the shape of a Z in the auditorium of the Sydney Town Hall, and placed theatre seating into the floor space within the Z. To Ravel's *Bolero* I opened the show with one lone model and stark pinpoint lighting. She was cocooned in a huge floor-length sheer pink cape and a head wrap. Then I added three more girls identically dressed, then five more, and so on. Each new group was picked up by the main group and stepped smoothly into the same routine like a huge pink wave. More models came on stage as the music grew louder until the climactic finale, when twenty-five girls all dropped their pink capes to reveal stunning hot-pink swimsuits. Out lights. Huge applause. That was a good one!

For another parade the following year, Carla had designed a superb summer collection. She had included many clothes in khaki and cream, including a fabulous line of khaki silk chiffon evening wear, and we came up with 'The Nile' theme. For the opening the models walked on stage with their faces hidden behind wonderful gold Nefertiti masks. I wanted a dramatic finale and Roger suggested clouds of yellow smoke. During rehearsals Jan came to me and said, 'Roger wants to try the smoke in the finale rehearsal. Is that OK?'

'No,' I said. 'It will go right through the room.' The waiters were starting to lay tables. It was already countdown.

'But he wants to be sure everything works perfectly.'

I couldn't argue so we let off the smoke. It hissed slowly out from the sides of the stage. The effect with all the models in khaki silk chiffon was sensational under Roger's strange moody flickering light. Suddenly alarm bells went off everywhere and the next thing the ballroom was filled with firemen. The hotel management, which knew of our plan, had omitted to tell the fire brigade. A smoke detection alarm had sent them racing to the hotel, and Jan and I were faced with some very tall, not very happy firemen and shortly after a very tall, decidedly unhappy fire chief. We pulled out all the charm stops, but for half an hour it appeared to be 'no go'. No, we could not let the smoke off again. No, they would not give their permission. We called on the hotel management for their support. Finally the fire chief reluctantly agreed. We could have our smoke finale but we would need fire officers on hand.

I raced out the back and just had time to slip into my outfit and do my hair and makeup as the first guests drifted in to see Carla Zampatti's 'Nile' collection.

Peter Weiss started out as one of MTA's most difficult clients, but over the years he became one of my closest friends. Peter understood the value of an element of surprise. In fact he insisted on it. For one Weiss parade a full military brass band, playing loudly, marched into the Wentworth Hotel ballroom, past the crowd of five hundred stunned guests and up onto the stage to join twenty-five models dressed in tartan. It brought the house down. Another time we had thirty broad-shouldered Bondi lifesavers carry models in swimsuits onto the catwalk, held aloft on lifesaving equipment. A knockout moment!

Peter demanded a lot from us but he also demanded a lot from himself. He had the ability to see the big picture, and if in the pursuit of excellence it cost more he always agreed to pay. In 1981 we were preparing for his biggest parade yet. It was to be held at the Wentworth Hotel. To fit the location we had a catwalk built that was twelve feet wide and ran the full length of the expansive ballroom. The hotel management was incredibly cooperative and had cleared a large storage area to accommodate our backstage space requirements. We had a sell-out show. All was in place, then late one afternoon, three days before the parade, Peter called me at home and said very simply, 'I've just had a call from the management of the Wentworth. The entire staff has gone on strike and there is no way they will resolve the matter in time for our show. We have to look at other sites.'

I sat stunned for a few seconds, the impossibilities hurtling through my mind. How do we notify five hundred guests of a change of location, that's if we can find one available and suitable? What about the stage built to size? The lighting plan? Where in hell can we go?

Suitable locations are not easy to find. It is amazing how many major hotels have splendid ballrooms and closet-size spaces backstage. With lighting and sound technicians, up to twenty-five models and a dresser for each, plus a bunch of hairdressers and makeup stylists and my office team, whose job was to control the backstage chaos and send the models on in the right order and at the right time, it was a considerable cast. Add to that all the clothes and accessories and you need a lot of room.

By noon we were at the Round House at the University of New South Wales. It was the best on offer, we had to make it work. Peter ran the location change like a military operation. He told Jan and me to concentrate on the show, he would take care of everything else. Five hundred guests were personally phoned or telegrammed. The media were seduced into giving us fantastic coverage about the change of venue. Roger Foley and his team spent a night redesigning and rebuilding the set. No easy task given they were literally fitting an oblong stage into a round hole. (Yes, the Round House is round.) Jan and I spent anxious hours figuring out how to accommodate everyone backstage. Our office team proved stoic.

On the day of the show, as we started rehearsals, one thousand live trees were delivered to the Round House. I marvelled at the transformation of the room. Peter's caterer performed miracles, aided by the Wentworth Hotel, which generously lent all the crockery, cutlery, chairs and tables. Backstage we had huge problems right up to curtain time. The space was small and stage access difficult. We arranged and rearranged models' locations, based on who had fast or difficult changes. John Adams and his hairdressing team worked under impossible restrictions in a space the size of a telephone box, as did Rickie Quesada, who boasted he was doing 'makeup in the dark'. But our team spirit, despite some frayed tempers, helped and everyone pitched in. We were going around saying, 'We will do it. We will make it happen.' It was one of the best shows ever and the guests gave us a standing ovation. The next day we received dozens of telegrams and calls of congratulations. The media gave the show a rave review. Satisfying for all of us.

Maggie Tabberer Associates changed the face of fashion presentation. Our shows were big, fast, professional and spectacular. They were also a lot of hard yakka. Personally they were very rewarding. I loved all aspects of the development and adored the thrill of a perfect presentation.

At MTA we were also developing the *Daily Mirror*/Grace Bros annual fashion spectaculars. The idea for these parades developed in 1974, when I was invited to join the inaugural Sydney to Athens flight of Olympic Airways. My friend Snow Swift had the Olympic advertising account and he thought I might write a piece about Greek fashion. One of my travelling companions was John Simpson, then a powerful advertising executive with Grace Bros. John was considered something of a genius in the business. We had enjoyed a good working relationship. He always advertised in my pages in the *Mirror* and I gave Grace Bros fashions editorial support.

The night after our arrival in Athens, a welcome dinner was hosted by Alexander Onassis, the son of the infamous Aristotle who happened to own Olympic Airways. It was held in the beautiful rooftop restaurant of the George Fifth Hotel on Constitution Square, with a fantastic view of Athens lit by a spectacular sunset. Our Australian contingent consisted of a gaggle of media and various distinguished and perhaps not so distinguished guests. During the rather sumptuous dinner,

Alexander Onassis made a gracious welcome speech without the benefit of notes and in perfect English. Then a rather funny old guy, clutching a bunch of handwritten notes, rose to respond. 'Who's that?' I whispered to John.

'Don't know his name but seems he's the mayor of some New South Wales country town and therefore officially the highest ranking amongst our mob.'

Well, the Aussie mayor rambled on, recalling his days in Greece during the war. Finally he took a deep breath, drew himself up to his full height and uttered a long, painful paragraph in tortured Greek. Our hosts looked rather embarrassed.

'John, for God's sake what do you think he just said?' I asked.

John reached for his glass of wine and replied, 'I think he said, "Your garbage night has been changed from Tuesday to Wednesday".'

While we were in Athens we came up with the idea of bringing a Greek collection to Australia and staging a joint promotion with the *Daily Mirror* and Grace Bros. We arranged for an exciting collection and a gorgeous Greek model, Psarakis, to come to Australia for a road show around the Grace Bros stores the following year. This was to be the first in a series of shows that ran for seven years. I took our big show format and style and scaled it down to store-size productions. They truly were ground-breaking in-store presentations.

From then on I would go overseas each year and organise a collection. Maggie Tabberer Associates would design and stage the shows on behalf of the *Daily Mirror* throughout the Grace Bros stores. I'd also compere the shows and back them with publicity in my *Mirror* pages. Initially these parades were staged to attract crowds into the stores, but clever John Simpson soon realised they also offered a great merchandising opportunity. Where possible we would buy collections from the country or designer featured. If the clothes were very expensive we would buy smaller quantities and Grace Bros would have compatible and less expensive items made up by local manufacturers, always following the theme of the show.

A travelling show was a lesson in organisation and stamina. We had a team of ten models. They would meet at our Double Bay office each morning, all dressed in our theme T-shirts, hop onto our little bus, and we'd chug out to one of the Grace Bros stores, such as Roselands. We would do three shows in a day, four if it was late-night shopping. It took two working weeks to do the rounds of the stores.

The shows were tiring but incredibly successful. The stores had to put on extra security for crowd control. I remember walking on stage one evening at the Bondi Junction Grace Bros store and the entire ground floor was a sea of faces. The management was in a panic — the crowd was stopping trade, and they feared the shoplifters might be having a field day. 'It's too successful,' said the store manager.

In 1976 I went to New York and met the formidable Eleanor Lambert, a fashion promoter and publicist with an awesome reputation. I was terrified when I went to see her in her Fifth Avenue apartment but we got on famously. Through this meeting I arranged for the American Coty Award collection to come to Australia, with garments by top American fashion designers.

After lining up the collection I stayed on for a few days to visit my old friend Barry Young, who all those years before had helped me to launch into the PR business. He had friends who lived in Connecticut, so on a golden autumn morning we drove up to see them. We had dawdled along enjoying the little towns and the wonderful scenery. When we arrived later than scheduled, our host was pacing nervously. It seems his neighbour, the film star Bette Davis, had invited us all for pre-lunch drinks and, as he said, 'You're never late for Bette.'

We walked next door to a little doll's-house cottage. Even before we'd knocked, the front door was flung open by a diminutive figure wearing an ash-blond wig and a yellow patchwork kaftan, with three tons of jangly bracelets on each arm. It was Bette. She mixed us enormous pink gins, flinging the ice into the huge glasses. Too bad if you didn't drink pink gin, that was what she was serving. She then threw herself dramatically onto a large white leather day bed, while we sat in a semicircle on spindly gilt chairs, and Bette proceeded to give a star's performance. She had just come back from filming, in Mexico I think, working with the British actor Oliver Reed. It seemed Oliver liked a drink or two or a thousand, and had a habit of riding a bicycle up and down their motel's corridors, slashing at the curtains and lamps with a sabre, whooping and hollering, and disturbing everyone's sleep. And most importantly, Bette's. One night, fed up with this she confronted him, ripped the sabre from his hand and threatened to use it to sever his manhood if he didn't go to bed and cease his noise. I didn't doubt her for a minute. She may have been small but, my God, she was feisty. In contrast, her house was very Dolly Varden. Every shelf, table and windowsill was packed with tiny, fragile glass animals. To my mind a nightmare and hell to dust.

On the same trip I was staying at the New York Plaza which I adored, with its big, airy rooms overlooking Central Park, and the Palm Court where you saw the world go by and ate the best hamburgers in Christendom. One night I had dressed in my finest. I was meeting Barry for dinner at the River Cafe, one of my favourite restaurants. As I stepped into the elevator I was met by a very familiar face. The big handsome face of the movie actor Anthony Quinn. He looked me up and down and said,

'You are a very beautiful woman.'

'Thank you, Mr Quinn,' I said. 'And *you* are a very beautiful man.'

The lift doors opened and we went our separate ways.

Ah, if only! Well, I console myself, he turned out to be a lousy philandering husband and he's fathering babies in his eighties. But the old devil is still very attractive.

In 1977 we brought out a collection from Mexico called 'Mexico Ole', after Alfredo Bouret introduced me to some other Mexican designers. They were wonderful, happy, colourful clothes that formed a spectacular collection. We also imported a full mariachi band, comprising eight dynamos who wore huge sombreros and beautiful skin-tight, dark tan suits, studded with silver buttons and worn with silver-embossed boots and spurs. In Sydney they would jump in taxis and ask to go to Crazy Bros. From then on in our office, Grace Bros was always Crazy Bros. The mariachis got so carried away with the warm applause they received at the Roselands store we practically had to lasso them to get them off stage!

The next year we staged a collection of the best of British design. I met and made friends with the talented Zandra Rhodes and the amazing Yuki, a Japanese-born Londoner, whose draped jersey evening wear was amongst the most beautiful clothes I've ever seen. From Italy came the collection of Livio de Simone, an exuberant artist who lived on Capri and painted designs on his colourful sportswear. He taught me how to make a frittata using every leftover in the fridge. He called it 'whose body's in it' frittata, and it's still a family favourite.

Most of these trips I took with John Cooper, who had replaced John Simpson after his retirement from Grace Bros. A tall lean man with a thin moustache and a very ready wit, he and

I developed a strong friendship, based largely on professional respect and humour.

John Cooper and I went to Japan in 1979 to meet with designer Kansai Yamamoto, whose clothes at the time were grabbing fashion headlines worldwide. Obtaining his collection would be a real win. We settled into our seats on Japan Airlines and took off. The flight attendant duly served us wine in the tiniest eggcup-size glasses. Gone in a flash. I said to John, 'That didn't touch the sides. Grab the hostie and order another.' He did and after what seemed an interminable time she produced another eggcup of wine. The weather was pretty rough and we were lurching around. 'Damn this, John,' I said. 'Let's ask for the bloody bottle.' The flight attendant came back with a bottle of wine, placed it in front of me and said ever so serenely, 'You enjoy drinking.' To which John quipped, 'She certainly does!' No matter how I tried, I couldn't convince him she meant to say, 'Enjoy your drink.'

In Tokyo we met a very shy and reserved Kansai Yamamoto. His collection was full of unusual and stunningly bold clothes. Instantly we knew we had a super show for Grace Bros, and I knew I had great photographs for my column. Having done the business we decided to 'do' the major stores. The cleanliness and efficiency in Japan is quite remarkable and the department stores reflected that. Like the pretty staff member, immaculate in her uniform, who stands at the escalator wearing white gloves with a dampened cloth in her hand, cleaning the handrail as it turns around and around.

Japan's fascinating and John and I really enjoyed it. In one small restaurant, tucked away in an alley off the Ginza, I assured John that ordering a meal was just a matter of pointing at the plastic mock-up dishes in the window. It worked, although the numbers somehow got confused and we had enough food for an army. We were also a bit stunned when the waiter brought to our table six very large opened bottles of beer. Oh well.

Shopping one day I spotted some superb greeting cards. They had intricately folded paper birds and animals on them. I am a great postcard sender when I'm overseas, so I gathered up a dozen. At the counter I noticed the sales girls whispering and eyeing me in a strange way. Finally one who was obviously given the task because she spoke a smattering of English, came to me and said, 'Madame, these cards for the death ceremony.'

'Fine,' I said. 'I'll take them.' I didn't think many of my friends would realise they had received a death ceremony card.

In Kyoto, in a shop the size of a shoebox, we found an ancient little woman and the most incredible array of bamboo goods. I wanted to buy the shop out, but with my suitcase already bulging I settled on small items. 'Look at these bamboo swizzle sticks, John, they're so chic!' I picked out twelve. The ancient one looked at me with a puzzled expression, slowly raised one of the bamboo sticks, held it in front of my face for a second then slowly put it to her ear and did a twisting motion. John said, 'So now you know if you take a gin and tonic at Maggie's place, the swizzle stick is actually an ear cleaner.'

MY WORKING life was hectic and exciting in the 1970s but I still had time to develop strong friendships. There is one person in particular I would like to write about. As I always say when I introduce her, 'Have you met my best friend Barbara?' I call her Barbarella.

We were born just six months apart at the same hospital in Adelaide. Then at an early age her parents took her to live in Sydney. She came from German stock. Her father, Norman 'Tiger' Turnbull, was a great footballer and also trained racehorses. Her mother, Alvina, was a fantastic woman — a great worker, cook, homemaker, gardener — who had a clear judgment of everyone and every situation. She was ramrod straight and very tall, even into her nineties, with wonderful piercing blue eyes. Barb had inherited it all, along with Alvina's 'no nonsense' attitude to life and her innate sense of style. Barb grew tall and strawberry blond while I grew tall and dark. She, as an only child, was indulged as a teenager and travelled the world. I, as the youngest of five kids, stayed home in Adelaide and took rowdy family holidays at Victor Harbour. I married very young and had two daughters. Barbarella married much later and had a son, Matthew, and daughter, Ash. She wasn't any better at picking a husband than I was, but at least she learnt from the experience and only did it once.

When her marriage broke up she went back to work teaching dress design at East Sydney Technical College, and then helped friends and later clients decorate their houses. She eventually tired of teaching, although she loved her students, her 'kids' as she called them, and they adored her. Stoic, Barb always managed and eventually the decorating side saw her work for some of Sydney's most prominent people. While I went to work because I had to support my kids, I also *needed* to work. God knows what I was trying to prove. Maybe that Margaret Trigar, daughter of poor rejected Molly, was as good as anyone. Barbara has never felt compelled to prove anything to anyone. It's one of her great strengths.

I first met Barb in the early 1960s. We were introduced by Jill Robb, who had just moved to Sydney. Jill took me to Barb's house, a stylish Paddington terrace she was blitzing at the time. In all the years I've known her since, it seems Barbara is always either knocking a wall out or painting it white. I don't know what it was but we clicked. We liked each other immediately. However, for the first couple of years of our friendship we would just meet for the occasional social lunch. Then in 1966 I had a major operation and Barb and Jill joined forces to care for my daughters while I was hospitalised. In an act of great kindness Barb took a spare pair of pink faille curtains and sewed adorable full-length empire-line dresses trimmed with deep brown velvet ribbon for Brooke and Amanda to wear to their first school dance. I was propped up in my hospital bed with nasty tubes running in and out of unmentionable places when Barb, Jill and my daughters arrived at St Luke's Hospital. I took two hairpieces and piled sixties'-style curls on top of their blond heads. They looked divine and were jumping out of their skins with excitement. Off they went to Paddington Town Hall with two surrogate, nervous aunts and strict instructions about behaviour and being home by midnight.

In the ensuing years our friendship grew and grew. Barb married her mad Hungarian and his paunch increased along with his fortune. The houses grew bigger too. When she moved from Paddington to a giant waterview house at Mosman, Barb skilfully turned it from an ugly old house into a magnificent home. A huge pool was installed, which projected out over the harbour. We spent many summer weekends there cooking up a storm, laughing, playing cards, drinking the best champagne and wines, arguing about whatever was in the news, and generally living a high old life. Our men were not perfect and nor were we. But we had fun.

When Barb turned forty six months ahead of me (I tease her about being 'my older friend'), I made a huge Mad Hatter's top hat of black cardboard plastered with a large sign saying, 'Nah! Nah! Barb's forty and I'm thirty-nine.' And I rode down the funicular to her house singing at the top of my voice, 'Happy Birthday to Barb. Happy Birthday to Barb. She's forty and I'm thirty-nine.'

'Bitch,' she said. We embraced and laughed.

When I turned forty we had a splendid dinner at Darcy's for twelve friends, and she generously invited the party back to her house for a swim. John Baker, a well-known man about town, was in his undies, swinging like Tarzan on a rope over the pool on that hot December night. But it was Barb and I who swung into action when the phone rang at five am and Barb's husband, back a day early from an overseas trip, called to say he was on his way home. 'Quick, you sweep up the sleeping bodies, I'll do the bottles and glasses.' I passed her husband's cab at the top of the street and drove home grinning to myself that both the bodies and bottles had been dispensed within a fast half-hour.

We were a great team. Hell, we still are! And we both love to travel. Pross often said to me, 'Save your money, Maggie, so you can travel when you get older.'

'Stuff that,' I'd say. 'Who wants to travel when they're old? I want to go now while I can enjoy it.' I haven't stopped travelling and neither has Barb.

We often went to the Pacific Islands. Barb's a barefoot and pareu, two swims a day, coconut crab and chilled riesling lunch girl. We both adore living with natural things: white canvas and cane furniture, wood, shells and primitive carvings, coir matting and plain white walls. On our holidays we collected interesting pieces from places such as Tahiti, Noumea and Vanuatu, and closer to home, Noosa, Port Douglas, Cairns and the Barrier Reef Islands — Dunk and Daydream. One of the funniest photos I have of Barbarella was taken when we were deep-sea fishing off Cairns. She had fought her catch for half an hour. Finally, turning red with effort, she screamed with excitement, 'I've got it. I've got it!' I poised my camera to record the haul. Suddenly her fish flew onto the deck. I clicked. But it was just the fish's head.

A shark had lunched well! The look on Barb's face was about as pop-eyed as her catch.

At the height of her husband's financial success, in 1976, he hired a 104-foot sailing boat, the *Eros*, which had previously been owned by the Greek shipping magnate, Niarchos. After a business appointment in London I joined them for a cruise around the Greek Islands. Days of lazy lunches, swimming over the side, long drinks at sunset and dinners on deck under the stars, or just moored on a still sea, nestled within those beautiful bare islands, listening to the goat bells and a friend strumming his guitar and singing the only song he could play, 'Starry Starry Night'. We loved to sleep on deck until one night Barb was woken by strange noises, went to investigate and was appalled to find the elderly captain engaged in an ancient act with the cabin boy!

One bright blue day we sailed to the island of Kos. Unlike most of the Greek Islands, Kos is green. Brilliantly so with an abundance of oleander trees surrounding its little white houses, their doorways and shuttered windows painted blue to keep the flies away, it's said.

Kaftans were 'the go' in those days. Barb wore a blue and white striped job. Mine was a soft strawberry pink. We went ashore and lunched well at one of the tavernas on the picturesque village square then wandered over to a small market to buy supplies for the boat. We noticed a little old man sitting in the shade of a large tree, mending a fishing net. He had a dozen tandem bikes for hire so, charged with some good retsina wine courage, Barb and I decided we would tour the town on a tandem. 'I'll ride up front and steer,' I said. Why do I always do that? We tucked our long kaftans up into our knickers, clambered on and took off. Our long legs peddled away, hair flying, kaftans flapping. It was exhilarating. We careered around the narrow streets with lots of shrieks and yells, and a couple of 'Oh Jeezuz' when we took a corner too fast. The Greeks loved it. They waved and clapped and yelled, 'Olympia. Olympia!' But as we started to head down the hill to the port the tandem rather got away from us. We were bouncing along over the rough cobblestones, going faster and faster down a steep incline, weaving to miss a donkey, an old lady and a fisherman, until we screeched to a stop, legs shaking, hearts pounding. We climbed off laughing until tears streamed down our cheeks.

Retsina is quite dangerous if you're cycling but so are two little ol' Adelaide girls when life seems just too good to be true.

BARB'S HOUSE was more than just a fun place for long lunches at the weekend. It was where I went, sometimes ran, to seek her wise counsel on the often complicated twists and turns in my life. My rocky marriage, other men, affairs, business moves, career moves, everything that crowded my life. She always had time for me. Yet when her marriage failed I believe I failed her. She is so private and strong. She never complains and always makes light of her problems. She never calls on our friendship, and for that I could strangle her. She might have a raging temperature, the roof's leaking, her teenage daughter has just dyed her hair green, the news is critical about a sick friend, and what does she say when I call by? 'I'm fine, darling. Just fine,' with a big grin and those sparkling blue eyes. I'm ashamed when I think what I've put her through and how little she ever asks of me. My mother always used to say, 'If you have one very good friend you are rich.' With Barb I won the lotto!

Barbara's bright and totally without ambition. She has always been accepting of her circumstances, whether she was working long hours and battling a budget, or moving first class around the world and coming home to a waterfront mansion. An avid reader, she can reel off a list of the best books, as well as the best boats, houses, restaurants, resorts, galleries, exhibitions, decorators and designers in the world. But she is shy, hard to drag to anything social. She hates getting dressed up, wears a polo neck sweater and jeans in winter, a pareu and sandals in summer. She wears her long hair in a simple plait or, if pushed, will twist it into a knot and pop on a bit of lipstick for special occasions. She can cook like a dream but would rather someone else do it. She has an uncanny knack of finding great recipes and planting them all over my house. It usually works! You have to dig to get an opinion out of her. I've heard her fib fabulously and convincingly rather than risk hurt or be critical. She makes everyone feel good — kids, teens, contemporaries and oldies. Her eye for style is uncompromising. She exudes a tranquillity and a peace with herself and her lot which is enviable. By comparison I'm a mess. She sends me up. My need for order and cleanliness, cushion puffing, styling dinner tables, cooking elaborate lunches and my 'work' neurosis. 'You're bloody mad, Margaret,' she will often say. But we speak every day and I can't tell you how much I value her and love her, and how much it means to me to hear her say, 'How are you, mate?'

Lovers
&
Others

As ENTERTAINING and titillating as it might be for the reader to peruse lists of famous or infamous lovers, such indulgent self-aggrandisement is not my style. Nevertheless, it would be dishonest of me to assume a convent-like demeanour towards my love affairs so, apart from those mentioned elsewhere in this book, let me now mention a few of my favourites in order not to appear puritanical. As if you thought I would be! Actually I've probably lived some of my sexual life with the freedom of a man. It's always troubled me that a man can have affairs, sleep around and be admiringly called a 'stud', a 'real womaniser' or 'a good ol' horny boy', whereas the same behaviour in a woman is referred to in salacious tones and she's branded with a lot of distasteful names. Well damn it, early in my adult life I decided what's good for the old gander is just as good for the goose. For a time I was sexually free and active.

The one-night stand was never my form. Frankly, I've always enjoyed the chase, the titillation, the phone calls, the flowers, the rendezvous and candle-lit dinners, as much as the actual seduction. Having one without the other is a bit like eating a pie without the sauce. So really I've only had three of these one-night affairs. I had flown from Athens into the island of Rhodes to await the arrival of friends. As I checked into the hotel a tall, well-dressed American with a soft drawl appeared at my side. Our eyes met briefly and while I was filling out the registration form he commented on some jewellery I was wearing, then charmingly asked me to join him for a drink that evening. Why not? We sat out on the terrace and watched the sun go down. A drink led to accepting his dinner invitation. His hand found my leg under the table just after the first course. He looked at me, I looked at him. We cancelled the main course and almost ran to his room. I left just before dawn. A few days later, back in Athens, a huge flower arrangement was delivered to my room at the Grande Bretagne. The note simply said, 'Unforgettable.' It was!

On the second occasion I had strolled from my Sydney house around to join friends in their picturesque garden for a lazy Sunday lunch. I was introduced to a beautiful young man with magnetic blue eyes. He was the son of a friend of my hosts, and I enjoyed his conversation. When I went to leave he suggested he walk me home. At my front door he made a move to kiss me. I found I was trembling with excitement. Inside the house we simply went up to my bedroom, undressed and had the most deliciously good sex. He was beautiful in every way. We never saw each other again, but I'd like him to know I have thought of him often.

I was in London seeing friends. It was the 'season' as they say, the town was crawling with Aussies. One night after a particularly good dinner in a fine restaurant, a very handsome and dapper senior newspaper executive suggested he escort me back to my hotel. I'd known him for a number years but this night was different. Slightly tipsy we decided on one for the road. The next thing I knew he'd skilfully undone my bra and we went to bed. It was sexual, not romantic. I see him frequently. I wonder if he'll be upset about my mentioning him. Then again, he'd probably be bloody furious if I didn't.

One very romantic incident didn't even lead to sex. I had boarded a plane in Melbourne to fly to Wodonga where I was to meet friends and drive up to their ski lodge for a few days. Just as they called my flight a very tall, extremely attractive grey-haired man raced into the departure lounge. On board I found we were seated together in the back row of a tiny aircraft. The weather was turbulent and so was the flight. We lurched and lunged all over the sky. As I've said before, I'm not a brave flier. Mr Handsome engaged me in conversation and we were very close in those rather cramped seats. At one stage the plane dropped. Some passengers screamed. I must have paled with fear because he gently took my hand in his and didn't let it go. As they announced we were about to land he leaned closer and said, 'I think you're the most beautiful thing I've ever seen. May I kiss you?'

'Yes,' I said, and we did. A long lingering kiss. After which not a word was spoken. We disembarked and stood waiting for our luggage, he on one side of the conveyor, me on the other. We kept looking at each other. Then he was joined by an attractive woman and a couple of teenage kids. Our eyes said goodbye. I went on to meet Barbara who christened my stranger 'The kissing bandit of Wodonga'. I wonder if he remembers that incident as clearly as I do.

I was in Melbourne travelling with my good mate Ronnie Fraser when a friend of his invited us down to Portsea for the weekend. He put together a dinner party of locals and it was a jolly night. There was a very attractive older couple. She was tall, elegant and grey-haired. He was well-built, very tanned and also grey-haired with a neat goatee beard. (Is there something about grey-haired men in my life I wonder?) Anyway the next day they invited us for lunch. It wasn't lost on me that he found me attractive, because I felt the same about him. Back in Sydney he started to call me. Would I have lunch? Would I have dinner? When could we meet? I finally gave in and we started an affair that dangerously ran for a couple of years. I was in Melbourne frequently and he came to Sydney often. Our affair was conducted on crisp white sheets in glossy hotel rooms. Inevitably his wife learnt about it and sent me a telegram while I was visiting London. 'No further contact will be necessary,' it said. I saw her point. I felt cheap. What in the hell was I doing? Back home I broke it off. It wasn't easy. It had been a very sexual relationship.

With a number of Channel Seven personalities I had boarded an Italian cruise ship to cruise the Pacific Islands for ten days. It was a promotional deal where we got a free trip and paid our way by socialising with the passengers and staging a mock 'Beauty and the Beast' show. Waggers and Pat Firman had also come along. I'm not a very good sailor in rough seas so I holed up for the first couple of days in my cabin until I found my sea legs. The night I finally thought I might keep some dinner down, our party had been invited to dine at the Captain's table. He was probably one of the most elegant ships' captains I had ever seen. During dinner I recognised a mutual attraction. Later that evening he found me in the ship's nightclub and we danced. Later, I had just slipped into bed when there was a sharp tap at my door. 'Who is it?' I said.

'This is your Captain!'

The next week was full of secret meetings, it was exciting and he was a skilled lover. Given his career and the opportunities it provided, he'd obviously had plenty of chances to hone his sexual performance. If I thought I was fooling my shipmates I should have known better. Pat and Waggers teased me constantly. I made the mistake of telling them over a bottle of wine how he'd come to my cabin and said, 'This is your Captain.' For months afterwards, Waggers would somehow manage to use those words on camera. It broke me up every time. When our ship sailed back into Sydney Harbour on a clear cold morning, 'my Captain' invited me to join him on the bridge. It was a wonderful finish to a short but sweet interlude.

There was a well-known Melbourne football player I met by the Parmelia Hotel's swimming pool in Perth. His handsome moustache proved to be very engaging but we both had high profiles and we were both involved with other people. It was short-lived, very naughty but very nice.

Holidaying in Vanuatu with Barbara, our artist friends, Nicolai Michoutoukine and Aloi Pilioko, invited us for lunch in their wonderful garden. They mentioned a French friend would be joining us, he lived in a thatched faré on the other side of a hedge of pink hibiscus. We were enjoying a long cold glass of rosé when this dashing man stepped through the hedge. He wore a Japanese blue and white *yukata*, had slick black hair and a neat, pencil-thin moustache and, as is the way in Vanuatu, he'd tucked a frangipani behind one ear. It was a staggeringly exotic look. His English was limited but his message was loud and clear. After lunch he offered to show me his faré. It was beautiful. Very simply furnished and just one large room with a minute bathroom and kitchen to one side. Nicolai had a rather noisy Vespa. We heard him coming and Barb calling out that they were going to town, did we want to go too? The Frenchman answered by slamming the faré's door. Barb and

Nicolai got the message. So did I. It was a ten-day affair in a wildly romantic setting. Very early one morning I was slipping back into the Le Lagon Hotel where we were staying, still wearing a long evening kaftan, when I was sprung by Dr Jean Battersby and her husband.

'You're up very early,' she said.

'No, very late,' I replied and sashayed down the garden path smiling to myself.

I had been going through a lot of stress before that holiday. My private life was in tatters and the business was very demanding. I'd complained to Barb about the vertigo attacks I was experiencing. They continued even when we got to Vanuatu. After a few days later, Barb said, 'How's your vertigo, Mags?'

'What vertigo?' I replied. The Frenchman sure as hell had fixed that.

I had met one of the most dashingly handsome men about Sydney at various social functions. He phoned and asked me to dinner. We dined in a small restaurant way over on the other side of town, maybe because he was in a relationship, although he wasn't married at the time. He had wonderful lazy eyes and a smooth European charm. Ultimately our dinner dates led us to his bed. The sex was good but in his passion he would bite me! It not only hurt (which is something I'm not into) but explaining his teeth marks was embarrassing. I see him across crowded cocktail parties from time to time. 'There goes the old biter,' I say to myself.

I was in New York when my friend Marcia Resche rang. Alan Bond was about to mount his first challenge for the America's Cup. She suggested we go down with another Australian friend, Grant Jagleman, and wave the flag for Bondy. I'd met Red and Alan some time earlier in Perth. I rescheduled my flights and decided to stay on for a few days. We took the shuttle down to

Newport. Naturally the place was packed and I worried about where we would stay, but Marcia said Alan had it in hand and all would be well. Grant was squeezed into the Bond's huge house they shared with family and crew. Marcia and I, it seemed, were to stay with neighbours. It was a huge, glamorous, over-the-top house. A maid showed us up to the first floor. Marcia's suite was all pale pink furnishings. Mine, pale lemon, even the carpet. It was luxury plus. The maid gave us the keys to a large pink Cadillac and said our host would probably be in residence in a couple of days. Four days later and we were still coming and going with no sign of him. We spent days at sea following the races and nights in rowdy restaurants with the Bonds and their gang.

On the fifth day I woke very early to be greeted with a strong smell of cooking floating up the stairs. Meatballs, I thought. I walked down and there in the kitchen was a tall, silver-haired man cooking meatballs. He wore an open-neck black shirt with lots of gold chains around his neck, black pants and very dark, black-framed sunglasses. I thanked him for allowing us to stay. He simply waved his hand and said, 'If you girls are free tonight I'm having some friends around for dinner. I cook Italian.' As it was, Marcia and I had prior arrangements. When we arrived home just after eleven, scattered through the house were a dozen or so guys who all seemed to look like the host — black outfits, lots of gold chains, silver hair and dark glasses — and everyone had a Barbie doll blonde hanging off his arm. The penny dropped. Two days later Bondy was out of the running and we took the shuttle back to New York. I had the distinct feeling we'd met the original Godfather and some of 'da boys'!

But I digress. Amongst the Australian contingent I'd met another tall, grey-haired man. Quiet, charming, it led to a brief, gentle liaison. It proved geographically impossible but it was nice while it lasted.

I was recording the 'Maggie' show in Adelaide one day when a guest on the programme proved fatally attractive. He was a Swedish astrophysicist working out of Woomera to 'send up a rocket'. It was a mutual attraction and a couple of weeks later his rocket had gone up and come down, and he had stopped over in Sydney before heading back to Europe. A friend had lent me his apartment. We made lunch and then made love. He was a very energetic lover. It must have been the sight of his white bottom, pumping up and down, but my friend's Siamese cat took an instant dislike to the action and leapt from the floor, sinking all claws into the physicist's derrière. He screamed in pain, the cat flew out the door in shock, I almost had a heart attack and the man was bleeding profusely. Worse, he didn't show much humour as I dabbed Dettol on his bottom, and got furious when I couldn't stop laughing. We met a couple of years later in London but old affairs are hard to heat up. Like warmed-over coffee they never taste the same.

In the mid seventies I had spent three summers in Greece. On the first visit I had started a relationship with a handsome executive of Olympic Airways. He looked like a black hawk, with a patrician nose and pitch-black hair. He had elegance and charm and certainly knew how to treat a woman. Each year thereafter we renewed our affair when I was in Athens. After sailing with Barb and her husband on his boat the *Eros* I had planned to spend another week in Greece. I called my Greek friend and we arranged a rendezvous in Athens. I would stay at my favourite hotel, the Grande Bretagne on Constitution Square.

The drive into Athens was a nightmare, the temperature hovering around forty-two degrees Celsius. I had packed a pure white crepe pantsuit to wear to dinner and travelled in one of my cool kaftans, but I was anything but cool by the time I arrived at the hotel. A leisurely shower and the air-conditioned room restored me, and I dressed carefully for my dinner date. We dined in the Plaka, then went on to one of the big clubs down by the coast to dance, listen to the emotional singers and smash plates. A woman selling white gardenias came to our table, and my Greek made the flamboyant and extravagant gesture of buying me her whole tray of flowers.

In the wee hours of the morning we drove to his brother's apartment. There was never a question of him coming back to my hotel — the Colonels were running Greece at the time and had 'eyes' planted everywhere. It was just not done, and anyway he was far too well-known in the city. We walked into the darkened apartment and sank onto an enormous couch. Sometime later, fumbling in the dark to dress he whispered that he couldn't find one of his socks. He said he couldn't drive home and be seen with only one sock. After crawling around for ten minutes I suggested he borrow a pair from his brother's wardrobe so we could get out of there before dawn. Duly dressed, socks and all, we drove back to the Grande Bretagne. He opened the car door and kissed my hand. We knew we might never see each other again. Neither of us had any silly thoughts about this affair, it was wonderful, exciting but contained.

I stood on the hotel steps and waved him off, then I walked up the steps, past the doorman and into the hotel foyer. I passed the two secret service agents, installed by the Colonels, who were permanently glued to chairs in the foyer, down the length of the room, past the bar and its bored waiters and a small group of late-night revellers, past a couple of cleaners vacuuming the carpet and up to the front desk where I asked for my key. The concierge wished me goodnight and I turned my back and walked away to the elevator. I rode up to my room. I had no guilt about this affair. I had had an open marriage for many years. My Greek lived a similar life. There was no threat to anyone. In the bathroom I took off my earrings then I reached for my pearls. As I started to take them off something caught at the back of my neck. I tugged then turned to look at my back in the mirror and there, laid out like a shop display in perfect profile against my pure white suit, was one gentleman's large black sock! I thought of the doorman, the secret service guys, the waiters and the revellers, the cleaners, the desk staff and the concierge. What a perfect view of the black sock they must have had, and I started to laugh. I ran a bath and sat in it laughing until it was a respectable time to phone Barb who was staying on the Costa Verdi and tell her. And God, we laughed.

I waited until late morning to check out, hoping a new shift of staff had come on. They all had, bar the beady-eyed concierge. As I paid the bill he looked at me and said in perfect English, which he'd never been able to summon up on my previous stays, 'And did Madame enjoy her stay in Athens?' I replied with conviction, 'I certainly did and could you mail this envelope?' In it was black sock and a short note of goodbye. There's nothing like the heady mix of sex, love and laughter. A few days later Barb and I flew back home to Australia. To this day, we can still giggle at the mere mention of a black sock.

Dr Ian Potts was a sensationally handsome man. He had been married to my friend Judy and he had always been sweet to me. I knew of his affairs from time to time, just as he knew of mine. But it was never a question for us, we were simply friends, something I valued. I was on another trip to Greece, Ian planned to be there around the same time so we met in Athens and enjoyed a few days doing the Plaka and dancing and making merry with my Greek friends. Ian was due to fly on to London, I had intended to go on to France. Then, over dinner one night, we decided it was ridiculous to turn our backs on Greece.

We swiftly cancelled our plans and through my friend Helene

Speronis, who worked for Olympic Airways, we found a small house in a small town on the coast halfway between Athens and Sounion. A friend of Ian's, a man I knew only as Chappy, flew in to join us, and a beautiful blonde Ian was seeing at the time also came over from London. A funny foursome, Chappy on the couch downstairs, me in a maid's room under the rafters and Ian and the blonde in the master bedroom. We toured the coast, discovered all the best little tavernas and made friends with the locals. Ian had me up each morning doing exercises, ambitious I thought. We turned nut brown in the sun, swam in the azure sea. It was idyllic. One morning on the beach we bought fresh fish from the local fisherman, Ian was a great cook and so we planned a dinner party on the rooftop. He and Chappy went off to buy the rest of the supplies and to find something to drink other than retsina, to which by now I had developed a healthy aversion. They seemed to be gone a long time. I'll never forget them arriving back at the house, Chappy was head to toe bandages — big ones, small ones, sticking plaster, white gauze and bandaids. Ian had fewer but was still a mess. Seems Chappy had found a bottle of Greek champagne, dusty with age and tucked at the back of the supermarket shelf in the local village. He had taken it down and as he bent to put it into his shopping bag the bloody thing exploded, showering him and Pottsy with glass and causing considerable damage. The store manager and his family were distraught and pressed numerous bottles onto my friends in an effort to repair the damage. One was a second bottle of champagne. I looked at it and remarked, 'Never trust a bottle of champagne with a hot-pink rose on the label.' We opened it gingerly, drank the contents and all paid for it the next day with scorching hangovers.

Dr Potts was my friend: he could be maddeningly pedantic, he could be scathingly witty, but he was intelligent, knowledgeable on a whole range of things and with me always special and sympathetic to my troubles. I loved him: He's gone to God now, I miss him — we shared some wonderful times together.

At a stage when I wasn't seeing my lover and eventual husband, Ettore, because I'd discovered he was still conducting an affair with another woman, I went out with several men. One a wealthy man about town. He was Jewish and very droll, witty and very funny. He would cook me dinner — always the same, a T-bone steak with instant Deb potatoes and a bottle of good red wine. Then he'd take me to bed. We laughed a lot. One night there was a frightening crash from the other end of his apartment. Ettore had been following me, trying to get me back. I think we both thought, my God, he's broken in! The man gingerly got out of bed and went to investigate. The next thing, stark naked, he walked through the room carrying a broom and a dustbin and said wryly as he passed, 'Woman's work is never done.' I cracked up while he swept up a bottle of disinfectant knocked down and broken by a window blown shut in a sudden gust of wind. I see him today. We are no longer lovers but we are still friends and he still makes me laugh.

There have been others. I won't mention them because maybe it will disturb their current lives. And by now you're probably appalled anyway — or perhaps not.

Maggie T

&

Corporate
Wardrobes

I T WAS no secret that I had battled my weight problem for
years. Throughout my television career one of the most printed
headlines had been, 'Maggie loses five kilos', and you could bet
your bippy that would be closely followed by, 'Maggie puts on
five kilos'. My weight went up and down with monotonous
regularity as I tried every fad diet that came along. Eventually
they all failed and I watched with a heavy heart as my bathroom
scales inched back up to my pre-diet weight, and then the
whole bloody cycle would start again. I longed to be thin but I
also I loved my food, I loved my wine. The social structure of
my life revolved around a table, usually mine. I really enjoyed
cooking and entertaining. For me it was the best way to relax.

Anyone who has battled the bulge will understand the
despair one feels. There were times when I hated myself. If I had

one ability, it was to know how to dress to disguise my weight or at least highlight my good points: long legs, thin arms, good bust. I carried all my extra weight in my torso. My legs and arms never seemed to get any bigger. Naked I looked like a rissole on toothpicks! I was probably Australia's best-known 'Big Girl'. But I made damn sure I was also Australia's best-groomed Big Girl. It helped. Good grooming goes a long way for any woman regardless of her size. However, I was in the wrong business. Television is not kind; it adds kilos. I would like a dollar for every time a woman, surprised at seeing me 'in the flesh' would come up and say, 'But, Maggie, you're not that big.'

I would reply, 'Well, it's a clever dress.'

'No, no,' they would protest. 'You're just not that *big*.'

It was quite comforting but not comforting enough. I guess a lot of Australian women recognised my problem and likened it to their own. As a leading advertising guy said to me once, 'It's valuable because it makes you real.'

My weight was my despair, but because of it I was eventually presented with a fantastic business opportunity.

In the mid seventies, John Geary, my partner Jan's husband, who was a fashion agent at the time, suggested we trade on that 'Big Girl' reputation. So together with a Sydney-based manufacturer we launched a range called 'Maggie Tabberer for Big Girls'. I had a lot of fun designing my sort of clothes for the collection, although I'd never designed before. It was simply a case of collating shapes I knew worked for me. The label met with some success. But after two seasons I had a blue with the manufacturer, having discovered that he was whipping up some styles in fabric I hadn't approved. We decided all round to abandon the project.

Then in 1980 I had a phone call that was to change my career. Rob Palmer, founder of the famous Jag label, and as smart as a tack marketing and advertising man, had been consulting for a friend, Carl Dowd. Carl Dowd came from a family of rag traders. Both his father Maurice and his uncle Bernard had built considerable companies. In fact, in the 1960s I had worked for Bernard Dowd, who owned and ran Hickory underwear.

Bernard's Sydney-based advertising agency, W. B. Lawrence and Partners, suggested that because of my television profile I would be an effective selling presenter for Hickory. Eventually I wrote Hickory ads, laid out like my *Daily Mirror* column, and we even used the same name, 'Maggie Says', along with my head shot. These advertisements were reproduced on the boxes of all Hickory garments. I clearly remember those writing sessions. Barney Greer was account executive director and partner of the agency. He was a quiet, calm man, unusual in the advertising business. Hickory was 'his baby'. He would call me in for writing sessions and we would take over the big, dark wood-panelled boardroom. Barney would sit at one end of the long table puffing clouds of blue smoke from his smelly but much loved pipe. I would sit way down the other end with a stack of paper and a little portable typewriter. Barney would hold up a control brief or a bra and read out its design features. Something like this: 'It has adjustable straps. It's made from imported Swiss lace and French lycra. It's finished with a tiny pink rose. And comes in colours — pink, white and burgundy.' Puffing on his pipe the whole time. I'd stare at the thing, then go into high-speed, if inaccurate typing.

'Want a little luxury in your life at a price you can afford? Then Hickory's new deluxe bra is just the thing. For night, wear it in rich burgundy. The adjustable straps ensure perfect comfort. Blah, blah, blah.'

Then I'd sit back and read this blurb to Barney, who would reply, 'Maggie, you forgot the pink rose. Hickory loves the pink rose.'

'Jeez, Barney, damn the rose.' But then I'd add a bit about the rose.

We would have four-hour long sessions doing this, made light by the sight of this rather sedate gentleman in his conservative tweed jacket waving knickers and bras at me from the other end of the table! I had enormous respect for Barney. He was a good advertising man. He was also a gentleman. His two young 'hot shot' lieutenants, Max Fulcher and Rob Hatherley, went on to direct me when I filmed Hickory television commercials.

They invented the 'Hickory halo'. An all-white set was mounted with huge black and white posters of problem figure spots and the Hickory garment that would provide the solution. In one commercial I walked along with a large black pen, planting enormous crosses on the figure problems, such as a bulging hip or a bad bra line. Then on the girl wearing the Hickory garment I'd draw a big tick and a Hickory halo. It was an extremely successful campaign for all of us, and it lasted about five years.

Therefore, when Rob Palmer phoned to say Carl Dowd ('Of *the* Dowd family?' I asked) had a proposition to make, I listened with interest. Carl and his brother Michael produced a fashion line called the Clothing Company. It was a basic, reasonably priced classic line, but increasingly the retailers were asking Carl to produce larger sizes. This led him to talk to Rob and they commissioned some research. It revealed a market waiting for the taking. These were the facts: around thirty per cent of Australian women are a size fourteen. Another thirty per cent are above that. This meant a potential market of sixty per cent and a clear majority who had been sadly treated as a minority.

The research also discovered that fuller figure women resented what was offered for their fashion needs. They didn't want just 'fat fashion'. They wanted to wear exactly what their thinner sisters were into. If it were denim, why not denim? Bold stripes and bright, why not bold stripes and bright? At a retail level they felt they were treated like second-class citizens: 'Sorry, Madame, we never have your fitting.' What stock was carried in the fuller figure departments was relegated to menopause mauve florals with crossover bodices and gored skirts, or huge shapeless shifts and, worse, bullet-proof polyester pants. Fashion just didn't exist for these women.

Armed with this research, Carl came to see me. Obviously I knew exactly what the problems were in the market. If it hadn't been for the generosity of my designer friends in the industry, including Inge Fonagy of Simona, George Gross, Harry Who, Carla Zampatti, Lizzie Collins, Mark and Geoffrey, and Peter Weiss, who made for me, I would have been wearing the menopause mauve jobs long before they were my due. I could never buy off the rack. I clearly understood the frustrations these shoppers faced because I was one.

I saw that this was a unique marketing opportunity. Carl could have named his new collection 'Carl Dowd' or even 'Joe Bloggs', but Rob convinced him that my name and public profile would give the label a running start. So the label became 'Maggie T' and we became partners, eventually owning half share interests in the parent company, Maggie T Licensing.

Maggie T took almost a year to get onto the market, and it was launched in 1980. The Clothing Company was licensed to produce day, sports and evening wear, and we licensed other top manufacturers to handle hosiery, knitwear, coats and lingerie. Later there were sunglasses and leather goods, and while today there has been a rationale of licensing arrangements, the Maggie T woman can still be dressed and accessorised from top to toe.

Pam Darraugh, who worked for Carl as his promotions and advertising director, organised the launch. Pammie firmly believed, 'You only get one chance to launch so let's make it the best.'

Carl spared no expense. We took the penthouse suite at the Hilton Hotel, Sydney. Carl and Michael set up in one wing, Pam, me and our 'Big Girl' models, Alison Chapple and Marcia Macarthur, set up in another. Pammie had Maggie T signature fabric printed for the catwalk and tablecloths. The Hilton's butler, Dennis, became part of the team, answering the door, pouring drinks, handing out refreshments to buyers and the press.

We worked gruelling hours to make everything perfect but it was worth it. On launch day Pam and I pressed each garment to perfection before six am and by six o'clock that evening, Maggie T had written the biggest single order ever with the Myer group on a first range, just over one million dollars. Eight months later sales exceeded Carl's expectations by one hundred per cent, with a figure of seven million dollars. We were certainly up and running.

After our first heady week of showings in Sydney we came to the last buyers' parade. The long hours and the high excitement had taken its toll. I was at the microphone, taking the buyers through the collection. Finally the all-black evening wear came on, the girls stepping smoothly through their paces. When they turned as one to walk off, with their back to the audience, they gave me huge smiles. I almost fell off the rostrum. The devils had blackened their teeth. I didn't even try to contain my laughter. We were all exhausted but deliriously happy and that evening we let it rip.

At first we adopted a rather classic approach to styling, but later we broke some rules and our clients and retailers loved us for it. We were the first to introduce 'Big Girl' walk shorts, and they literally walked off the rack. Our signature stretch denim jeans were *streeetched* to the limit. At first we styled them with a prominent 'Maggie T' signature embossed in silver across the back pocket. However, after following a size twenty-four customer along an airport causeway one day and seeing my name reading more like 'MMMAAAAAGGGIIIIIEEE TTTT' across her derrière, I suggested our design team opt for something a little more subtle. When our saucy French knickers hit the market we thought maybe we had gone too far. They were sold out in days. I had a stack of letters from women thanking Maggie T for putting some glamour back into their lives, and even some from husbands thanking me for putting something else back into theirs.

Over the years Big Al, as we came to call Alison, and Marcia were the staunch Maggie T model girls. They were always professional and they were always fun. On many an occasion their humour lightened the load, particularly when we went on taxing overseas shoots to photograph our Maggie T brochures.

I found a great deal of satisfaction in the early days of building Maggie T. At times there were differences of opinion, which is normal. But generally we worked as one and it was exhilarating. Initially I was also the face of Maggie T. Pam did a fantastic publicity job persuading *Women's Weekly* to put me on the cover with a four-page story on the launch — not bad considering that was the week Lady Diana got engaged to her prince. There were also television interviews, press interviews, radio interviews — what is called saturation coverage.

Pam and I worked on the brochures together. I found they embraced all my experience as a fashion director, collating the clothes and accessories; and as art director, selecting locations and settings with our photographer, Greg Barrett. I'd then model the collection for photography and finally I'd go back to my room at night and bash out the copy for the brochure with Pammie talking me through the selling points. Finally, dog-tired, she and I would press the garments needed for the next day's shoot.

We took off to exotic locations for the brochure shoots, including Club Med, Moorea, Tahiti and Cherating, Malaysia.

A fringe benefit was the opportunity to see my gorgeous Brooke who was then working with Club Med in Moorea. Our team consisted of Pam, Greg Barrett, Big Al, Rickie Quesada as makeup stylist, and me. Those shoots were hard work: seventy or eighty shots in just six days, often in searing heat. In Malaysia I got up at four am, and Greg would do my shots at first light, because I hated the humidity, my makeup would run and my hair would be saturated. This meant long days but it was the only way. Pammie says I was the worst to be photographed. I hated it. I bitched and blued and carried on, but as soon as my shots were in the bag and I could go back to being a director, I was happy. Then I'd pull on an old T-shirt or a pareu and enjoy the rest of the shoot. While we worked hard we always found time to play and have a laugh. They were the happiest of times, with a good team of good mates who got the job done and did it bloody well.

In 1985 I received the Sir Charles McGrath Marketing Award for the marketing of Maggie T. I was the first fashion identity to win the award and the first woman. While my name was on the medal it really belonged to the team: to Carl and Michael, Pammie, Greg, Rickie, Big Al, Marcia, the design team and all the others who contributed so much in those first exciting days of Maggie T. I wouldn't have missed them for the world.

Today Carl and I still have our half shares in Maggie T Licensing. Carl has taken another partner into the Maggie T Corporation. They run some twenty-six stores around Australia and New Zealand. The nature of the business may have undergone some changes but the spirit is still the same, proving 'big' can be beautiful and fashionable.

Over the years, like all partners, Carl and I have had our differences. We were actually born one day apart so both being strong-willed Sagittarians probably didn't help. But now we are older and wiser, our collective egos having been dented enough times to make us finally see the light. We are friends.

IN APRIL 1983 I was back in my home town of Adelaide for a Sudden Infant Death Syndrome fundraiser, staying at the Hilton, when the receptionist rang to tell me that a Susan Mitchell was on the line. Susan Mitchell. I didn't know a Susan Mitchell, but I took the call thinking it was probably someone from the SIDS committee and a voice said, 'Maggie, you don't know me but …'

Damn, I thought. How many times have I heard that line?

'Yes,' I replied with caution.

Susan went on to explain that she was writing a book celebrating Australian women. She had in fact already interviewed a well-known designer to represent the fashion field. But the designer had since decided she didn't want to go public on what she had told Susan.

'So I'm the second choice,' I challenged.

'Well, yes,' said Susan.

But she had got me, I thought such honesty was commendable. After all, she didn't have to tell me about the previous interview. Susan lived in Adelaide, I in Sydney, so we arranged to meet halfway in Melbourne when I would be there the following week to present an award at the 'Logies'.

Susan rang on the dot of nine-thirty in the morning — our appointed time. She had watched the interminable 'Logies' on television the night before, and she couldn't believe that I would be up and ready for the interview. I told her I was a morning person and, yes, I was ready. Ten minutes later she arrived wearing a Maggie T outfit (not lost on me), and with her friend Mary Beasley we had coffee while we sized each other up. My daughter Amanda poked her head into the room and said something cheeky. We all laughed and the ice was broken.

Over the next couple of hours Susan interviewed me. What I didn't know at the time was that Mary Beasley had been a member of the Keswick and Wayville Tennis Club all those years before when my first husband Charles Tabberer played there. Because of the club's stuffy rules I was not allowed into the clubhouse until Charles and I were married. Mary had cautioned Susan about me, it seems she and her young friends had decided I was 'stuck up' because I never talked to them. At the time I was seventeen, dead scared, came from the wrong side of the tracks and was banned from going into the clubhouse. I wasn't stuck up, I was petrified.

While I sat there about to tell the story of my life to a woman I'd known for fifteen minutes, Mary was sitting there thinking, so this is 'Miss Stuck Up' thirty years on. Susan was probably wondering if I was going to tell her the truth.

Susan has penetrating hazel eyes, a vibrant, ready laugh, a great sense of the ridiculous, and she doesn't interview, she interrogates. She also has a unique ability to become your best friend in a very short time, and I found to my surprise I was spilling the beans on the real me. When, in the course of the interview, I told her about my days at the bloody Keswick and Wayville Tennis Club Mary's eyebrows shot up in surprise. They stopped, looked at each other, burst into gales of laughter, then told me about 'Miss Stuck Up'. Well, we rocked, and a friendship was founded between the three of us that remains today.

Susan's book, *Tall Poppies*, was published in May 1984. At the time I was sitting in as host of 'The Mike Walsh Show'. We invited Susan on to talk about her book. She says when I held it high and said, 'Buy this book, it's a terrific read with some great inspirational stories about women who've achieved,' her publishers said, 'Press reprint.' *Tall Poppies* remained on the bestseller list for months, and Susie has since gone on to write seven more bestselling books. For me she has been inspirational — she has also nagged, pushed, bullied and cajoled this book out of me. I've lost count of the times I said, 'I can't do this,' and she firmly said, 'Yes, you can. Now get off your bum, Maggie May, and get on with it.' She showed me how to get started, how to be courageous and tell the truth. I think the greatest moment I've known since I began to write about my life was when Susie read my first hesitant chapters, looked straight into my eyes and said with a big grin, 'You've found your voice.'

She is my friend, I now call her Susie, and Mary Beasley from the Keswick and Wayville Tennis Club and I are now the best of mates.

ONE DAY in 1986 my secretary announced that Will Bailey, the Group Managing Director of the ANZ Bank, was on the phone. Mr Bailey wished to commission a new corporate wardrobe for the ANZ staff of 23,000. The bank had drawn up a short list of six designers and I was one. Would I care to compete for the commission? It took a flat three seconds to say, Yes please. I thought it over for a while and came to the realisation that a project of that size would require enormous production and management skills.

As I was already working with Carl Dowd on the Maggie T range, it made sense to team up with his clothing company. I called Carl and we arranged a meeting with our team. Some years earlier at MTA I had worked for a company called Uniform Specialist. They made off the peg uniforms and wanted to expand their business. Jan Geary and I had known that in order to expand, they had to improve their collection. We collated some new designs, chose exciting new colours. I filmed a promotional video around the city, shooting the dos and don'ts of a working wardrobe. Let me tell you, there were a lot more don'ts than dos out there. In general, uniforms at that time were usually dreadful bright turquoise, button-through jobs with too-short skirts, usually topped with a tired too-long cardigan and teamed with horrible cork-sole shoes. It was not a good look. The rejuvenated Uniform Specialist range was a terrific success. However, it was still off the peg, and therefore not exclusive to any one company.

The ANZ wardrobe needed an exclusive and individual look that would spell out what the ANZ Bank was about. Security, reliability, professionalism, strength and service. I scribbled these thoughts on the back of my boarding pass as I winged my way down to see Carl. I had a strong image in my mind but I realised that as well as a design profile, a corporate wardrobe needs another essential component: performance. To design for those 23,000 staff we would have to consider all their different shapes, sizes and ages. Also, the range would need to comprise interchangeable, versatile pieces that could be worn in numerous ways to meet the individual's needs, while still retaining a strong ANZ image.

Carl and Kay Gorski, his fabric buyer, got busy researching high-performance fabrics. Pam Darraugh and I concentrated on the presentation format, and with Kathy Flambo, head of the design team, I put together the range. I had always admired airline captains' uniforms. The navy with gold sleeve stripes, epaulettes and service pips to me represented a quiet, classy authority. This became the inspiration for the design. As a base cloth we chose a dark navy-blue, hard-wearing wool blend, adding epaulettes and gold buttons to the jackets. I insisted we incorporate the ANZ coat of arms, so we had it embroidered on jacket pockets. We wove the ANZ logo into a print for softer dressing and blouses, and incorporated it onto men's ties, shirt pockets, belt buckles and knitwear. It came together beautifully.

We worked extremely long hours but the team spirit never flagged and it was incredibly exciting. The only other bank that had gone 'big' with a new corporate wardrobe image was Westpac, dressed by my friend Peter Weiss. I have to acknowledge that he was supportive and generous with his experience and advice.

As the presentation day drew near we all suffered nerves, but as Carl, Pam and the gang reminded me over and over again, 'It's all in the presentation, Maggie.' I found I was losing a lot of sleep. The decisive meeting with Will Bailey and his senior executives was scheduled to take place at ANZ Head Office in Collins Street, Melbourne. As we walked from the carpark I recall thinking, I really want to win this account, but if we don't at least we can say we gave it our best shot. I said so to the team as we stepped into the elevator. They looked at me and said as one, 'Yes, Maggie, but it's all in the presentation.'

'You buggers,' I fired back and my tummy turned. I had written my opening address based on the need for an authoritative, confident look and likened it to my airline captain.

'When I step onto a jumbo jet and put my life in the hands of the captain I need to feel assured, I don't want to see him wearing a tired old pair of jeans and a sloppy T-shirt. I want to see him dressed in his sharp blue uniform with his service pips and gold sleeve stripes. It's authoritative, it instils confidence. ANZ customers, when they step into your bank, are looking for confidence too. They should feel assured their money is safe and they are dealing with the best professionals around.' I went on to stress one of my firmest beliefs: 'If you look good you feel good.' Staff 'feeling good' are obviously going to work more enthusiastically and efficiently.

Having opted for a direct sales format, we presented detailed charts showing how the manufacturing, delivery and promotional aspects would operate. We explained that each staff member would receive a personalised catalogue and order form. We planned a video showing the collection, along with details on 'How to measure', and the many options on how to wear the coordinated range. Boasting 'A different look a day with six easy pieces', we guaranteed a garment size exchange and a 'help line' for those staff who needed advice. Pam then presented the packaging and promotional plan. Carl talked them through the nuts and bolts of the deal. Kathy and Kay explained fabric samples and sketch design details. Will Bailey thanked us, but bankers never give anything away. I knew the presentation had gone well but the question was, had it gone well enough?

Suddenly we were ejected into the bright sunlight of Collins Street. Carl insisted on taking us all for lunch where we rehashed the whole meeting in minute detail and agonised over our chances. I can't recall how many days we held our breath. It was probably only a few but it felt an eternity. Then I received a call. We had won! A formal letter of acceptance followed. We were in the corporate wardrobe business. Hoo-bloody-ray. Winning heralded a period of arduous work hours and impossible deadlines, but we did it. And a few months later we presented to the media the new ANZ corporate wardrobe.

Will Bailey generously allowed us to have the launch in the executive reception area on the top floor of ANZ, Collins Street. A magnificent large room with spectacular views over Melbourne. We planned the presentation down to the last detail. We built an all-white catwalk and had twenty young models show the range live, as well as showing the video, skilfully produced by my mate Peter Wynne. We had shot the video in the oldest ANZ bank in Melbourne: a cathedral-like building, brimming with banking tradition. We also included film footage of Greg Barrett shooting the models for the all-important brochure. We finished by illustrating how these young Australians would look in their corporate wardrobe, out and about on the streets of Melbourne. We were all very proud of that video. Still are.

The launch gained extensive press coverage right around Australia and made the national news of two networks. Our ANZ project won numerous marketing awards, including: Best Australian Corporate Video; a gold award for Direct Mail Media — Australian Direct Marketing Awards; Aussies at work — Australian Lifestyle Fashion Awards; and a gold award, Order Generation Catalogue — Australian Direct Marketing Awards. It was very, very satisfying and in 1992 we did it all again for the giant AMP Corporation. Carl went on to build a hugely successful business in corporate wardrobes with his new company Dowd Corporation. Although he sold his interest a couple of years ago to John Laidlaw, the renowned owner of Yakka, I'm still involved with the Dowd Corporation and proudly dressing ANZ and AMP.

Working with the Best

M Y CAREER has been curious in one respect, much of my early success was based on the way I looked. However, while that opens doors, I had to contribute more if I wanted to keep a job and move onward and upward. As my career path changed from modelling to television, to fashion journalism, promotion and publicity and design, I quickly recognised the value of working with the best — the best professionals in the business. The people who make your show, your production, your promotion or business look good. The people who make the difference with their exceptional talent. Let me introduce you to some of them.

Early in my fashion promotion days, I persuaded one of my accounts, Lurex, to stage a show for the fashion trade. We needed more Australian designers and manufacturers to use Lurex fabrics, so I figured a fashion show was the way to go. A glitzy cocktail party with attractive displays of Lurex fabrics was planned and I knew who I wanted to work on them with me. My friend Hazel Craig was a diminutive girl with a huge talent, who for several years had styled the window displays of Sportsgirl stores. Under Hazel's guidance Sportsgirl boasted the best windows in Australian fashion. I always swung by one of their stores on the day they changed the windows to 'see what Hazel's done'. She was a legend, so I took my Lurex idea to her. Making a fabric display look good is no easy task, Hazel did it brilliantly. After hours of setting up the show, she had to be dragged away from 'just fixing another swoosh', as she called them, even though to my eye it all looked perfect.

When I went to Melbourne I often stayed with Hazel and her husband, the Italian photographer Bruno Benini, in their big rambling terrace house in Carlton. There was always something happening in their home for Hazel's displays. Once I walked in to find eight six-foot tall cardboard giraffes in the living room. Another time everything in the house was covered in gold glitter, Hazel was preparing the Christmas show. She had the ability to make something splendid out of nothing. She could work within even the most limited budget and still perform magic; I admired her talent immensely.

In my early television days in Sydney I met a young hairdresser called Xenon. A young Tom Jones look-alike, he was tall, long-legged and lanky, with remarkable black golliwog curls. He was a junior with Alexandre in Double Bay but went on to have his own salon in Rose Bay and then earnt a considerable reputation working in America. When we met it was the era of wigs and hairpieces. His motto, it seemed, was 'Big, bigger, better, best'. He would back-comb my limited locks to hell then plant one, two, my God maybe three hairpieces onto my scalp. Fabulous. There were days when I wore a bigger mane than the Metro-Goldwyn-Mayer lion. Xenon was responsible for the exaggerated and incredible hairstyles I wore when David Franklin photographed me for the opening credits of the 'Maggie' show.

Inevitably, as for all women of that era, so much back-combing and pinning had an effect. My baby fine hair was damaged by the rigours of time. But I recall Xenon with great fondness. He was a true artist, although at times he tortured me.

Later, after I'd let my hair grow quite long, I was in Melbourne when my friend Janice Wakely, a model turned photographer, suggested Bob Leopold cut my hair. 'Come on, Maggie. Go for a radical change,' she said. 'I'll take the snaps.' The result was a sharp asymmetrical cut, brilliantly executed. And Janice's shots found their way into a double-page spread in the Sydney *Daily Mirror*.

In the following years my hair went up, out, in and down again and again until a young man at the Edward Beale Salon, two doors along from my publicity agency in Double Bay, convinced me to go 'short' again. His name was Max Pinnell, and he created the look I've worn for the past twenty-five years. Our friendship grew and I had the pleasure of working with Max for several years before he took off for the big time in New York, where he now has a golden list of famous clients. He still comes home each Christmas just to terrorise us. Max was one of the funniest characters in the business. He worked with me filming fashion awards, staging parades and on photographic shoots. He has a wicked wit and a tongue to match. If teamed with his good friend and mine, makeup stylist Rickie Quesada, you were at risk. They were outrageous together and any occasion involving both was bound to be hilarious and at times totally out of control.

Cuban-born Rickie arrived at my agency clutching his portfolio. He had a heavy cold, a red nose and was miserable. But I was so bowled over by the photographs of his work and reacted with such enthusiasm that he was soon wearing a big grin.

We were mates from the start. Rickie was really more than a makeup stylist. His exquisite taste guaranteed I wore the right look for the right shot. He always had a worthwhile opinion when shooting my fashion spreads, and I was always willing to heed his advice. He has an 'eye' as they say in the business. Rickie, along with his partner, Ray Freeman, became my close friends. Ultimately we spent long lunches and memorable dinners at their house, my house and on my boat. We travelled together, laughed together and from time to time they helped dry my tears and nudge me back into some semblance of shape.

When Rickie returned to America for a time I started to work with Richard Sharah. Richard is a huge man. He should be an artist, he paints the most superb faces, his skills honed on the competitive American market. Here he worked with me doing my makeup for two series of the 'Home Show', numerous television commercials and parades, along with my fashion pages in *The Women's Weekly*. He called me 'Mum', which I loathed. But I'm still admiring of his great talent. I hope he remembers me with the same fondness I recall when I think of him.

John Adams was brilliant as a parade hairdresser. He never caused a problem backstage, even though at times we had him sandwiched into impossible places, then gave him less than an hour to dress twenty models' heads. John and his first stylist, Michael Comino, would just get cracking and always did a splendid job. It was through John that I met Helen Cornish-Bayer. My friend Helepops, as I affectionately call her, has been my makeup stylist and hairdresser for several years now. We've flown a lot of missions together and I think she's put my 'special occasion' face on more times than either of us would care to count. Faces for television commercials, the 'Home Show', TV series, photography for various clients, road shows for the same, parades and big deal functions. I don't know what I would have done without her.

She's always calm, reliable and professional, and she can cut hair brilliantly, even fine wimpy hair like mine.

I've talked about Alan Nye, the photographer. It was after our inevitable split that I looked around for another regular photographer, someone I could rely on, someone I could build a good working relationship with. The work was pouring out of Maggie Tabberer Associates and I would be spending two or more days a week in the studio with them; I needed a professional without dramas. I found David Franklin. David was a quietly spoken Jewish man. His Sydney studio was the antithesis of Alan Nye's Paddington chaos. In David's studio everything had a place and everything was in place, the dressing room was stocked with tissues, mineral water, good mirrors and good lighting, and it was clean. My God, you could eat off the floor of David's studio. He had an awesome amount of equipment and it was cared for with precision. His shots were beautifully lit; he worked calmly and quietly; he hated being rushed. For David nothing short of perfection was acceptable. A few years later, his life was cut short — far too short.

I have to mention Greg Barrett. I met Greg way back in the early seventies. He was a young model working around Sydney and I bumped into him a few times at Alan Nye's studio. He took off overseas and when he returned in 1976 he came to see me with his portfolio. Greg had become a photographer. He recalled how I looked at his book and said, 'I think we will be working together, darling.' He says he then went home and didn't sleep for two weeks until I called to make a booking. Then he claims he didn't sleep at all until the day of the shoot. He also says he will never forget when on the first shoot he was firing off a million frames, he felt my hand on his shoulder and I said firmly, 'I think you've got it, darling.' He now reckons he's 'One-roll' Barrett. That's not strictly true but it sounds good. In reality Greg will keep shooting until he's got the right shot.

He's never let me down. He's taken wonderful fashion shots for my pages over the years, for my clients at the agency and covered all my big fashion shows. He's photographed me a zillion times and made me look good on days when I know I sure as hell didn't. And even better on days when I knew I was looking OK. When a girlfriend saw some head shots Greg had taken of me she remarked, 'He should be bottled, he's so damn good.' She was right. I was proud to be his first Australian client all those years ago. Since then we've taken fashion shots, high above Hong Kong, on the smelly Klongs in Bangkok, the white beaches of Tahiti. We've worked in luxury hotels and grubby back lanes. We've been boiled on beaches, frozen in high hills, and risked life and limb on bad flights and worse drives. All in the name of getting *the* shot. I salute him and I love him.

Roger Foley, who I've written about elsewhere in this book, has to have a mention. Roger's laid-back, sometimes laconic nature and pace gave me near heart attacks more times than I care to remember. But he always came through. He was my light and sound man for all the big MTA fashion shows. He could turn a stark white catwalk into a myriad of moods — he would surround the room with awesome sound. With his signature curly black hair, 'white tie' printed T-shirt, he always presented himself to me as I came off stage, eager to know whether I was pleased with the production. I always was — Foley is unique.

In my years of staging the *Daily Mirror*/Grace Bros fashion spectaculars, I came to know John Cooper, the Grace Bros group promotional director. John was another professional to be admired, he 'saw' the decor and staging from the moment we looked at the clothes. When we were in Bangkok he dragged me all over town buying props and shipping containers of goodies back to Australia, even before the collection was ready. His innate sense of style was not all front of house gloss. He turned impossibly small spaces in the stores into workable areas for the parades. He was always aware of the backstage realities, we had generous space for accessories, and dressing rooms for each girl and her dresser. This made for smooth shows, as smooth as John. He never lost his cool. He can send me up brilliantly, does a marvellous take-off of me on the microphone compering a fashion show, and I adore him.

From day one of the 'Home Show' series, Ian Marsden was my cameraman. He fought off bad weather, agitated directors and impatient guests to always make me look good. Mind you, he shot houses, furniture, objects, interiors and all manner of other things with the same professional passion, but mainly he really cared for me. When a girl's in her fifties shooting a tele-vision series she needs all the help she can get. Ian gave it in unlimited quantities, I'm a fan.

Peter Wynne cared for me with the same passion. He produced the award-winning *Australian Women's Weekly* Australian Fashion Awards and shot my ANZ corporate wardrobe launch video. He put equal effort into both productions. No one can cut film like Wynne. I used to marvel at how he could take some raw footage, some wonderful music, and blend them together to create an inspired piece of film. He's still at it and doing it better than anyone in the business. And above all, he still has that wonderful sense of humour and he's still laughing.

Pammie Darraugh I worked with on both the development of Maggie T and the ANZ corporate wardrobe. She had an enthu-siasm for every project, which bowled me over. Pammie saw the big marketing picture, she also saw beyond the pretty shots and the perfect video. She would sit at my elbow and point out the finer details that should be emphasised. The awards which both Maggie T and the ANZ corporate wardrobe gathered for me really should have her name on them.

I first met the designer Inge Fonagy way back in the seventies. We became friends, and our families became friends. Inge 'I'm just a dressmaker, darling' Fonagy is one of the most endearing characters in the fashion industry. Our relationship started out as designer and fashion editor. Eventually though, Inge started to make one-off garments for me whenever there was something important, such as the David Jones Fashion Awards or a special television show. Inge never compromised. She always insisted I go in for lengthy fittings and every aspect of the garment had to be perfect. She'd be frantic with her collection or about to take off on a fabric buying trip to Europe, but she always found time for me. Her stamina and dedication are inspiring.

George Gross and Harry Who have also been great professionals. Their labels today are as high class and important on the Australian fashion market as they were twenty-five years back. Such longevity has to be acknowledged. It takes true talent and strength to stay on top for so long. They have also made me special garments, for special occasions: the dress of char-grey paillettes for *The Australian Women's Weekly* Australian Fashion Awards has to go down as the all-time winner. They are friends I value. We've had some very funny times together and, no Harry, I won't spill the beans about Tahiti!

There is also my friend Peter Weiss. As I've remarked elsewhere in this book, Peter started out as my most difficult client and became one of my closest friends. He demands excellence, not just of others but, more importantly, of himself. Together we put on some of the most memorable fashion shows. I learnt an enormous amount from him, namely, that it is all the little details that make a great show, that make a great night. We've cried on each other's shoulders when our personal lives were blitzed and we've both pulled through. I value his friendship enormously and I admire his tenacity and skills.

Jan Geary and I were partners for some twenty years at MTA. I was the creative side of the agency but no matter how brilliant the promotion, the parade, the photography, or the concept, it doesn't work if it's not backed up. Jan was that back-up. She managed the agency, the clients, the staff and probably *me* with stunning efficiency. We were a great team. Working together was an experience I wouldn't have missed for the world.

We always had fun at MTA. My daughter Amanda and Rhonda Pemberton became firm friends while working there and ring-leaders in mirth. For instance, I'd had my portrait painted some years before; it didn't fit in the house so I hung it in our large, open-plan office where five of us worked together. Giving 'The Boss' a new head became a regular game, cutting large heads from newspaper posters or magazines. I'd arrive to find I was Winston Churchill with a big fat cigar, Maggie Thatcher with her cast-iron hair, or Mick Jagger in large-lipped horror. It was cause for a lot of hilarity.

I had some remarkable girls pass through MTA. Most went on to bigger and better careers; a few opted for babies and marriage. And in their time they all worked hard — Sue, Margie, Rhonda, Amanda, Inge, Shelley, Sam, Penny and others. I'm sure they'd tell you they learnt a lot at MTA, and I know they'd tell you we had a lot of laughs along the way. I remember them all with great affection.

Finally, my agent of almost thirty years, Harry M. Miller. Harry steered me through a maze of lucrative contracts, listening to my instincts when I thought it wasn't my bag and always believing in me and my judgment. Even when it meant the loss of a healthy commission. He's tough but fair. He taught me that any deal has to work for both parties to work well.

To all those mentioned here I say, thank you. Thank you for your time, your talent, your friendships and your professionalism. You're the best.

Joining the Women's Weekly

I HAD been writing for the *Daily Mirror* for sixteen years when one day I received an invitation to fly to Rupert Murdoch's sheep property, Boonook, in country New South Wales for a luncheon to be held in conjunction with the Australian Wool Board. Harry Miller and Peter Weiss were both going and my daughter Amanda agreed to join me. We flew into the property on a hot dusty morning. The airstrip was studded with private jets and marquees were set up around the beautiful gardens. A fashion parade of wool garments was held, then there was time to wander around the pens and admire the prize rams. All before lunch.

As I walked with Peter and Amanda along the path to the lunch marquee we bumped into Kerry Packer. I knew Kerry well enough to say hello, he had always been friendly to me. Nevertheless, he is a big man, intimidating in his size, stature and reputation. This day he was charming and we chatted away.

During our conversation we were interrupted four times by women coming up to me to say such complimentary things as, 'I have always admired you,' and 'I am a great fan of yours.' I noticed Packer's interest in this, but nothing was discussed until later at lunch when he said quietly, 'Maggie, call me in the office on Monday. I want to discuss something with you.'

I duly called and was summoned to his office at Consolidated Press. Kerry offered me the Fashion Editor's job on *The Australian Women's Weekly*. I was more than flattered. I knew the benefits of writing for a national magazine with the staggering circulation the *Weekly* enjoyed. Also, the advantage of colour for my fashion pages could not be denied. It was a great opportunity. When Kerry said that we should discuss money, I replied, 'Let's leave that to Harry to sort out.' Harry Miller had been my agent for a number of years and I never did a deal without him.

'No,' said Mr Packer. 'I won't negotiate with Miller.' I went on to explain that Harry was my manager and any dealings would have to go through him. I held out and Packer held out. Finally he called in Trevor Kennedy, Editor-in-Chief of Consolidated Press, and said, 'You sort it out.'

Eventually Harry negotiated a lucrative deal for me. I was thrilled to be going to the *Weekly* and they were thrilled to have landed me. It was to be a happy union for a number of years.

The hardest part was telling Ken Cowley, Chief Executive of News Limited, that I was leaving the *Mirror*. Ken is one of the nicest men I have had the pleasure of working with. He said he was sad to see me go but he clearly understood the opportunity I had with the *Weekly*. He called in his top columnist, Ron Saw, and we had a drink. Ron then wrote a 'Goodbye Maggie' piece that I will treasure forever. It was run on page three of the *Daily Mirror* and it covered almost the whole page, generously singing my praises and wishing me well. It was a gracious and charming end to sixteen happy years. And so in 1981 I became the new Fashion Editor of *The Australian Women's Weekly*.

When I first joined the *Weekly* it was just that — a weekly magazine. Initially my columns were just two pages, although frequently I shot an additional two pages of what was called an advertorial — an accepted practice in those days where paid ads were made to look like editorials, in this case like my 'Maggie' pages. Later when the *Weekly* went monthly, my pages increased to eight per issue. With twelve issues to plan over a year I always endeavoured to cover different fashion styles, figure types and varying budgets. For the most, from day one, I worked with my favourite photographer Greg Barrett. Greg and I had established a creative compatibility since I'd started working with him at MTA. Occasionally I'd used other photographers if he wasn't available, but generally he was around and I liked that.

Briefly my job involved viewing collections, selecting garments and accessories, finding the right models and choosing suitable locations, ably assisted in the fifteen years I was at the *Weekly* by five different girls — Alyson, Kym, Sarah, or Sas as I called her, Emma and Kate. They were all fantastic. I hope they know how much I valued them.

I always directed my own fashion shoots. I was told that a former fashion editor merely sent the clothes to the studio and left the poor photographer to cope. But I had a clear idea of how I wanted the pages to look and that involved overseeing all the details. I also have a very demanding eye; I'd tug hems, adjust sleeves, worry about a hat or shoes and swap jewellery around until it worked. Greg shot polaroids so I could 'see' the layout evolve as I'd planned it. I would take these polaroids back to the office and write my copy while my assistants would gather price and stockists' details from the various manufacturers and designers. Finally I'd work with the layout artists. Usually they were cooperative and it was a team effort, but in later years there was one who drove me bonkers. She would agree to all I suggested then go off and do as she wished. My pages for a time bore embarrassingly garish typefaces and electric coloured borders and headlines and I hated it, I *hated* it. But for the most it was a smooth operation.

Only a few months after I'd joined the *Weekly*, MTA was again approached to stage the Australian Fashion Awards. Jan and I decided we were strong enough to return to the fray. Also because of my new association with Kerry Packer, his *Australian Women's Weekly* and his Channel Nine, I saw a new opportunity for the business I loved to stage the biggest Fashion Awards ever. The *Weekly* would produce a fashion issue that would appeal to both readers and advertisers, and Channel Nine would have a spectacular fashion show. So it became '*The Australian Women's Weekly* Australian Fashion Awards', and from it the fashion industry would gain huge exposure.

Kerry probably indulged me, he didn't really believe fashion worked on television, and said so. When I assured him it wasn't going to be any simple old fashion show, he handed me on to Sam Chisholm, the Director of the Nine Network. Sam can be one tough cookie but we got on and he gave the project his fullest support. He appointed Peter Wynne, a dynamo young producer, to work on the awards. I grew to love and admire Pete. He has enormous talent. He's also a bloody nice guy. I never saw him lose his good humour. Later Peter Faiman was appointed director of the show. Eventually this production proved to be the most exciting show of my career, and I know Pete Wynne feels the same way.

Jan and our assistant Rhonda Pemberton took on the mammoth task of 'operations' centre. Their initial task after the FIA had completed its judging procedure was to draw up a schedule for Amanda and me to see the ranges. My daughter Amanda had come back from spending a few years in Europe and was working with us at MTA. Our job from there was twofold. I would put together the *Weekly* Fashion Awards special issue, selecting garments for photography, and we would also set aside garments to be filmed for the television show.

The *Weekly* shoot took two weeks, day-in day-out. We shot seventy-one pages of fashion, from sportswear to kidswear, city clothes and evening wear, young designers and fantasy. The talented photographer Greg Barrett shot the pages superbly. It was a challenging schedule but the results were immensely satisfying. The *Weekly* advertised it as 'The Greatest Issue Ever'.

In the meantime we held long meetings with Pete Wynne and Channel Nine. We settled on the Sydney Town Hall as the venue. It would become a logistical nightmare for caterers, not to mention the question of where we would put the network's musical director Geoff Harvey and the Channel Nine orchestra. Once the enormous stage was designed all was resolved. Channel Nine set designer Geoff Howden produced the most beautiful 'sail' concept inspired by the Sydney Opera House, with a vast triangular cat-walk stage. We also decided the format would involve footage of some of the nominated fashions filmed at various locations around Australia, others would be presented live in the Town Hall. One of the greatest difficulties with a production like this is not to sacrifice the live audience over the TV viewers. Pete solved this dilemma by planning to install giant monitors around the Town Hall. This way the guests could see the film clips and the television viewers had the benefit of the entire production, with the recorded inserts linked to the live presentation.

With our locations locked in, models booked, airline tickets at hand, wardrobe vans, garments, accessories, makeup and hair stylists, Pete, his camera crew, Amanda and I hit the road. We shot swimwear off Heron Island in Queensland. We had a hard time convincing Ben Crop, our underwater photographer, that models are not professional divers and he'd better get his shots in two or three takes, or we would be fresh out of live models. Our main cameraman, John Bowring, who shot the entire production, got some memorable footage at dawn on the beach at Heron Island, thanks to the perfect weather and his not inconsiderable talent.

A few days later we filmed menswear at the Twelve Apostles on the Victorian south coast. After climbing around the cliffs, dressing models in the open and trying to keep the garments looking good in a force ten wind, we fell ravenous into a funny little country motel. It was all of eight o'clock when we hit the dining room, but that's late by local standards. The cook, a burly big bloke, lumbered out from the kitchen. I'd never seen him before in my life but he greeted me with, 'G'day Maggie.'

'Hi. What's special for dinner?' I asked.

'I'll tell youse what you can have,' he said. 'Yer can have steak … steak … or steak!'

'Oh, OK. So how would I have that cooked?' I asked.

'You'll have it cooked my way,' he replied.

Sometimes you just have to go with the flow.

We shot equestrian wear at dawn on Melbourne streets. A wonderful model, who was cast because she could ride, was filmed on a magnificent horse, clip-clopping through the deserted CBD; it was quite haunting. In Canberra we took the models to the top of the Telecom tower, a dramatic pinnacle that overlooks the city. Jackets and capes blew in the breeze. Visually it was to be one of my favourite sections. It was also the last day of the shoot. John Bowring had to catch a plane to the Northern Territory where he was going to film an important job early the next day. But first he wanted to grab a low-tracking shot of two models striding towards the camera with the tower reaching up into a blue sky behind them. He was lying on his tummy on a trolley clutching his camera, pulled by two of the crew. One take, two takes.

'John, you're going to miss the plane.'

'No. One more.' Then, 'Just one more.'

'John, you're seriously going to miss the plane.' Again and again we begged him to go, but until Bowring got the perfect take at the perfect pace he wasn't about to leave.

John was a very quiet man with a dry sense of humour. He called Pete Wynne 'Lucky Pierre', and he wasn't averse to a couple of Bundies and Coke at the end of the day.

During the weeks of preparation and filming, Pete would fly to Sydney and we would hold meetings at my house to get away from the madness of the office. One of the most complex challenges for me was with the set. It was spectacular, but a triangular stage is completely different from a traditional catwalk, and I'd only ever choreographed catwalk shows. Added to that, it was to step down in three different levels. I spent a long afternoon with Geoff Howden and Pete walking out and counting my planned routines, and explaining why they would have to move the steps. It seemed a bit manic at the time but we were dealing with models, not professional dancers. The step down or up *had* to finish on a count of eight. They agreed to make the necessary changes and it was worth the effort. Not one model put a foot wrong.

Thanks to all this hard work, I was losing kilos by the minute. George Gross was designing my dress, a long column of char-grey paillettes with a skirt split to almost my altogether! I think he took it in three times.

I also worked closely with Geoff Harvey. I'd sit in his office at Nine and talk him through the clothes and the musical style needed. 'This is kidswear. We are going to have Humphrey Bear on stage. It needs cute, ba bompity bom music, Geoff.' And he would play it right onto the keyboard for me to hear. Having settled on the sound, Geoff would record it with the orchestra so that I had a tape to work with when I was choreographing the steps at home.

Finally all was in place. Show day dawned, 26 March 1982. It didn't escape anyone on the team that we were going out live — no chance to correct a mistake or cut it out. Pete would yell, 'Live, baby. Live!' And my tummy would turn. But throughout the day I was so busy taking the models through rehearsal I didn't have time to get nervous. That is, until I went backstage to dress and makeup, having done the rounds and wished my team, 'Chukkas, kids.' Minutes before the show went to air we lost contact with the outside broadcast van. Peter Faiman calmly worked his way through the problem, solved it and, *Bingo!* We were on air. I stood at the centre entrance backstage and suddenly I realised the enormity of it all, my stomach almost hit the floor. I heard the voice-over announce: 'And now, live from the Sydney Town Hall, the Nine Network is proud to present *The Australian Women's Weekly* Australian Fashion Awards. Ladies and Gentlemen, Miss Maggie Tabberer.' And all I could think was, 'Oh Jeez, I need to have a pee!' Too late.

As I walked on stage there was a roar from the audience. It was the warmest reception I've ever had. After that I was on automatic pilot. We had imported some 'name' presenters — the colourful British designer, Zandra Rhodes, with her hot-pink hair and distinctive dot-dash eyebrows; European beauty, Princess Ira Von Furstenberg; and designers David and Elizabeth Emmanual, the cherubic couple responsible for Lady Diana's wedding dress.

The ninety-minute presentation seemed to evaporate. There were only two hitches. One group of five models moved on stage too early. But like real troupers, realising their error they just froze and waited for the next group to come on and parade in the right order. This was important because camera shots had been plotted at specific points. No one picked it except those involved in the production. In another section, which had been choreographed for up-tempo music, the orchestra started to play very, very slowly. Alarmed I turned to Geoff Harvey whose orchestra was adjacent to my podium, rather uncomfortably sandwiched into a tight space under the balcony of the stalls. I caught Geoff's eye and using one finger determinedly beat out the up-tempo pace. Geoff, Mr Magic that he is, realised the mistake and slowly increased the tempo with his baton. The orchestra stayed with him and more than that my models stuck with the beat. Several people remarked what a clever routine it was. A slow wind up!

Pete Wynne had stationed himself on the floor just off to the side of my podium. He really nursed me through the production with quiet little nods of approval and encouraging grins. And when the audience roared and clapped at highlights of the presentation he'd give me a wicked little wink. Then it was over. The house went mad during the finale. All of us who had worked so hard on the show were bursting with pride. I was summoned to Kerry Packer's table. Sam Chisholm was there. They both said flattering things. Backstage it was hugs and thanks all round. I think we all felt dizzy with the success, then I went to find Pete Wynne. He wrapped me in a bear hug. We were both emotional.

I'd planned to take the next day off but the phone didn't stop ringing. Flowers, telegrams. The press gave the show a huge wrap. I finally went to the office for a couple of hours but I felt odd

— useless and wrung out. Jan suggested I go home for a couple of days. I remember wandering around the house unsettled, almost depressed. I phoned Pete. 'I feel the same way, Tabs. It's called "the let down".' After weeks of intense focus on the project there was now a void. Mind you, it didn't last long. We were soon up and on to the next job, and we did *The Australian Women's Weekly* Australian Fashion Awards again two years later.

THE FOLLOWING month, April 1982, Peter Wynne told me Nine had entered the show in the international Emmy Awards. I didn't give this much thought until a couple of months later when Sam Chisholm called to say we were a finalist in the Emmy's Light Entertainment section. I was at my Consolidated Press office, and on the spur of the moment I rang Kerry Packer's office. Yes he was in. Yes he'd see me. Gulp. Courage, Margaret! I took a deep breath.

'Now look K.P., our fashion award show has been nominated as a finalist in the Emmy Awards. It's a fantastic thing for both Channel Nine and the *Women's Weekly*. I think you should send me and Peter Wynne to New York for the Awards announcement.'

'Oh you do, do you?'

'Er well, yes I do.'

'You go,' he said.

'No, I have to go with Peter. We lived that show for almost three months. It wouldn't be fair.'

So the boss and I argued for a bit then he gave me one of his disarming grins — disarming because he doesn't often grin — and in a mock growl, he said, 'Well, just make sure you bring home the bloody trophy.'

I belted down to my office and rang Pete, singing when he came on the line, 'New York, New York's a wonderful town.'

'You little bloody beauty,' he hollered. And so in November

we went to New York. Kerry was generous, he gave us first class air tickets and accommodation, and arranged for Peter Faiman to be with us in New York.

Before we flew out I'd had a killing week at the office and two days filming a Maxwell House coffee commercial. I had broken a fingernail on the weekend, it would have been noticeable in the commercial so I'd had one of those synthetic jobs built on. After flying awhile I felt a pain in my finger. The synthetic nail, probably affected by cabin pressure, was slowly curling into the sides of my finger. It became excruciating.

'Warm brandy,' said Peter. 'That will fix it.'

'Peter, I can't drink warm brandy, it will go to my head.'

'Not to drink, to soak the finger.'

You know what? It worked. I sat with my finger in warm brandy all the way, and back on the ground the nail resumed its former shape and the pain went away. We had twenty-four hours in Los Angeles, doing Rodeo Drive and nudging each other a lot. 'Have a look at that one.' 'Get a load of that car.' All the stuff you do in LA. Then it was on to New York. The next night we met Peter Faiman and like the Three Musketeers took a limo off to the Awards ceremony.

Well-known actor Michael Landon, the President of the Emmy jury, took time to move around the pre-dinner drinks party and meet all the nominees. The ceremony was compered by the witty Tony Randall, one half of 'The Odd Couple'. The music was provided by the Don Costa Orchestra, Frank Sinatra's old mates. At tables of ten we were seated with some very friendly and witty characters, not surprising when we learnt they were from Mary Tyler Moore Enterprises. They cheered when our nomination was announced and there we were up on the biggest screen we'd ever seen. 'Makes our monitors look a bit puny,' whispered Pete.

There were three finalists. I only recall one, a strange aesthetic documentary shot in somewhere like Peru with a dialogue of off-beat poetry and a guy riding a donkey up and down mountains. It won! But the three of us went on stage to receive a High Commendation Award. And that's no slouch out of a worldwide competition. The Petes looked at me and teased, 'How are you going to explain this to the big fella back home?'

'With difficulty,' I replied.

But nothing was going to spoil our night. We partied hard and spent a few fabulous days in New York. We met up with Lorrain Willison, then publicity manager for Channel Nine, and her brother George, a reporter with the network, and we enjoyed a huge Thanksgiving dinner in a wonderful restaurant. When we boarded our flight home a friendly Neil Sedaka chatted from his seat opposite, and as we raised our first champers Pete said, 'I tell you, Tabs. It doesn't get much better than this.'

KERRY DIDN'T ball me out. We just had a tussle over who would keep the special citation Emmy Award: Kerry? *Women's Weekly*? Pete and Channel Nine? Or me? Calm restored, we had copies made. Kerry insisted he keep the original. Fair's fair. After all I'd had the trip to New York.

A LITTLE over a year after I started writing for the *Weekly* I began to work on the magazine's commercials. In those days it was still a weekly, which meant I would spend half a day every week filming. They were always hectic shoots by the sheer nature of the product. For instance, we were often kept waiting to shoot the cover because it was still being printed! We could go with a mock-up, but directors hated it because it never looked natural and I couldn't flip through the pages, which was often required. Locations were difficult. A 'home' environment was preferred because it suited many of the shots necessary to illustrate the content of the magazine — a kitchen for the cooking pages, a table setting for the style pages, somewhere to shoot fashion, an attractive room setting for my openers and closers. And of course it had to be reasonably quiet, away from flight paths, bus routes, main traffic flows, marinas or building sites. But sound problems were persistent. You'd arrive at the quiet, leafy North Shore street to what was thought to be the perfect house, only to discover the agro guy next door was going to mow his lawn no matter what, or the council had moved in with chainsaws to lop the street trees. It could be a frustrating business. And why was it that homes which met all the requirements were always located way over on the far side of town? For years I was often the only car driving across the Harbour Bridge at the crack of dawn. My happiest moment came when they found a large house on the southern side of the Bridge and we spent a pleasant year filming with a very accommodating family. The master of the house always had an espresso coffee waiting for me. Generous and nice.

At one stage the well-known journalist Mike Gibson joined the *Weekly* as a columnist. It was decided to team us together for the commercials. I liked Mike enormously, he has a ready sense of humour. Mind you, it was often tested. Like the time the *Weekly*'s Craft Editor came up with things to do with wooden pegs and paddle-pop sticks. A concept Mike and I found, well, unbelievable. There we were, sitting on a verandah, with Mike holding this silly little carousel. He gives it a little whirl and the peg and paddle-pop sticks fly around with little horses attached by strings. Then as we start to speak our lines we get the giggles. Second take. We break up again. Third take. We are in gales of laughter. Fourth take and I have tears streaming down my cheeks and mascara everywhere but on my lashes. The director begins to lose patience, but laughter is infectious. The whole crew were doubled over. Somehow we finally got it together and shot an acceptable take. Neither of us was comfortable with the silliness of it all. I think it did Mike in. Shortly after I was working alone again and Mike returned to more serious journalism.

I did the *Weekly*'s commercials for almost fourteen years, which I believe is something of a record for presenter ads.

WHEN HARRY Miller approached me to become my manager he obviously realised I had a commercial future. Well, in addition to the ads for the *Weekly* I've made a hell of a lot of endorsement commercials, and I'm grateful and proud of the fact that most led to substantial long-term associations. Right from the start Harry and I laid down some ground rules: I would never endorse a product that wasn't honest and didn't provide quality. I would only make commercials for products that had a credible association with me. In truth I've said no to more commercials than I've said yes to. Since the 1960s, I've been the presenter for some pretty terrific companies and some pretty terrific products: Hickory lingerie, Osti fashion, Taubmans paint, Crown Corning cookware, Logan Homes, Club Méditerranée holidays, Maxwell House coffee, Wiltshire Staysharp knives, Cussons soap, Bristile roofing tiles, Parker pens, Black & Decker electrical goods, *Woman's Day*, TNT courier bags, General Electric, Summit Homes and Luxaflex. Not necessarily in that order and I've probably forgotten a few (to do with age, I suppose).

I've always retained script approval and insisted on my own makeup stylist and hairdresser. This makes me sound like a pain in the arse, but I'm always on time and word perfect. It's part of my professional pride.

John Mostyn headed up Osti. They produced budget fashion, good quality at staggeringly low prices, and they sold volumes. The first Osti commercial saw me as myself, Maggie Tabberer,

Fashion Editor. I was with John Mostyn being shown the latest Osti collection. There was a moment when, admiring a particular dress, I was to say, 'But John, what about the price?' John replies, 'Maggie, just $19.95.' We'd done several takes because there were lots of models moving around in the shot. Timing was critical and John had marginal nerves. There was a bit of tension building and the director wanted a perfect take. On the spur of the moment I thought I should break the ice and get a laugh going, so in the next take when John said, 'Maggie, just $19.95.' I replied with an incredulous, 'Shit!' We all cracked up. Later clever John made good use of that tape. He would show retail buyers the range and explain that Osti would back them with a national television advertising campaign, then invite them to see Osti's latest commercial and play the rogue tape. Some fell off their chairs, they were so stunned but it always got a laugh. Naturally, only the proper version went to air. I was with Osti for around seven years.

Ad man John Singleton had the Taubmans paint account and I was engaged to make television and radio commercials, appear in their point-of-sale print material and on their colour charts. Years later when I was painting my farm I went to the Taubmans centre and had them mix a particularly wonderful charred green for the cottage woodwork. The guys took great delight in dragging out my twenty-something-year-old colour charts and hooting at my hairstyles. 'Oh, give me a break, fellas.' In the seventies, when Harry M. was about to present his stage show *Jesus Christ Superstar*, he had Taubmans paint the entire exterior of Sydney's Capitol Theatre in what was to become 'Superstar Brown' on the colour charts. This colour became a bestseller but, for the record, is my all-time pet aversion colour. More like 'down brown'! 'I hope painting the Capitol isn't coming out of my side of the deal,' I'd tease Miller.

Singo at the time was hotly involved in politics, promoting the Australian Workers' Party. He called one day and said, 'I'm sending a tellie crew around. I just want you to endorse the Workers' Party.'

'No, John, don't because I won't. I never had anything to say publicly about politics and I'm not about to start now.'

In an effort to convince me he added, 'Well, Maggie's doing it' — his wife at the time being the beautiful model Maggie Eckhart.

'Yes, John, but she's married to you. I'm not.'

I like Singo. He's a first-rate ratbag, but I like him.

Filming for TNT courier bags, a production problem arose when the noise of the objects I was dropping into the handy courier bag drowned out the dialogue. The director fixed this by cutting a large hole in the base of the bag and putting foam rubber underneath. On screen I popped a magical and endless array of things into the bag ever so silently!

I was with Maxwell House coffee for three years and the commercials were always bigger than *Ben Hur*. Harry and I went to the ad agency to meet the client and discuss the first commercials. An over-enthusiastic art director took us through the story board. The commercial was to be set in an open-cut coalmine. I was to be the Fashion Editor shooting a fashion spread with models and guys in hard hats. There would be huge trucks rumbling by, lots of action and even mock explosions going off behind us. That all sounded fine, then the writer gushed, 'The explosions represent the transference of power that happens when you drink a cup of Maxwell House coffee.' Was I hearing right? What garbage.

Appalled, I pushed my chair back, looked at the guys and said, 'If you believe that ad-speak bullshit then I'm going to open an ad agency.'

We went on to shoot the commercial under great difficulty. The location, trucks, so many people and explosions created a logistical nightmare. No one mentioned transference of power to me again and nor would they need to.

On another Maxwell House shoot it was to be a Maggie fashion parade, capturing all the pace, excitement and hurry-scurry of backstage at a fashion show. At the end of the commercial I was to sink into a chair and obviously be saved by another refreshing cup of Maxwell House coffee. There was no voice-over or dialogue spoken throughout the commercial, just the live sound of models chatting, dressing, panicking, stagehands and the music of the parade. My only script was right at the end — a satisfied, 'Mmm, great cup of coffee.' It was one of the rare occasions I found the director impossible. He was obsessed with details that were time consuming to shoot, and although I wasn't needed he wouldn't allow anyone to leave the set, he was obviously winging the shoot. Frankly, I thought he just wanted an audience. It was a big ego show and inconsiderate. At the end of something like nine hours on the set he announced we were going to shoot my close-up.

Oh thanks, I thought. Now that I'm sagging with fatigue he's going to shoot my bloody close-up. Furious, I took my place and duly sipped the coffee. But before I could deliver, 'Mmm, great cup of coffee,' he called, 'Cut.' Then, 'We'll shoot once more and I think we've got it.' I waited. We did a second tape. Again he jumped in with, 'Cut. That's a wrap, ladies and gentlemen,' he announced, very pleased with himself. I waited a full thirty seconds, fighting the temptation to not say anything, but then relented.

'Excuse me, but what about the dialogue?'

The look on his face was worth it. I would have loved to have walked off and not reminded him about the undelivered line, but I knew that would mean coming back and going through the whole business again. It wasn't a consideration. Still I felt I'd certainly made a point. Close-ups at the end of the day, indeed!

When I filmed a refrigerator commercial for General Electric it again had a fashion show theme, only this time the models were fridges. They were to glide down a catwalk and open their doors, just like a fashion model would open a coat. I was to compere, pointing out the models' features: 'Instant icemaker, big crispers' etc. Sounds good? No. A nightmare. There were three young grips under the stage pulling an apparatus that moved the refrigerators along the catwalk. They either went too fast or too slow or too jerky. Take after take after take. I always try to stay calm in these situations. It doesn't help to have talent bitching on about the delays, the director has enough to contend with. But it was excruciatingly hot under the big spotlight and I started to feel faint.

This may sound barmy but by habit I rarely walk off the set, and I never sit down during a shoot. I know if I walk away I have to crank myself up and into the mood again, and if I sit down my garment will crease. And anyway, I'm a standing sort of person. On this occasion they finally sorted out the pusha-me pulla-me business and we went for another take. Refrigerator model one moves out smooth as silk. I deliver the lines. Second model moves out. Perfect timing. We had almost come to the end of a faultless take when *boom*, *bam*, *crash*, there was an enormous explosion. A giant lamp had blown above my head. I was showered with glass. The silence that followed was eerie. Everyone was shocked. Rickie picked the glass out of my hair while the lighting director fixed his lamp. Back to square one. Just another day at the office.

I had a fantastic association with Black & Decker. Paul Harrison, the company's marketing director at the time, was the man who came up with the Maggie 'Black & Decker suits me to a T' concept. He was one of the smartest marketers I've ever worked with and also one of the nicest. My association with Black & Decker lasted ten years and survived many Black & Decker executive changes. John Callaghan directed the initial commercials. His high-tech, sharp-lit, black and white look had enormous impact. About the only colour on the set was the food and my lipstick. They are amongst my favourite commercials and started a tradition. I always wore white for Black & Decker.

Staysharp knives was another years-long contract. Initially we shot several commercials over two days from their Adelaide-based agency. It did nothing for my confidence to walk onto the set and notice both cameras had lens filters fashioned from black pantihose, and the crew hadn't bothered to chop off the legs or disguise them in any way. Gawd, was I looking that rough? Anything that involves food can be difficult and certainly time consuming. In one closing shot I had to chop some vegetables. We tried several different vegies — out of control carrots, tomatoes that were overripe and cabbage that just didn't look good. Finally we settled on zucchinis. I started my lines, going chop, chop. The final chop saw a ring of zucchini roll around and around like a spinning top until it went plop. Like a full stop it landed. When they put the commercial together the Staysharp logo came up 'pop' just as the zucchini went 'plop'. Looked bloody amazing. Of course if it had been planned it would never have been possible.

After several years with Staysharp the association had run its course and we parted. I've never been dismissed with so much grace and style. They held a special dinner for me and presented me with a superb gold-plated Staysharp knife, fixed to a chopping block and with a message of thanks inscribed on a gold plate.

Making the commercials I generally worked with some wonderful people and I enjoyed the camaraderie of a crew. It would be stupid not to make friends with these guys. After all, your fate is in their hands but I genuinely came to appreciate their skills: the director who has total control but is always happy to let you contribute some little 'business', such as an inflection, a telling pause or a certain move to camera; the cameraman who makes you look good simply by changing an angle; and the lighting director who can miraculously make the years vanish. Then there's the grips with the fast-cracking quips who keep the team's spirit up when you're starting to flag. The caterers who come to the rescue with comforting lunches. The makeup stylist who performs miracles with your face then nurses you through the day. The hairdresser who has a sharp and discerning eye. I salute them all. Too many people to name individually but they'll know who they are. We had some good times and we did good work. It doesn't get much better.

One Door
Closes,
Another One
Opens

I WAS looking forward to a few days break. Jan Geary and I had had a bumper year at the agency. The last appointment for the week was to be lunch with John Fink, who was trying to persuade me to write a fashion column for his publication, a small magazine about Sydney. I'd said I just couldn't take on anything more but he insisted we go for lunch anyway. It was the Thursday before Good Friday, 1980. We met at a trendy city restaurant, quite new and rather glamorous. It didn't take me long to convince John I couldn't accept his offer, and he was charming about it. We settled down to enjoy good food and trade gossip.

As we lunched I noticed a few tables away an extremely hand-some man giving me the eye. Cheeky, I thought. He persisted to the extent that I became mildly embarrassed. He was with three 'suits' — CBD business types — and he looked different, casually dressed in shirt, jeans and a jacket. He also had a very deep suntan. Bet he doesn't spend his time in an office, I thought. When they stood to leave I had the distinct feeling they were aiming for our table. I found myself slightly flushed. John knew one of the guys, John Jost, a well-known journalist, so it was introductions all round — one 'suit' was a solicitor, Tony Hartnell, and the casual one was Richard Zachariah. He had been a journalist but was now on the land in Victoria, hence the tan. The suits left, but Richard more or less invited himself to join us. John courteously bought a second bottle of wine and we started a 'let's find out who you are' conversation. John moved to leave and I went to join him, but Richard insisted I stay to finish the wine. By this time we had discovered we had mutual Melbourne friends, I was enjoying his company. Why not!

As he walked me to the car he mentioned he was staying with a friend, Andrew Clark, son of Manning, and that Andrew had arrangements for Easter. Richard sounded a bit lost and lonely. 'Well, if you get bored with your own company call me, there's a lot of nice people in this town,' I said.

Early the next morning he phoned: 'What's happening?' I explained there was a great party each year at Di and Tony Yeldham's. The Yeldhams ran Double Bay's hottest fashion spot, the Squire Shop. They were old mates and I didn't anticipate it would be a problem to invite Richard. I rang and Di said, 'Fine, the more the merrier.' When I arrived at the party Richard was already ensconced, pressed close to a leggy blonde. Occasionally he caught my eye and at one stage we spoke briefly. 'Having fun,' I teased, nodding toward the blonde. He laughed. Bush boy out to have a good time, I thought.

The following day he phoned and said he'd had a very late night but great fun, and he thanked me for organising the invitation.

He then pressed to see me. 'Sorry, I'm really busy.' He was very insistent. God knows why, but the little-boy-lost attitude obviously got to me. 'Well, I'm lunching with great friends, the Jacovides. Let me see.' I have generous friends. 'Sure, darling, bring him,' said Chris. I collected Richard and he gave me a bottle of French champagne to say 'thank you' for organising his Easter.

At lunch were Chris and Judy Jacovides, my maddest and dearest mate Ronnie Fraser, politician Paul Landa and his beautiful wife Ann. The conversation was spirited, the food as always at the Jacovides' was great, and the good wine flowed. It was a jolly day. There was a strong mutual attraction between Richard and me. I felt mildly uneasy that it hadn't gone unnoticed. 'I'll call you,' he said as we parted. 'And next time I'll buy you dinner.' It would be almost two years before I gave in to that invitation.

Ettore and I had stopped sleeping together years before, soon after we lost our son. In grief I let it be. By the time I wanted to resume our sexual life Pross had bad arthritis and used it as an excuse. Did he blame me for the baby's death? Did I blame him? I honestly don't know. But it hung like an invisible curtain between us. We didn't argue, we did love one another. But we both quietly had affairs. I had no intention of ever leaving Ettore. We were as one, and had been for a long, long time. It never occurred to me that it was any different for him. He was my Rock of Gibraltar and I was sure he felt the same. But we never spoke about it.

I always knew when he was having an affair. Men do silly things like go on fruit juice diets, buy six new pairs of white undies, and supposedly play cards a lot with the boys! I also knew when Ettore was lying to me; he yawned. 'I'm a going to *yaaawn*, meet Jimmy. He wants to show me this house *yaaawn* that he's going to buy and then we will have a pizza *yaaawn* and go to Gino's to play cards *yawn*.' Oh sure, Pross! But I didn't rock the boat. These affairs never last, I thought.

Unless one of us was overseas, I insisted that the family be together every Sunday. Sometimes Pross would try to get out of Sunday lunch, saying he had to go to the restaurant and do the books. I knew otherwise. It was wicked but I took a perverse pleasure in stacking his plate with food, knowing full well that when he slipped away in the early afternoon his mistress, whoever she was, would be hard pressed to get a second lunch into him!

In the weeks after Easter Richard rang a few times and once sent me a rather suggestive postcard. I was frantically busy by then, locked in heavy negotiations with Carl Dowd and Rob Palmer about creating the Maggie T line. At the agency we were staging the big shows for Weiss and Zampatti. Our client list had burgeoned and I had travel plans. Time went by. Richard came to Sydney only to discover I was in Melbourne. He'd phone every so often, and he seemed to get cross if he suggested a date and I couldn't make it. I suppose this was flattering but I had enough to manage in my life. Then almost two years after meeting Richard I found out about Brigitta and my husband.

Brigitta was a beautiful Austrian-born model I had used occasionally for photography for the agency but never for parades. The day before we were to stage a big Weiss show, one of the models fell ill. 'Just get me someone the same height and size,' I said to Jan, 'so we don't have to do fittings. And she must have the same shoe size.' We had a day of rehearsal only. My 'girls', as I called them, had all worked with me before. The shows were demanding, and nothing but perfection was acceptable. At first I treated Brigitta with kid gloves. I realised it was daunting to come into a different style of show as mine were and learn the routines in a day. But as the rehearsal progressed I felt she was not trying. 'Just focus, Brigitta.' I placed her in the middle of five other girls, I suggested she just follow what was happening in front of her. But she wasn't getting it. She also had a totally different walk from my models, slow and sombre. She sort of sat on her bottom with a hip thrust. I hated it. My girls walked tall, I had them stride out. As the pressure of time built I did yell at her a couple of times. But was that any excuse to steal my husband?

I'd heard rumours. Ettore was on yet another diet, wearing his new undies and yawning a lot. Something was going on. I ignored it for a while but then, painfully, the truth exploded. Ettore had finally made a move to come out of his five-year retirement. He had negotiated a restaurant lease on premises in Cross Street, Double Bay with the Scarf Brothers. While they were building the restaurant Ettore took off to Italy to 'find a new chef', he said. In the space of eight months he went three times. And for the first time in our life together he refused to give me his travel agenda. 'I don't know where I'll be. I'll be travelling by car. I need to search out a chef.' I knew he was lying. What if I need him? I thought. What if something happens to him? It was unsettling. He never did find a chef, by the way.

Somehow we staggered on for another year. I was totally immersed in work. It was May of 1982 when he came home one night and we had words about the rumours. They were persistent and growing. I was getting messages from all sorts of people. 'Come on, Maggie, where would I have time to have an affair?' He yawned and went to bed. Ettore was always very careful with his private papers; his briefcase was almost glued to his wrist. That night I went to the study where we watched TV and saw his briefcase on the floor. I have no idea what made me do it, but I opened the case and took out his cheque book. I scanned the butts. The last entry said, 'B airfare Italy'. I started to shake. The rumours were true. I raced into his room, he woke and I punched and hit him with all my might. My diamond ring scratched his face. There was blood. I sobbed and sobbed. This was never supposed to happen. I was hysterical.

I can't recall how it finished. I probably went to bed and cried myself to sleep. The next day we were very quiet. We both knew we had reached a crossroad, and I don't believe either of us really wanted to be there. Amanda came to see me: 'Mummy, I have to talk to you. It's about bashing up Daddy.' How's that for a line? When we did get around to talking he was uncertain. I didn't, couldn't, push for a conclusion. I guess I thought it would be like all the others; he would finally give her up. I threw myself into work. Days passed, weeks, months. Finally he said, 'I need to think, I need my own space.' Oh purleeese, Ettore! He stood at the bottom of my bed and told me I was 'too strong a woman'. What in the hell did that mean?

I was capable, I was independent, I ran the house and business efficiently. I could whip up his favourite meal. These were all things he had admired — now I was 'too strong'. We had been together so long. Sure, it had lost its sexual side. That wasn't easy on either of us, but it was a deep love, he was Pappi, my Pappi. So what in the bloody hell did 'too strong a woman' mean? Too strong for what? To be helpless, in need of a protector? He could never ever tell me. It was torturous and I guess it also changed my attitude to the tall, blond and handsome Richard. After all, if Ettore could get a younger, trimmer woman, I could get a younger, trimmer, taller and more handsome man. Oh Maggie, wrong, wrong, wrong.

I hadn't heard from Richard for some time, when out of the blue there was a call. 'I'm sick of you refusing my invitations to dinner. Now if you don't have dinner with me in Melbourne I'm coming to Sydney,' he said. I was to be in Melbourne on business a few days later so we made plans. As usual I was staying at the Regent Hotel, now the Sofitel. At the appointed time I opened the door and there he was, drop dead gorgeous. We drank the management's gift of champagne then decided to eat in the hotel's best restaurant. It was easy, witty conversation. He was so different from the men I'd known. Eight years younger than me, very Australian, with a larrikin sort of attitude. We talked about his great loves. Wildly diverse — Essendon Football Club, Auden's poetry. I liked him enormously. He was physically incredibly attractive.

Careful Margaret, I said to myself, this could be difficult. It's hard to confess, but with previous lovers I had it all worked out. Only have affairs with married men. It's safer. They have responsibilities so they'll understand yours. Keep it discreet, keep it controlled. That way it wouldn't threaten my life with Ettore. But Richard, I sensed, could be dangerous and the game play had changed. I knew by then that Ettore was in love with someone else, and I guess I wanted to fall in love too. Revenge? Who knows?

Back in my room for a nightcap we started a kiss that led to more. I don't know why, but I didn't want to just jump into bed. I was alarmed, I think, at the passion I felt. The hunger. Somehow I fought off my rising desires. He left. Very early the next morning the phone rang and a voice said: 'Lunch.' Weak at the knees with excitement I rearranged my day. Again he came to the hotel and again we ate in the hotel restaurant. I didn't even mind that it went on my bill. That afternoon we made love. It was passionate, ravenous. The sense of discovering that we were sexually compatible was wondrous. We were not shy with each other. I hadn't for years had the greatest figure in the world, but with Richard it didn't matter. He told me I was beautiful. I felt beautiful. The hours evaporated. His demands seemed endless. At one stage I fell back on the pillows dripping in perspiration and said, 'Richard, no, stop. I know you've been in the bush for a long time but this is ridiculous.' And we laughed. Oh God, how we laughed.

Perhaps it's hard to understand how, having taken this lover, I could still love my husband, but I did. Over the next year I kept my life in little compartments: work, lover, home and husband. All neatly wrapped in a different space and time, although my husband was more out of home than in. My diary records that in 1983 Ettore moved out in February, back in March, out in April, back in June, out in August. Then back for several months. We staggered on in endless pain. I can't explain why I tolerated it. I trod water at home and snatched happiness with Richard whenever I could. I was often in Melbourne for business. I still couldn't get Ettore to sit down and talk honestly about where we were heading. I suppose I didn't want to admit the end was near.

A couple of years earlier I had bought a boat, a twenty-five foot Bertram, and had busied myself learning to drive it. It afforded me a great escape at weekends with my mates, Ronnie, Barb, Rickie, Ray, the kids and their friends, and overseas friends, including Lord Piers Wedgwood. At first I was intimidated at the thought of entertaining a lord, but he proved to be a pleasant surprise. 'Call me Piers.' He was a wonderful, roly-poly man with a healthy sense of fun and a taste for good food and wine. Lord Wedgwood worked hard publicising the company and product that bore his name. He had been introduced to me by my friend Ray Freeman, who had joined the Wedgwood company in Australia. Piers always endeavoured to find time in his demanding Australian schedule 'for a spin on Maggie's boat'. Then there was my gorgeous friend, Libby Reeves Purdy. Once when I was going to Los Angeles, Trevor Kennedy from ACP suggested I look up Libby. At the time she worked out of Kerry Packer's Channel Nine office in LA, where she lined up all the

Hollywood star interviews for the Nine Network. She handled everything and everyone with incomparable style and ease and always a smile. Mind you, Libby had the benefit of experience in dealing with the big names, she had worked as personal assistant to David, later Sir David, Frost for ten years.

Libby and I loved one another immediately we met, and it was a friendship that would grow over the years. Having her on board was always a joy. Through her I made another close friend, Vicki Jones, who at the time was publicist for Channel Nine. A bubbly, brilliant girl who went on to become programming director for the Nine Network, and was later snaffled by Channel Ten.

For lunch on the boat I'd cook Friday night or very early Saturday and head down to Rushcutters Bay to the *Maggie T*, as I called her, toting big eskies packed to the gunnels with goodies, then prepare for the mates' arrival. We'd head out, usually do a round of the harbour and finish up at our favourite haunt, Taylors Bay. Lunch was never simple: fritattas, huge chunks of rare fillet beef, salads and cheeses. Rickie and Ray would contribute stunning pud and there was always good wine. Thank God I was never tested by the water police. It was irresponsible, it was an escape. When I bought the boat I told friends it was to stop me having the menopause. It did for a long time, but eventually my hormones held me hostage.

I adored the boat and felt a great sense of achievement in mastering it. My instructor was a burly bloke called Ron. He was incredibly patient with me, but in truth I really didn't find it too difficult. When I first arrived on the dock at Rushcutters Bay all the regular boaties eyed me sceptically. A lot of people buy boats, use them for a few weeks then leave them idle for months before selling them. I didn't. Rain, hail or shine I was there every weekend. If the weather was really foul I was happy just to sit on the boat at the dock, play my music and read. Sometimes after work I'd go down and sit and watch the sun set over the harbour and listen to the clink clank of the yacht riggings or take an evening spin. I got my money's worth out of the *Maggie T*. She provided hours of joy. It was peaceful, probably the most peaceful I felt in that turbulent time.

Ettore had been gone from our house for something like four of his proposed six weeks 'to think about' separation. Richard had come to Sydney. It was hot and sunny so we took off on the boat and swam the day away. The evening was so incredibly beautiful we decided to stay out overnight. In a snug Taylors Bay mooring we sat on deck for hours, talking about life, love and the whole damn thing. The next morning at about five we cruised back to Rushcutters Bay. A nasty little breeze had whipped up and I was concentrating on bringing the *Maggie T* safely back into her mooring. I failed to notice a dark figure standing on the dock. Richard had picked up the mooring ropes, I'd switched off the engine and raced back to help him secure the boat. Then I looked up. It was Ettore.

'You get off that boat, Maggie, and you go home and pack your things and get out of that house now,' he shouted. I was stunned. After all, he had left me. He was the one who'd dragged me for two years through his on again, off again indecision about his mistress. And there he was making demands. As the saying goes, I let him have both barrels. Richard remained silent. Ettore turned on his heel and strode off down the dock. Then my knees gave way. I was shaken. Where did that anger come from and why? What game was he playing? Did he just love the drama of it all? Suddenly I felt very, very tired. This had to stop. Our relationship almost from day one had been turbulent. I'd played out so many scenes I didn't have the stomach for it any more. It had to stop.

While the eastern suburbs rumour mills were spinning over-time, Ettore and I had managed to keep a lid on the details of our impending separation. He was still coming and going from the house. A week living with me, the wife, then a week with Brigitta, the mistress. I hadn't given any real thought to the fact that inevitably the media would be interested. I was just living on memory, rising each morning at six and going to work. Work was always a panacea for pain. One morning I was woken with an indecently early call. A male voice said, 'Maggie Tabberer, this is the *Truth* newspaper in Melbourne. Would you confirm you — .' I didn't give him a chance.

'No comment,' I said and I hung up. Shaken I rang Harry Miller.

'Sit tight for a bit, don't panic,' he said.

I loathed the thought of *that* newspaper breaking the story, even though I knew it was inevitable. Not that sordid little rag. I rang Richard. His advice was, 'Talk to Andrew.' Later that day I had lunch with his great friend Andrew Clark. Andrew knew journalism inside, outside and upside down, and I confided in him. 'Maggie, make a statement now to the media in general. Just announce that you and Ettore have decided to separate. It will kill the story.'

Harry's office prepared the statement and it went out. The next day one evening paper crowed: 'Tabberer has announced her marriage is over to Ettore Prossimo. Who cares?' Well, that sure as hell killed off the *Truth* story. I was forever grateful for Andrew's advice.

Richard had been married for fourteen years. We never ever talked about his wife and we rarely talked about my husband. Our affair was passionate, sexual, played out in the clouds of the fiftieth floor penthouse of the Regent in Melbourne. Isolated from the grim reality of infidelity and lies. Eventually it all caught up with us and we caused a lot of hurt. It sits uneasily on my conscience but this was the situation when Ettore and I finally agreed it was over.

TOWARDS THE end of 1984 I realised I was doing too much. Something would have to go. After hours of agonising it seemed it would have to be my involvement in Maggie Tabberer Associates. I'd been in the PR business for more than twenty years. It really didn't hold any more challenges for me. And I felt it wasn't fair on Jan to continue in a half-hearted manner. I knew she was disappointed when I told her but after some discussion Jan decided to buy my interest in the company. Today, as Publicity Partners, she is still successful and active in the business.

Rhonda Pemberton, an account executive at MTA, was a delicious girl, thoughtful and generous. Quietly she went about organising a surprise farewell for me. She coerced my friend Ray Freeman into inviting me to dinner at Kables at the Regent in Sydney. On arrival, Ray told me friends of his were having a cocktail party in one of the function rooms. 'Let's pop in for a drink before we go up to dinner,' he said. Not suspecting a thing, I went along. We walked into the room and it took me a few seconds to realise that all my old fashion mates were there: Peter Weiss, Brian Rochford, Marylyn Said, Barry Taffs, Rickie Quesada, Greg Barrett, John Cooper, a heap of others, and lots of my favourite models — the girls who had walked my shows and helped make me look so good. I was stunned. But I still didn't comprehend what was happening until Rhonda said, 'Maggie, welcome to your party.' Tears, hugs all round, laughter, a huge cake in the shape of a catwalk with tiny models on it strutting their stuff. Model Di Sweeny had made a special dress to wear — white cotton decorated with 'Maggie Parade instructions' in black felt-tip pen. They were diagrams of the choreography. So clever. We drank for Australia that night. It was such a generous act on Rhonda's part and very touching that so many friends took time to come and let me know I would be missed.

I knew deep down I was going to miss those shows too. Despite all the hard work they were always the most rewarding, creative experiences. The beautiful girls, the fabulous clothes; when it all came together and the house erupted with applause, there was nothing like it. But I closed that door and moved on.

SEPARATED FROM Ettore, I had to face the reality of where I was going to live. We had argued on and off about who would get our house in The Mews. Ettore changed his mind every other day. 'You have it, Maggie.' 'No, I want it.' Ah hell, I thought, let's get this over and done with. Then in a rage I said, 'Ettore, you bloody well have it.' Finally I just didn't have the energy to fight for anything any more. I agreed to what really was an unjust settlement, but I didn't care. I felt as though I had been swimming underwater for two years and I needed to come up for air. In 1985 I decided to buy a new house, to start afresh. It would be a white house and I would never live with another man again. No full ashtrays, no dumped damp towels, no shaving cream splattered on the bathroom mirror. No endless shirts to iron, dinners to cook, trays to carry. No, no, no …

I found my house in Edgecliff. I went with Barb to look at a highrise apartment. We were standing in the street gazing up at it when an acquaintance, Bill Shipton, who was a builder of some note, walked by toting his dry cleaning. He asked what I was up to. 'Trying to find a new home, Bill.'

He eyed the highrise and said, 'Maggie, forget it. You'll hate travelling in lifts with strangers, you need privacy. Look, I built these townhouses across the road. Only three in the block. I live in one, know the people in the second and the third I believe could be bought.'

Slowly and painfully I packed up The Mews. And strangely and painfully Ettore was still coming and going; a few days at home, then out again, to his hotel and girlfriend. We couldn't look at each other without one of us bursting into tears. It was the longest six weeks of my life. By right I owned all the furniture, I had redecorated a couple of years earlier and financed the changes. Ettore was still saying he intended to live alone, but we both knew he was lying. I left his bedroom and the study furnished so he had some rooms of comfort. A close friend told me that this was total madness, but you do what you have to do. I still loved a lot of Ettore Prossimo. Then I moved into my new pristine white house.

After I'd organised extensive renovations it was gorgeous and I enjoyed unpacking. But one night, a few days later after family and friends had all come to see, I found I was home alone. I'd unpacked all the boxes, the house was in order, everything perfect. I wandered from room to room. Upstairs, downstairs, out onto the terrace. I took a spa. Took a shower. Made a snack, poured a glass of wine, turned on the TV. Turned it off. What in the bloody hell was wrong with me? Then it hit me — I was alone. I was living alone. I can't tell you how terrifying it was. I had been born into a big rowdy family. I had married, had my kids, divorced, lived with my kids and nanny, then lived with and finally married Ettore. I had never lived alone before. Icy fingers encircled my heart. I knew I had my daughters, my stepson, my family, my friends, but for the first time I felt so incredibly alone and I didn't like it. Not one little bit. In the next few months I again threw myself into a frenzy — working and seeing close friends.

My life was daily becoming more and more complicated. Months before Richard and I became lovers I had been having an affair with another man. It was comforting for a time, but gradually I became alarmed at his demands. He wanted to know where I was every hour of the day. He phoned me at the house even when he knew Ettore was there. To surprise me he would appear on planes when I was flying interstate. He would leave notes tucked in the windscreen of my parked car. This was dangerous and I loathed it. I backed off and he pursued me even more. Finally I had to tell Richard about it. When he and I arranged a few days escape to Queensland this man was there on the plane. It's an understatement to say we had a horrific flight. I had told him it was over. He was relentless. When we came to fly home he was again at the airport. Finally the airline contacted me to tell me he was making constant enquiries about my travel plans. Don't tell him a thing, I said. I know I probably treated him badly and I'm sorry. The reality was, he was obsessed, I wasn't. He was gentle, intelligent, a hopeless romantic.

So time rolled on. I was travelling to Melbourne regularly, seeing Richard, working hard, hating living alone. I filled my social hours with friends and too many glasses of white wine. What was hardest was the tenuous link Ettore maintained. He would phone for no reason. One day he rang and said he would like to see my house. He came and went, popping in and out of my new life. I swore to myself after every call that I would demand he stop this. Finally I did. He stopped for three or four weeks, then one day he rang. He sounded ill. He said he was incredibly depressed, he had been seeing a shrink. He needed to talk to me. I went to see him at The Mews.

I hated how it looked; this house I had loved so much, found, decorated and adored. Now there was a dark 'Grandma Moses' European dining-room setting. There were bows and frills on things. My God, it wasn't Ettore. Another force had had a hand in this. We talked. Sad, emotional. He told me it was over with Brigitta. He would have to face his life alone. Immensely sad, angry and confused, I ran. As I drove away I knew I couldn't put it all together again. Too much had happened between us and other people were now involved. I had just started to put my own life back together. No, I couldn't get involved again. I wouldn't.

About a week later I lunched with Barb at her home. I'd been trying to reach Ettore earlier in the day about my insurance. When I phoned The Mews again he answered and sounded strange. I don't know why but I said, 'Is that woman there?'

'No, Maggie.'

I knew he was lying. We had words. I was outraged that only days before he had put me through another emotional hoop. How dare he play with my feelings like this. I went bananas. I grabbed my car keys and, despite Barb's pleas not to, headed off to The Mews. I no longer had keys to the underground garage but I drove down there, parked in a visitor's spot and walked back out to the street then down, through the gardens to his front door. Our front door. I hammered loudly. 'Ettore it's me, let me in.'

'Go away Maggie,' he replied. 'There is nothing for you here.'

A bomb exploded in my head. 'Nothing for you here!' Days before he had summoned me to this house and now because his mistress was with him, 'there is nothing for you here!' I pounded on the door, screaming language that would make a wharfie blush. The rage took hold. I've never been so totally out of control. All the years of hurt burst to the surface. I grabbed a brick from the garden and hammered it against the door. I kicked the door repeatedly, my shoe indents are probably still there. 'Open this bloody door!' When he still wouldn't open it I stood back, aimed the brick and threw it with all my might at the door again and again. A neighbour yelled, 'Hold it down out there.'

'Get fucked!' I shouted back. For once in my life I couldn't give a damn about what the neighbours thought. I heard Press say, 'Ring Barbara.' I knew they were standing in the kitchen just to the left of the front door. It had a high window above it, and for a brief second I contemplated hurling that brick through the window. But some tiny shred of sanity remained. I paused. Then Ettore shouted, 'Maggie, I've called the police.' I had a rush of adrenalin. Good, I've scared them. But then, oh God! I could see the headlines: 'Maggie Tabberer Arrested.' I dropped the brick and sped back through the gardens down into the garage. I was shaking so much I couldn't get the key into the ignition. As I started to pull out I saw a sea of navy-blue serge legs at the entrance to the drive. I stopped, took a deep breath, quickly wiped my tears away, then drove very, very slowly up the ramp to street level. As I eased past a young policeman, I said, 'Good evening, officer.'

He tipped his cap. 'Evening, Ma'am.'

And I drove sedately to the corner. Then gunning the engine and sobbing, I raced back to my white house. In the meantime Barbara had grabbed her son Matt and searched in vain for a taxi. By the time she arrived at The Mews the police were just pulling out in the Black Maria. She thought, they've got Maggie in there. 'Matt, quick, see if you can see her.' Young Matt ran the length of the street, jumping up, trying to look through the back door grill to see if indeed I was in there. Barb finally arrived on my doorstep, followed minutes later by my stepson Nicolas.

'Why, why does he do this to me?' I cried. 'Why does he continue to lie? Why? Why?'

Nicolas gave the saddest reply: 'My father always lies.'

By now I was hysterical. They fed me neat brandy and my dear Barb put me to bed. I woke the next morning and knew I had to get professional help. I knew I couldn't find my way through this alone. I was ashamed of my behaviour but I was also very frightened. I had truthfully wanted to kill them. I rang my doctor, told him all. He arranged immediately for me to see a shrink, who was patient with my tears and generous with his time. I sobbed out the whole sordid story and along with Kleenex he gave me some positive tools. Don't talk to Ettore. Don't accept his calls. Don't drive down his street trying to see them. Get on with your own life. Simple? No, hard, very hard. But I did it and after three or four visits I found the strength to move on. Lugging a lot of bad baggage I suppose, but at least moving on.

A few days after my attack on Ettore's front door my dear mate Stuart Wagstaff called. I was in a depressed mood and related the story. He was comforting and sympathetic. A couple of hours later he phoned again and said, 'Tabs, are you going to be home in the next hour? I have something for you.' He rang my garage bell and I went down to let him in. At the time he drove a big Mercedes. Sticking out from its boot was a long object. He grabbed it and I saw it was an old wooden door. He carried it into my garage and propped it against the wall. As I stood there speechless he tied a house brick onto the door handle with a long length of rope.

'Now, Tabs,' he instructed, 'the next time you feel like taking out your anger or frustration or whatever, you just come down to the garage and belt the shit out of this. It's safer.' And we laughed and laughed. I love that man! I kept the door there for a long time. I never did use it again. Mind you, there have been times since then when I've thought it would have come in handy.

ONE MORNING in August 1985, the phone went. It was Richard.

'Darling, are you sitting down?'

Alarm bells sounded. 'Richard, don't do this. What in the hell's the matter?'

'Nothing, darling, but I thought you should know I've left my wife and I'm coming to Sydney to live with you.'

'Oh, my God,' I heard myself say.

After we hung up I sat thinking for a long time. I had pledged to myself that I would never live with a man again. In the past months I had gradually built a new life. I could look back on my relationship with Ettore and acknowledge that from the start it had been founded on lies. I don't know why he lied. Nicolas had a theory it was a result of his traumatic childhood in war-torn Italy. I don't know. I do know that I didn't like the way I had developed in the past years. My lovers, my lies. It's very uncomfortable to confront your sins. Now here was this man who had broken his marriage and said he was coming to live with me. As always when I'm in trouble I went to see Barb. I remember her so clearly, fixing me with those baby-blue eyes and saying very deliberately, 'Maggie, before you allow this to happen you had better be very sure.'

In the next few days Richard and I spent hours on the phone. I put up a lot of arguments against his move. He only responded with confidence and proclamations of love. 'It's a big love. I know this is right.' We discussed the fact that this relationship would be a real commitment. We had both experienced unfaithful partnerships — been there, done that. Now, mature, we wanted something more. It would be total, monogamous and, we said, forever. Any uncertainty flowed down and out my toes.

Richard had been running a restaurant in a country town with his wife and reading the news on a local television station. He still had three months of his contract to see out. He had moved out of the family home they had built on a property owned by his wife's father. The first night he'd gone to a caravan park then he had found a house to share with a couple of people who worked at the station.

'I'll be there with you in three months,' he said. I hadn't planned it this way. It was Richard's decision. But I discovered that I really wanted this relationship. I was in love. 'It's a deep, deep love, darling, isn't it?' He would say. And I so wanted it to be.

I should mention that Richard's wife behaved in an exemplary manner. She never called me, abused me or, to my knowledge, badmouthed me. Given my own aggression and angst when I'd discovered Ettore's deception, I often wondered how she coped with Richard walking away from their marriage. She chose what seemed a passive path. Me — well, I guess you could say when I'm passionate, I fight dirty.

Our divorce had become final in 1986. Ettore had served me with divorce papers. The irony was not lost on me. I had been married twice, both husbands had left me, then both divorced me! I knew it was because I couldn't or wouldn't face the fight and divorce them. 'Lily-livered idiot,' I scolded myself. But I was so happy with Richard by then it didn't seem to matter. A divorce is a divorce, regardless of who files it. Later, Richard even suggested that we should think about getting married. 'Oh no!' I said. 'Let's not spoil a good thing. If ever you feel like that again, darling, go and lie down until it passes.' From time to time he did raise the subject and I always gave him the same answer.

I heard rumours that Ettore and Brigitta had married. I rang Nicolas. He assured me it wasn't true. But the rumours persisted and I rang Ettore. He denied it. Within days I met two people who had been at the wedding! Why not tell me the truth? Why not at last tell me the truth, Ettore? I never asked him. I don't suppose he could have answered. He hadn't been able to for the twenty-nine years of our relationship. He will never change, I thought.

They were married in August 1987. It didn't last. They separated and divorced in 1991, after which he bought her an apartment in Double Bay. I felt a mild bitterness. I'd worked so hard and contributed so much financially to our long marriage, and in the end, our divorce settlement was largely in his favour. Brigitta had got an apartment after only a few years. Life isn't always fair, I thought, but by then it didn't matter. Pross stayed on in their marital home.

A few months later, in 1992, he sold the house and went back to live in Italy. God knows why I still worried about him, but I did. When I heard about his plans I begged Brooke and Amanda to counsel him. 'Tell him to lease the house. It will be worth a small fortune one day. Tell Daddy to rent something in Italy until he's sure that that is where he really wants to be.' It made sense, but he told them he wanted to be near his sister. I wryly noted it had not been a close relationship since I'd known him. But what's that old saying about homing pigeons? He bought an apartment in Catania, Sicily, right under Mount Etna. Ash rained down on him day and night. He complained to Barb on a visit back to Australia that he had to dust three times a day. And he'd had bars fitted to all the doors and windows. This was Mafia country, polluted with grime and crime. Oh Pross, how silly.

IN OCTOBER 1985, Richard and I prepared to live together. I had a photographic shoot for several days in Melbourne. We arranged that Richard would drive to Melbourne in the afternoon, pick me up, return to his television station where he would read his last evening news, then we would head for New South Wales. We spent the night in a funny little motel in Moe, then drove across the Monaro with Dire Straits at full belt on the stereo. It was heady, romantic. We arrived at my white house. He had his car and a boot full of clothes, and that was it. Within days he had a job at Channel Seven News as a reporter. Our new life took shape.

My psychiatrist had suggested to me that both my first and second husbands had been father figures. Well, Richard was eight years younger. He certainly wasn't a father figure. Finally I'd got that out of my system, I thought. Living with Richard was a new experience. He was desperately untidy, but I was so much in love I just picked up, tidied up, shut up. Years later it would drive me to distraction. The white house had a great vibe, it had a sunny deck and a huge spa. At weekends there was the boat. Richard was fun. There's a lot of larrikin in him: the antithesis of any other man I'd known before. There was football and races and Aussie humour and chiacking around. It was so very different and suddenly I could laugh again. I'd fly home from the office, we'd have wonderful little candle-lit dinners then make love in the spa. It was very romantic. Occasionally I'd think, living well is the best revenge.

If there was one moment that raised an alarm it was in the December of that year. Amanda was coming home, bringing her big strong Italian boyfriend, Sergio, to be introduced. I was, as always, mad with excitement at her return. I was filming so Nicolas went to collect them. They were going to stay with him. Late in the afternoon Amanda came running up the stairs — tanned, healthy, gorgeous, long blond hair flying. She hit the room at a thousand miles an hour. I was coming down the stairs from the upper level. Our arms outstretched, we raced to embrace. Suddenly Richard stepped in between us and snatched me away from Amanda into a tight embrace.

'Darling,' I protested, 'let me hug my daughter.'

He said something like, 'No, you're mine!'

It should have been a warning of what was to come. Richard wanted to be the centre of my universe. He didn't want to share me with anyone. This would cause great problems for him, for me and sadly for my kids. But at the time I pushed the thought away and we spent a happy Christmas that year all together at Barb's. We saw friends, Richard introduced me to Henry and Sarah Crawford. Sarah's brother was an old mate. He and Richard had spent some of their youth together in England smoking a lot of dope and learning how to exist without working. I introduced Richard to my circle: Georgie and Snow Swift, Barb of course, Peter and Adele Weiss, Rickie Quesada and Ray Freeman, Waggers, Ken Stevens and Vicki Jones, Glen Marie Frost and Bob Frost and Leo Schofield. They were all very generous and willing to accept him. He often didn't make it easy. I learnt he had a sharp tongue, and often it lost all discretion. Occasionally he invited someone from Channel Seven home and we saw a lot of his old journo mate Andrew Clark and sometimes bad, mad and funny Peter Blazey. Peter and Richard had met in their early journalistic days. Blazey had been a biographer, a political speechwriter and an advertising copywriter. And if he'd told me he was a brain surgeon, I probably would have believed him. And when Nic Columb came to Sydney, he would visit us. Nic had gone to school with Richard and was probably his longest-running friend.

Late 1985 Channel Seven offered Richard a programme called 'Eleven AM'. He would start early the next year. There was great excitement. I was thrilled for him. However, it wasn't without its problems. Clive Robertson had been hosting the programme and naturally resented Richard taking it over. Robertson had moved to a late-night news spot. When they bumped into each other in the corridor Robertson used to snarl at Richard. I mean snarl, like a cranky dog. Years later he wrote Richard a letter of apology. He had obviously had his problems with the network too. Richard was to know all about that but not for a couple of years.

So we zoomed into 1986 with our expectations high. The critics were indifferent about Richard's 'Eleven AM' debut.

I believed it was just a matter of time before he 'owned the chair', but his performance was often coloured by his moods.

We travelled a lot, grabbing short breaks in Queensland's Port Douglas and Noosa became a favourite escape for us. Frequently we stayed just south of Noosa at Peregian Beach with my friend of many years, Ross Stay. Ross had headed the Design School at East Sydney Technical College, and I had met him through Barbara, whom he had taught. Ross was a straightshooter with a wacky sense of humour, a passion for Egyptology and old movies. He could make us laugh like no other. I had been visiting him for many years. He knew all of my highs and lows in life, was always kind and kept my visits extremely private. The local press were frequently put off by Ross and he did it brilliantly. I know he felt happy for me when I first took Richard to meet him. He could see we were very much in love. A few days with Ross, in his sunny house, walking along the wonderful beach, was like a six months' resuscitation programme.

On one occasion I had been invited to the opening of the new Caloundra Racecourse, close by. The organisers decided to fly us into the course in a chopper which landed to collect us on the beach. Tottering across the sand in high heels and holding onto a silly hat wasn't my idea of a great way to start the day. But as Mother would say, 'They meant well.' When we reached the chopper, its blades whirling above our head, the pilot jumped out, grabbed the huge sliding door and shoved it open with all his might. It appeared all his might was too much. The door just kept travelling, landing some metres away in the sand. No amount of fiddling would get it back in place. Time was ticking away. Finally the pilot just strapped us in and up, up and away we went. I was terrified but Richard was worse, so I had to sit closest to the open door. Not gallant of him, I thought. It was like flying a mission in Vietnam. However, it was a good reason to drink a lot of champagne.

Back in Sydney, Sam Chisholm, the James Cagney look-alike head of Channel Nine, and his wife, Rhonda, invited us to dinner. I liked Sam. I always felt his bark was worse than his bite. But then I didn't work full-time at Channel Nine. I did, however, baby-sit a lot of programmes when their regular hosts were away, the worst being the 'Today Show'. This involved getting up at four am and trying to think sensibly. By six we had been given the final rundown for the programme. If the show's co-host, Steve Leibman, and the producer of the time, Ian Frykberg, hadn't generously nursed me through the week I don't think I'd have made it.

Knowing how the good drinks flow in Sam's presence I suggested we get a hire car for safety. Thank God I did. As I recall we were the first to arrive. Sam and Richard downed a couple of enormous beers while we waited for the other guests. And what a star-studded media group they were: Gerald and Irene Stone, Mike and Kerry Carlton, Max and Geraldine Walsh, Ian and Caroline Frykberg. Richard was more than impressed, and his glass seemed to empty faster and more frequently than anyone else's. Suddenly to my horror I heard Richard's voice rise aggressively. He and Max were in some sort of heated debate and Richard was leaning across the table and wagging his finger at Max. That stopped all other conversation, and then all the boys got into it.

I knew I had to get Richard out of there. I called our car, tried to joke and keep the conversation going until, with Sam's help, I could ease Richard out and away from the table. In the car he turned green. I was furious with him. He kept saying Sam must have doctored his drink. 'Which one of the thousand?' I said. He was turning an even stranger colour. As we came over the Harbour Bridge I just had time to tell the driver to stop and Richard heaved. Fortunately not in the car. It was very embarrassing. At home he was extremely ill. I put him to bed, bathed his face with cold towels and eventually he went to sleep.

I lay awake for a long time, thinking it was probably the most unbearable social occasion of my life. I was mortified, and I hoped he would be too in the clear light of the morning. This wasn't how you built a good reputation and a solid career. All that boozy boys' journo stuff just wasn't on any more and certainly not in that circle. This wasn't the first time I'd seen Richard out of control. Unfortunately it wasn't to be the last, either. The next day I suggested he phone our host and the other guests and apologise. He was filled with remorse but I don't think he really learnt from the lesson at all.

Country Girl

I T WAS in May 1986, on a chilly morning, when I slammed the door of the white house to drive to one of those terrible six am makeup calls. I'd been filming television commercials for many years and still couldn't figure out why makeup calls had to be at such indecent hours. There were always hold-ups, technical or temperamental. And you could bet your bippy you'd be lucky to get in front of a camera and speak two lines before they said, 'Break for lunch!' As a precaution against boredom I usually took a good book but on this particular day I scooped up *The Wentworth Courier*, the local real estate bible off the front step, thinking it would fill in the hours. I'm crazy about real estate and the old *Wentworth* is always a good read and dream.

That's where I found Boree Bills, or rather that's where Boree Bills found me. I do believe houses find people. At the bottom of a page, tucked away from the big glossy eastern suburbs agents' ads, was a tiny line drawing of what looked like a small French farmhouse. The advertisement simply said: 'Stone Cottage for Sale.' It was like a magnet. I kept leafing back to it. I had some knowledge of the area; the McDonald Valley, better known as the Forgotten Valley, was up through Wisemans Ferry. Jan Geary and her husband John had at one stage owned a small property there, where Jan rode her horses and I'd spent the occasional weekend as their house guest.

Although I'd never harboured a desire to 'go country', I knew Richard loved the bush and felt it was a part of his life that he would miss. We both enjoyed my boat and nosing around Sydney Harbour, but maybe it was time for a change. When I got home I showed him the ad and suggested we contact the Sydney agents. They had a couple of photographs so I prepared dinner while Richard drove down to Double Bay to collect them. Though blurry, they showed a house of some considerable charm. Richard agreed it would be great to have a weekend retreat. A phone call to Barb, who I consulted on all my property buys, and we decided to drive up to see the cottage the following weekend.

We met the local agent, Ian Robinson, at Wisemans Ferry. It was a glorious, cold, crisp, sunny day; the road into the valley was truly terrible. Eventually we crossed an ancient wooden bridge, worn and twisted from years of floods, but bravely still standing. We drove down an embankment, across a shallow river and on to Boree Bills. The property — fences, sheds, outbuildings and twenty-five acres — looked a bit tired, but the house? Well, the house was something special, and it did look like a French farmhouse.

The two main sandstone rooms were part of the original structure, which the agent figured was more than one hundred years old. 'Squire' Baily had raised eleven kids in those two rooms and carved his initials in a verandah stone before he left in 1905. Clever and sympathetic extensions were added in 1983. Eventually we met the man responsible for them, Peter Robbins, who was living on an adjacent property in another unusual house he'd also built.

In the extensions, thankfully, the 'new' was 'old'. Old slate roofing tiles covered the floor of the two main rooms; the timber ceiling beams, felled on the property, were left in their natural state. The tall internal wall, which ran the entire length of the main living room, and a huge eat-in kitchen were creatively constructed from panelled doors salvaged along with a timber staircase from a demolished Surry Hills mansion. As were the two main stone fireplaces, skilfully reconstructed to match the cottage originals. On the down side, the timber was painted a dull brown, and some of the ceilings a lethal tobacco tan. There seemed to be built-in bunks everywhere and the bathroom could only be described as primitive. It obviously required a lot of TLC. But the house had good bones, and Barb and I immediately knew we could really do something with it.

I also instantly knew I couldn't do without it! I couldn't even risk letting it go to auction, so an offer was made there and then. Followed a couple of days later by a larger offer and suddenly Boree Bills was mine, or 'ours' as I always referred to it. I didn't want Richard to feel uncomfortable about my funding our life. I felt he had given up a lot to come to be with me and I never had any concerns about who owned what, so I always said 'ours'. Ironically, Richard frequently said 'mine'.

The former owner was a sweet man. He said he was getting old. His wife was ill and he just found it all too much. I bought his old David Brown tractor, some harrows, a slasher, twenty head of Hereford cattle, and even a few pieces of furniture, including a great rocking chair his father had made. I still have it today. While they moved out I used the time to assemble the furnishings for the farm in the double garage of the white house. I couldn't have done it without Barb's help. We made lists on lists on lists. We drove each other bonkers, daily phoning with some new 'essential' for the list.

Left: The 'Beauty and the Beast' gang on the cover of *TV Times*. 'Beast', Eric Baume, and a few of the 'beauties': from left to right, Dita Cobb, me, Pat Firman and Hazel Phillips. I'm wearing my Mexicana black dress, which I wore ad nauseam on the programme. As you can see, eye makeup at the time was seriously BIG!

Below: Stuart Wagstaff, Pat Firman and me strutting our stuff at the Perth Telethon, having a ball and belting out 'Together, Wherever We Go'.

MAGGIE'S BOY
'He's so handsome, so divine'

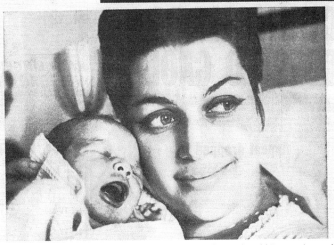

The front page of *The Daily Mirror*, 7 September 1967, with two-day old Francescino and his proud mum. (Copyright *The Daily Mirror*)

I had many famous guests on the 'Maggie' show. Here I am interviewing Sir Robert Helpmann and, above, dancing with Ronnie Arnold. One a gentleman of classical ballet, the other of jazz dance.

Mad hairstyles by Xenon, photographed by David Franklin and used for the 'Maggie' show credits. (Courtesy Channel Seven)

Above: Winning gold — Gerard Kennedy and me at the 'Logies'. Incidentally, this was the dress Ronnie Fraser borrowed for my send-up on the 'Mavis Bramston Show'. (Courtesy Pacific Publications)

Left: Me and my shipmates cruising the Pacific Islands: 'Ugly' Dave Grey, Diana 'Bubbles' Fisher and Stuart Wagstaff. *Up front:* 'The King', Graham Kennedy and Joe Hasham.

My darling, funny friend Ronnie Fraser. I still miss him.

My agent Harry M. Miller. He has steered me through almost thirty years of contracts and negotiated my divorce from Ettore Prossimo and my split from Richard Zachariah, proving he is also my friend.

My much-loved daughters, as teenagers.

The trade launch of the Maggie T range at the Sydney Hilton in 1980. My business partner, Carl Dowd, and I are in the centre, surrounded by licensees and models. Second from the left in the back row is my friend and Maggie T's PR director, Pam Darraugh.

I was Fashion Editor of *The Australian Women's Weekly* for fifteen years and frequently cover girl. Amazingly on one occasion I even ousted Lady Di and Prince Charles — they were relegated to a small box! *Top:* Launching the Maggie T range, March 1981, left; my first issue as Fashion Editor, August 1981, right. *Bottom:* With my grandson, Marco, July 1991, left; with Richard Zachariah, October 1992, right. (Courtesy Australian Consolidated Press)

At a *Women's Weekly* birthday bash. Max Gillies as Robert Menzies, complete with eyebrows! Me, Kerry Packer and David McNicoll as ourselves.

In New York at the National Television Council's Emmy Awards. Peter Wynne, left, Peter Faiman, right, and I received a special citation for *The Australian Women's Weekly* Australian Fashion Awards, screened on Channel Nine in 1982. And don't we look pleased with ourselves!

Couches were made by Freedom. 'No, Maggie,' said Barb, 'you can't have white canvas in the country.' I compromised with sand linen. I bit the bullet and invested in two glorious tables. One a three and a half metre long dining table in early Australian pine, another a magnificent server for the living room. Richard discovered two old chests in, of all places, Noosa. One stencilled with the trade name 'Singer Sewing Machine Company'. A third Barb found in a friend's shed. I got to it with my trusty Black & Decker sander, and to this day feel proud of its handsome restoration. There was bedding, a new stove, first and second fridges (necessary as the corner shop was a good hour's drive away). We even got down to linen, pots and pans, crockery, cutlery, needles and pins. It seemed endless. Both our cars were now parked on the street as the garage was chockers with all the furniture for Boree Bills.

Finally the big moving day arrived. The 'Game to go anywhere removalist', China Bear, loaded 'the farm' into the pantechnicon. Barb and I crawled aboard my little car with all the food and wine for the weekend, and off we set. One hitch was discovering the power would not be connected until the next day. We stopped and bought candles and ice. We were nervous about the van crossing the river but it was fine. Getting up a steep and slippery drive proved to be a bit heart-stopping but they made it. By the time Richard arrived after work that evening Barb and I had the entire place in order. Beds made, fires blazing, candles aglow. Without electricity for the stove we barbecued chops over the kitchen fire, made a simple salad and opened a bottle of good red to celebrate. Well two, actually. I thought, I have never been happier in my life. I was in love. My man was there, my best friend was there, the house glowed. It was a very special night.

Over the following weeks the house changed considerably. The down brown was painted a rich dark green that Taubmans patiently mixed and remixed until we had the perfect colour. We painted the entire interior white (that's no surprise) with the exception of the panelled wall of doors which was already painted just the right 'aged' mellow cream. We hired a local tradesman to create a tiered rockery garden across the back of the house, built with huge stones from the property. We also built a barbecue, which was much used and loved. We extended the narrow front verandah and topped it with old slate roofing tiles found in Peter Robbins' garage. It was the perfect place for breakfast or a sundowner.

There were some natural hitches I had to come to terms with. The flies drove me mad, but Richard finally persuaded me not to be so 'townie'. A fly's a fly, let it fly in one side of the house and eventually it will fly out the other. He was right. The fieldmice had to be persuaded to move out. And I learnt to keep all food stocks in sealed containers just in case the mice decided to move back in, which they did every year when the rains came. When we first bought the place the owner told us about a rather large goanna that had got in under the roof and fell through the bedroom ceiling! My heart stopped. But we didn't see it until a couple of months after we moved in. It was a particularly warm, sunny winter's day. Richard and I were alone at the farm and we decided to have a barbecue. I'd marinated some pork fillets and made a delicious salsa. Richard loved to cook on the barbecue. He was quite inept in the kitchen but king of the barbie. I was wandering around, fiddling in the garden, with a glass of white in my hand. At the rear of the house was an old stone and timber table. I don't know why but I stood up on it and looked up over the big slanting roof of the house, straight into the yellow-green eyes of this huge, I mean seriously huge, goanna. I'm not sure which of us got the bigger shock. I let out a bloodcurdling yell. It took off and up over the roof.

Richard nearly dropped dead in shock. It wasn't to be our last encounter. Mr Goanna and his two-metre long missus regularly popped by.

On one occasion, a scorching hot day, Richard had flaked out after lunch on the couch in one of the big downstairs rooms, which were wonderfully cool in summer. The doors onto the verandah were open. A hissing noise woke him and it was his turn to look into those yellow-green eyes. Richard ran to the door just in time to see Mr and Mrs Goanna disappearing down the slope, waddling along at the speed of sound. After that we saw them up trees, by the dam or simply passing by across the verandah. Soon they just became part of the landscape, often giving heart-stopping moments to visitors. But by then I was wonderfully blasé about them. Greg, our local handyman, did give me some concern when he told me straightfaced, 'If you see a goanna, lie down. Otherwise he might think you're a tree and try and climb you.' Oh great, Greg! The one thing I never got used to were the black snakes. Richard downed one with a shovel as it was very close to the house. Another in the rockery one day 'got away'. 'Got away to where?' I yelled.

I wasn't amused when after months of toil in my garden, the cows broke in and ate the lot. But as one of the locals said, it could be worse and at least they fertilised as they went. Our small herd of Herefords provided us with great joy. They all had names. The gang leaders being 'Maudie', 'Old Roney' and 'Cussons Mum'. Maudie provided us with our first birth, twins aptly called Black and Decker. After all, it was my contract with Black & Decker that had largely funded buying the farm. 'Cussons Mum' was named after Cussons Imperial Leather, for which I'd also made a commercial. I discovered that the only problem about naming your cattle is sending them off to market. I cried every time and our local transport man used to say I made him feel like a monster, bawling my eyes out while he loaded the cattle for market.

Early one evening when we had a house full of guests we discovered a cow in distress. She wasn't going to deliver her calf without help. All hands were called and we rounded her up, got her into the crush, and Richard prepared to pull the calf. He succeeded, but my rather lavish dinner was barely touched by our guests who were all feeling decidedly squeamish. When the feed got low our cows turned feral. They would break into Peter's place next door, and either Richard or I would have to load bales of hay onto the tractor and go and lead them back with promises of a big dinner. 'Come on, Maudie. Come on, Roney. Come on.' They would amble along, drooling, and we would lock them back where they belonged. Two days later we would be doing it all again. Or they would break into the big open shed where we kept bales of feed. In the absence of a front wall Richard had strung a hot wire across the shed. It worked for a while, but then the cows would simply break it down and help themselves.

I had always been a good runner at school and I could beat any kid on our block in a race down the length of our street. This speed came in handy at Boree Bills when the cows broke out of the paddock and were heading into our newly planted avenue of trees along the driveway. I took off and beat the bastards to the open gate, much to the amazement of a gaggle of friends who were lunching with us. There was great hilarity. 'Boy, Mags, you sure as hell can move!' one of them exclaimed. Richard was the most astonished: 'Jeez, old girl, I wouldn't have believed it if I hadn't seen it with my own eyes!'

One Friday I drove up to the farm early. Richard and guests were to arrive that evening, and I wanted to have everything ready and dinner prepared. I had opened the house, unpacked the food, picked flowers and generally got it all in order, when

I heard a strange noise. I wandered down to the shed and to my horror there was Maudie, lying down. 'You naughty old bugger,' I said. 'How dare you break in and feed your face, and now you're so full you can't get up.' Then I noticed her front leg. It was caught in the blades of the harrow. I thought, don't panic, Maggie, for God's sake, don't panic. Think it through.

I knew Peter wasn't home next door and our other neighbours, Jenny and Walter Cavill, hadn't arrived. I'd noticed their car wasn't there. Everyone else was too far away. Maudie was distressed. She tried to stand and fell back. I started to talk to her in what I hoped were comforting cowy tones. 'There, there, Maudie. Hang on. I'm here to help, we can do this.' I thought I was soothing the cow, more likely I was soothing myself. I stood and took in the situation. Standing her straight up was not the answer. I had to get the hoof to slide back, then out of the blades. Still talking to her I went around to drag the harrow back away from her hoof. She panicked and tried to stand again. I was terrified she would break her leg. But I sensed she knew I was trying to help her. I backed off, talking more and more. 'There, there, Maudie. It will be alright, old girl.' I sat down on a bale of hay and thought about it for a minute. If I approached her from the front her natural inclination would be to back off. Hopefully it would work. Somehow, don't ask me how, it did. She backed off, heaved, pulled, strained and pulled some more, and the foot came free. She could barely stand but she hobbled off down the paddock to join her mates.

I was shaking from head to toe. I headed inside and poured myself a very large, very stiff drink. Richard, when he heard the story later that night, was thrilled and proud of me. 'I'll make a bushy of you yet,' he said. Eventually he did. The sad thing is that by then he didn't want to be a bushy himself.

We bought a horse from a neighbour down the valley, a white

stock horse called Cobber. He was a gentle giant. Not a great ride and a bit undisciplined but Richard enjoyed poking around the property on him. Richard and the Cavills would ride every couple of weeks up over the rise and come back thirsty and tired. Richard then bought a horse from the Hunter Valley, a polocrosse pony called B.A. It didn't take us long to work out how he got the name. He was very definitely B.A! One day Richard suggested I take Cobber, he would take B.A. and we would go for a ride on a deserted property adjacent to Boree Bills.

I hadn't been on a horse for years. I wasn't confident but I wanted to please Richard. It would be fun if I could gain my courage and we could go riding together. We mounted up. He went ahead and led Cobber. It was a superb day. The kookaburras sent us off with a laugh. (Perhaps they knew something I didn't.) The crested doves were busy in the bushes and our resident eagle was working the river with his enviable grace — gliding, diving, rising on the current. Just wonderful. We gently eased across the river and worked our way along the track. My bum and legs were starting to talk to me, and after a while I suggested we head back. We had just turned for home when Cobber decided he'd like to travel a different path. He went straight off the track and down a steep embankment. Whoa! Heading for a stand of poplar trees at considerable speed, I have no idea how I stayed on. But I did, and somehow reined him in. By the time Richard had caught up with me we were both as white as the horse. I walked the last half mile home, on very shaky pins. I kept thinking how silly it was to risk my bones with a fall. I had to work. I had contracts in train. No, I'd better leave riding alone.

Boree Bills became the centre of our life. It was wonderful having neighbours in and friends up to stay. I had to lug all the food and wine and laundry to and fro, but it was worth it. I simply kept a large pad and made lists and more lists. I loved the challenge of running it efficiently. And there was Mr Bliss. Oh dear, dear Mr Bliss. He was a large ginger cat. The previous owner had suggested we inherit him, and we were thrilled to take him in. Prior to our arrival he hadn't been allowed past the front door, but he very quickly wangled his way into the house, our hearts and lives.

He was fiercely independent. A large box sat on the back verandah, which we kept stocked with a bag of his favourite food and a warm rug. He lived happily there during the week, but come Friday he would sit high on a sandstone outcrop below the house and await our arrival. As we hit the drive he would dart across the garden and be there at the gate to greet us, purring like mad and pushing into our legs for a cuddle. In the evening he would sit on the back of the couch nestled into Richard's neck. Richard loved Mr Bliss. They were great mates. Put out at night, at dawn he would position himself below our bedroom window. As soon as I drew the curtain back he would call us. I'd go down and let him in and he'd dart up to the bedroom and settle on the end of the bed. If it were really freezing, well, what the hell, we'd let him sleep at Richard's feet. I imagined my mother would have been horrified: 'An animal's place is outside, Margaret.' Sorry Mum.

We had been at Borees a couple of years when the vacant property next door was sold. We noticed a large flash car driving in and out, but we hadn't met the new owners. There was only a ruin of a house on the land so they never stayed. Then we learnt that a development action had been approved for the land. On further investigation we discovered it was to be a conference centre: a series of accommodation huts and a central building. All this on a property that not only had a high fire risk but a flood-prone river crossing the only access in and out of it.

Along with our neighbours we went to council and protested. While the development was put on hold because of our challenge I received the most unusual of letters. Amazingly it came from a well-respected, high-profile legal firm in Sydney, but the language and tone of the letter was decidedly threatening. It more or less stated that unless I withdrew my opposition the new owner would have no alternative but to lease the property to the Comanchero Bike Club. Members of this gang, incidentally, were currently up on murder charges. A council meeting was scheduled. The new owner presented his plans for the property, finishing with a heart-felt plea as to his honourable intentions to respect the environment, consider the aesthetics, etc, etc. With our neighbours and the help of Ian Robinson, our local agent, we had done our homework. We could estimate traffic flow on an inadequate road and several other factors that obviously made the development both dangerous and unsympathetic to the valley. These were presented by Walter Cavill. Then it was my turn. I addressed council, reiterating the safety problems and said, 'I would like to tender to council a letter I have received from the developer's solicitors. I believe it clearly indicates the true nature of this man, his questionable intentions and disregard for the valley.' Case closed. Development denied.

Christmas at Borees was both a challenge and a joy. Planning menus for a houseful of family and friends took some doing. One year the temperature soared above forty. I recall my dear English friend, Libby Reeves Purdy, coming down for breakfast wearing a short pink jumpsuit. She is blonde and as pretty as a picture, but by eight am her face was as pink as her suit. Our neighbour, Walter, played the organ at the local church, and one Christmas we all trundled off for evening service and sang our hearts out. Then we wound our way back; a river of car lights travelling home to Borees where we dined and laughed to the wee hours of the morning. They were truly happy, happy days.

We talked with our neighbours, the Cavills and the Slaneys, about each putting in a swimming pool. I can't recall who came up with the idea but it made sense to arrange a joint deal. By the time they started to dig the three pools a huge wet descended. It was a painful, expensive and protracted business, but finally we all had our pools. It changed our summers at Borees. We spent hours floating in it or simply going for a quick dunk then getting on with whatever business was at hand. Sometimes I'd be cooking, run out, jump in and be back at the stove in less than a minute, totally refreshed.

I bought a ride-on mower and took on the responsibility of keeping the lawn and drive neat. I'd be out there for hours mowing away as happy as Larry. We made improvements to the property, putting in water storage tanks and a pump, planting the drive with trees and building the garden. Richard and our neighbour Peter would do a 'cool' burn in the evening on the hill behind the house. I hated it but the fire hazard in summer was very real. Many a time we drove through considerable fires along the road to get to Borees. I felt afraid for the safety of the house on more than one occasion, sitting on the verandah at night watching the fires come up or down the valley.

One of the most joyous times I experienced at Boree Bills was a solitary moment. Richard had burnt off a huge cluster of reeds in the centre of one of the main paddocks, and it was decided we would plough them back into the land. I went down to take my turn on the tractor. I was covered in black soot, but happily driving up and down. There's a great sense of achievement in getting the lines straight. Richard had shown me how to do it and I loved it. I was ploughing along, watching the kookaburras dive in for dinner and in a second of great clarity

I thought, I am blissfully happy. I'm dirty, dusty, tired, in love and very happy. I love this land and I don't look anything like the public Maggie Tabberer. Great!

The only problem with Boree Bills proved to be the river. The crossing was really nothing more than some heavy rocks sunk across the river bed with a few steel guideposts at one side. When the river rose we could only see the tips of these posts. If it really rose and the posts disappeared, which they did frequently, then we said a prayer, took aim at the road on the other side, gritted our teeth and drove into it. I always took the precaution of opening all the windows of the Range Rover before I drove through, believing that if the car went under and the electrics failed I wouldn't be able to get out. If the rain bucketed down I'd spend an uneasy night, driving Richard mad — who incidentally could sleep through anything — waking him every hour or so to ask, 'Darling, should we pack up and get out?'

I had work commitments and getting flooded in just wasn't responsible. Eventually it happened. I called Kerry Packer's secretary, Pat Wheatly, who gave me the number of a reliable chopper pilot. He flew in, snatched us up and took us to Sydney, in time for Richard to make the studio and me to fly to Melbourne for Maggie T. It proved a very expensive weekend. On several occasions our neighbour, Walter, came to the rescue with his little boat. Richard would wade across with a rope, holding tight to the steel posts and occasionally disappearing from view in a hole. Then he would tie the rope to a tree on the other side. We would load up the boat with our weekend supplies and, using the rope to secure the boat, hand over hand, ease our way to the other side across the rapid flowing waters. I was never really comfortable with this method of transport but grateful to Walter anyway. He and Richard loved it. I guess it was gung-ho boys' adventure stuff. On one occasion we had a house full of guests who had to risk the rising water and wade out at dawn. Thank God we had taken the precaution of parking their cars on the other side of the river. They all drove home with damp bums.

The worst experience I had was arriving one sunny Friday to find the river up and flowing fast. I looked at it for a while then thought I'd better be cautious, so I drove further up the valley to where Peter Robbins was building another house. I explained I was a bit nervous about the water level, but he laughed and assured me he'd come out only an hour before and it was fine. I went back, eyed the level, concluded it looked dangerous but decided Peter really knew what he was talking about. So I took a deep breath, said a prayer and all alone, slowly drove in. At one stage the water swept over the bonnet of the Range Rover and I almost died but I made it to the other side, cursing Peter. Later that afternoon he rang, concerned and apologetic. He was in the local pub because he couldn't get across to his house. The river had risen a couple of metres from the time he had gone out that morning and he was fearful for my safety, if impressed with my courage. By this stage I had decided it wasn't courage but stupidity. When Richard came up later that afternoon, Walter got out the boat and he made it across to keep me company.

After a while we started pleading with the council for a new crossing. They'd come along, drop a few more rocks in the river to raise the crossing a little, then another flood would sweep the rocks away. It was hopeless. The alternative was to build a serious cement crossing but it would be expensive. As there were only three houses on our side, that was not really viable. I understand a fine crossing is now in place.

One year we were hit with a very big wet. Don Burke had asked if he could film our garden for his programme. As the day drew near I had to phone from Sydney and explain about the flood waters. I also mentioned I was anxious about Mr Bliss.

'Great!' said the producer. 'We'll chopper you in, you can feed the cat and we can knock off some footage for the show. It will be fantastic.' Mmm, another member of the gung-ho boys' club, I thought. Well, I'm not particularly mad about helicopters, but flying up the Forgotten Valley that day was an experience, looking down onto the swollen river, which had flooded out across roads, farms and bridges. We circled Boree Bills and there on his rock, as though by some instinct he knew I was coming, sat a little ginger and white cat, Mr Bliss. The chopper frightened the hell out of him as it landed, but I called and he came quickly, purring like crazy and pushing his nose into my legs. I put a big new bag of feed in his box, gave him an enormous saucer of milk and a cuddle, then with Don explored the house.

There was little damage save for some water under the ground-floor bedroom door. I checked the cows and horses. All was well, so we climbed aboard and flew away. A couple of weeks later Don returned, by road this time, with his crew and we filmed a nice piece on our humble garden for 'Burke's Backyard'.

Full Speed Ahead

MY DIARY records a frantic business year in 1986. Three constant messages I wrote to myself that year were: 'Just do it'; 'Must achieve etc, etc, etc'; 'Keep free to die!' I look back and wonder how Richard and I had time to have so much fun. Along with all my other commitments I was still recording voice-overs for Val Morgan's Cinema Advertising, which I had been doing for the past ten years with my old mate Graham Kennedy. No one could dispute Graham's great talent. I only had to look at him to laugh. He had a quick-fire wit and you could never, ever top him.

Once a month he and I would sit in a recording studio for a few hours opposite each other with a tall stack of commercials typed on cards. He'd read one, I'd read one. No rehearsal, just do it! We plugged everything from smash repairs to floral arrangements, health studios to hiring ditch diggers and drotts. Graham couldn't help the odd irreverent remark and I'd break up and get the giggles. So he'd grab my card and read the commercial, then say, 'Now they'll have to pay me more.' We started getting fan letters. 'Hated the movie, loved the commercials,' said one. But Graham could also be maddening.

On one occasion he arrived in a bad mood. The young girl from the agency had asked us to keep the cards for each theatre in order after we read them and slip the rubber band on at the conclusion. It would save her hours of sorting them later. I thought that was reasonable but it seemed to inflame Graham's mood. He started to read his cards and toss them off the table onto the floor. In a break I suggested this was pretty mean, not to mention childish, but he continued to do it. When we finished he made a grab to scatter my cards. I slammed my hand down hard on top of his. 'No, Graham, don't.' For the first time since we had begun working together I raised my voice and gave him a no-holds-barred opinion of his behaviour. He never tried it again. As difficult as he could sometimes be, generally he was adorable.

We once had to record the ads for a theatre in Perth. We started to read. The first commercial was for a Thai restaurant, the second for a Chinese, the third for an Italian. No one had bothered to tell us that it was restaurant special, and it amused us no end. I mean, where were the florists, swimming pools, smash repairs and hiring of ditch diggers and drotts? Kennedy moved into top gear, his ad libs were hysterically funny. I really lost it. We were both laughing so hard I couldn't continue. 'No, no Graham, stop. We must do this sensibly.'

'No, no,' he said, 'carry on, carry on.'

He refused to go back and record again. The director had no alternative but to keep going — you didn't argue with Mr Kennedy. Val Morgan had to send the tape to Perth. The theatre probably only ran it for one night, because all you could hear was hysterical laughter. Val Morgan behaved generously considering the lost business. They did, however, request that Mr Miller pull us into line. I have a tape somewhere of that recording. Harry Miller says he plays his copy when he wants to have a good laugh.

IN JUNE that year I received a citation for my services to fashion from the Fashion Group of Australia, which is associated with the original Fashion Group founded in New York. Its key members are all involved in fashion: editors, writers, designers, promoters and publicists. It is always flattering to receive an award, but this one was very special because it came from my peers. I guess all those years as a columnist, a fashion promoter and designer had established my name in the industry. How lucky I am to have worked for so many years in an industry I love so much.

RICHARD AND I made a commitment early in our relationship to always do everything together, so I was reluctant to accept an offer to go with Ray Martin to London in July to cover the Sarah Ferguson and Prince Andrew Royal Wedding for the Nine Network. Harry was insistent and Richard reluctantly agreed. So for the first time in our relationship we were separated.

I had a maxi-length cream coat made to go over matching trousers and a cream beret of the same fabric. I figured that on camera a hat with a brim would cast shadows on my face. I had a job to do and I wanted to be comfortable. When Richard saw the beret he said, 'Well, darling, if it blows off don't chase it!' Now that's how to boost a girl's confidence. I flew to London.

Ray Martin is always easy to work with but we were sorely tested. We had both spent a few busy days filming stories for the hours-long television coverage. Then came the big day. While the rest of the world press were stationed in one location, we were to telecast from the open top of a double-decker bus, brilliantly parked by the Nine Network almost opposite the main entrance to Westminster Abbey, with a clear view of the street where the royal carriages would arrive. Our surprise guest was none other than Dame Edna Everage. The interior of an adjacent bus was fitted out as a makeup, wardrobe and rest room. I found myself standing in my trousers and a bra pressing my coat. I glanced up and there at the other end was the Dame pulling on her pantihose before stepping into a screaming wattle-yellow silk ensemble. I did think, The world is mad, mad!

Up atop the bus we got into position for a live cross. We had some time to fill before the wedding carriages arrived, and the producer had arranged live link-ups all over England to illustrate how the Brits were reacting to the Royal Wedding Day. I was given a long voice-over script. The Red Berets were to parachute into some small town and Ray and I had to voice over a mini history of both the famous Red Berets and the town. The problem was that the script was cued to the visual — a visual we quickly discovered we couldn't see on our monitor because of the suddenly bright English sunshine. Who could anticipate bright English sunshine? So there we were looking at each other in growing panic as the countdown diminished. We bumbled along reading bits of the script and ad libbing the rest, hoping to hell both the visual and our commentary would finish in unison. I think it did.

Then, like a sunny tornado, Dame Edna arrived on top of the bus and the Aussie crowd gathered below went bananas. She tossed her ever-ready gladioli at the gathering and said, on camera, that my hat looked as though I'd baked the wedding cake! Ray was doubled over with laughter. At last the royal carriages started to arrive. Princess Anne spotted the Dame and waved so hard she nearly toppled out of her carriage. In fact all the royals acknowledged the Dame. Some with a gentle nod, others including Fergie, Anne and Edward with enthusiastic waving. Only the Queen turned her head away, but was she smiling?

From London I went on to Europe to visit my daughters. Amanda came from Positano, where she was now living with her beautiful Sergio Bella, to meet me in Rome. We shopped

and talked, talked and shopped for two days then flew to
Athens. Brooke, who had been travelling the world working for
Club Med, arranged for a car to drive us a few hours north to
Gregolemano. We arrived there late in the afternoon, just in time
to catch a ferry to the club village on the island of Evia. It was
a gorgeous reunion. A hot summer's night, blessed with a full
moon. Because I'm always so horribly organised I had packed a
couple of my favourite white linen pieces in the top of my
suitcase, wrapped in tissue paper to avoid crushing. So when
Brooke told us we had to hurry to the restaurant to catch the
last serving of dinner, I was dressed in a flash.

The restaurant was packed but we squeezed into a table on a
narrow balcony overlooking the sea and that incredible moon.
There's a strong family feeling amongst the kids who work for
Club Med. They were all keen to meet Amanda and me, and to
join us so the table was rather crowded. I was Brooketta's Mum,
not Maggie Tabberer. It was a nice feeling. The waiter appeared
with an enormous platter piled with pasta in a rich, red sauce.
He had to lean across behind me to serve Amanda. I felt something warm on the top of my head. It moved in a slow slide
down my neck. I was looking straight at my daughters' faces.
I watched their parallel expressions, first horror, then disbelief
and then the little buggers both broke into peals of laughter.

Brooke blurted out, 'Yannis, what are you doing to my mother?'

Suddenly I realised the warm feeling was the pasta. A big
rich, red pasta! It had slid off his tray onto my head and down
my neck. Now there are two things my daughters tell me I'm
manic about, my hair and my white linen both have to be perfect.
Dear Yannis had got both in one! Even I had to laugh. The girls
took me to the nearest bathroom where, doubled over with
mirth, they picked the pasta from my hair and sponged the
sauce from my white linen shirt. They then sat me under the

blower hand-drier. In fifteen minutes I was back at the table to a round of applause from the entire restaurant.

After a few glorious days in the sun with my daughters it was time to say goodbye, drive back to Athens and fly home to Richard. I recall thinking that absence makes more than the heart grow fonder. We were still passionate about each other. Most lovers have pet names for each other. I almost cringe as I write this but I was Boobie and Richard was Boobie. How our friends put up with our 'Boobie?' 'Yes Boobie?' 'Oh Boobie, so-and-so', I don't know but when you're in love you're in love. And we were. Truly, madly, deeply. Oh Boobie!

Amazingly, my fiftieth birthday was approaching. Naturally I didn't want to know about it but friends don't let you forget these things. As one pointed out, 'It's hardly a secret, darling. The world knows you're going to be fifty.' For the past few years my kids had always surprised me with a party of sorts. One year I thought I was going off for a quiet family dinner. I drove around to collect Barb, we were to meet the kids at the restaurant. Barb complained of a headache and asked to pop back to my place for a Panadol. I parked the car in the garage and made a dash up the stairs to be greeted by 'Surprise, surprise,' and forty friends screaming, 'Happy Birthday.' How they did it I'll never know. I'd only been gone twenty minutes but there were all these people in my house, not to mention waiters, food and champagne. It was terrific.

Another year I'd declared it a 'cancelled due to a lack of interest birthday', and headed out onto Sydney Harbour with just a couple of friends. I planned to dine later with the family at home. We moored at my beloved Taylors Bay and suddenly pulling alongside came my old friends Georgie and Snow Swift in their beautiful yacht and on the other side was another friend in his cruiser, followed by Nicolas in his speedboat.

'What's going on? How did you know I'd be here?' I yelled.

Then bursting out from all three craft came Amanda, Brooke and a gaggle of other mates. They had all brought fabulous food, bubbly and gifts galore, including a blow-up rubber dinghy, which was the best present ever from my kids. I'd paddle around in it for hours. We tied the boats together and had, as they say, a ball. There's nothing like a good surprise.

But in 1986, for my fiftieth, I decided I'd give myself a party. A super-duper party. My friends Sarah and Henry Crawford generously offered their stunning home in Woollahra. Sarah came from the well-known Victorian Darling family. 'Darling by name, darling by nature,' I used to say to her. She had met Richard years before in Melbourne. Henry had produced the very successful Australian film *A Town Like Alice*. We had spent a lot of time together since Richard's arrival in Sydney, sitting around the big handsome table in their stylish kitchen. Sarah could send Richard up better than anyone I know. After staying a weekend at Boree Bills once, she said to Richard, 'Do you always blow-dry your hair on Sundays?' She could understand why he would blow-dry it on work days for television. But Sundays? And at the farm?

We discussed caterers and decided, damn the expense, after all, a girl doesn't turn fifty every day. I would bring in Peter Rowlands, the exceptional Melbourne caterer, to manage the food, wine and staff. Sarah volunteered to do the flowers. Brooke organised a white baby grand piano and her friend, the musician David McLeod, to play it. I hired my old lighting mate Roger Foley to transform the garden, and Amanda and Sergio advanced their planned Christmas trip to be here by 11 December. I wrote invitations to fifty friends: 'Please join me for my fiftieth at the Crawfords …' Kerry Packer, when he read it, said he thought 'The Crawfords' was a new nightclub! Harry Watt and

George Gross made me a white silk duster coat with a jewelled 'T' and straight pants.

The evening arrived, golden and warm. We mingled for drinks in a perfect setting by the Crawfords' crystal pool. I'd made a gaff with the seating. I sat a certain gentleman next to a very attractive lady whose 'husband-to-be' was the ex-husband of the first man's current mistress! Oh good one, Margaret, I cursed myself. It didn't matter a fig. It seemed everyone was enjoying themselves. My dear mate Peter Weiss had been asked to say a few words. I said, 'Pete, make it brief, OK.' He did a brilliant job. Then I felt I had to thank a lot of people. I stood to their warm applause and I don't know what got into me, probably the champagne, but I started at one end of the room and simply went on and on, talking about each of my guests and why it was so important for me to have them there. I gave a sort of thumbnail sketch of our friendship. When I got to Kerry I said, 'Well, K.P. and I have a very special relationship. I know he's the boss, he sure as hell knows he's the boss, and that's that.' Everyone laughed. I sat down and the party resumed.

We were all rather merry, but out of the corner of my eye I noticed Pete Weiss and Richard in a huddle. A tiny alarm bell sounded but before I could move, Richard was on his feet. I remember thinking how handsome he looked in his white dinner jacket, tall, tan, terrific. 'How lucky can a fifty year old be?' I asked myself. And then he spoke. I knew he'd imbibed too much but nothing prepared me or anyone else for what he was about to say. He spoke of our love, our life, finding one another and then the unthinkable came out of his mouth. 'And finally I want you all to know, she's a fabulous fuck at fifty!' For a nanosecond you could have heard a pin drop. Everyone was stunned. Oh Richard, I thought, how could you? Again his tongue hadn't connected with any sort of barometer. I bit my lip to stop the tears of embarrassment. Embarrassment I felt more for Richard than myself. Someone coughed, someone giggled nervously. Then they broke into polite applause. I could feel every eye in the room on me. I had to bluff it. I smiled broadly, got up and hugged him. I loved this man so very much but by God I could have killed him at that moment. I'm sure he knew instantly his brand of humour was too lateral. It landed in the poor taste field, often to be mentioned, never to be forgotten.

When Richard and I finally broke up many years later, I had a call from my old friend David McNicoll, the *Bulletin* columnist, who had been there on the night. 'Well, Tabs,' he said from his hospital bed at St Vincent's where he was recovering from surgery, 'as far as I'm concerned and almost everyone else I know, he went downhill rapidly from the night he gave that outrageous speech at your fiftieth.'

I can't pretend that this was an isolated incident. Richard frequently spoke the unspeakable. His acid tongue quickly won him a reputation. Always after one of these incidents I would try to discuss it with him. He had two ways of dealing with this. One was to turn the argument around and criticise me: 'Where's your sense of humour, Maggie?' Or he would mumble a brief, half-baked apology and win me over by wrapping me in an embrace and kissing my neck. And as much as I adored having him kiss my neck, nothing would diminish the unease I felt with the slow realisation that this was perhaps the real Richard. I started to warn him to behave himself before we went out. Eventually I began to slowly remove us from those social occasions where I felt threatened by his possible bad behaviour. I refused a lot of invitations.

Richard and I continued to lead a frantically busy life. It was full and, I thought for the most part, great fun, but little by little I noticed some of my nearest and dearest friends seemed to be too busy to spend a weekend at the farm, or couldn't make it for dinner. Was I imagining it? I didn't want to believe the gnawing suspicion that it had to do with Richard's attitude so I just pushed it away. When we were alone it was great. Richard would always be sweeping me up in his arms, we would kiss passionately. I adored cooking special dinners for him, ironing the perfect shirt. We would play our music or watch a great movie. At home, alone, we were very happy, for some years anyway.

In a moment of sanity, I sold the boat. It seemed we were constantly torn: if we were on the boat we thought we should be at the farm. If at the farm, particularly in the heat, we wondered why in the hell weren't we on the boat? So I sold it, and I'm pleased to say, sold well. I had, after all, kept the *Maggie T* in immaculate condition. She had cost something to run and moor at d'Albora Marina but I'd spent very little on repairs, so I got back almost my entire initial outlay. I choked up as I walked down the dock away from her for the last time. I'd been good to the *Maggie T* but she had also been good to me. I had wonderful memories of happy days on the harbour.

There was only one sad note. A close friend who frequently came out on the boat with me enjoyed sunning herself on the deck. She had a very pale complexion, but she insisted on slathering herself with sun oil and baking to a rosy red. Eventually a small mole on her foot turned into a very nasty melanoma. There were anxious days leading up to and following the inevitable surgery. When I went to see her in hospital, Professor Bill McCarthy, head of the Melanoma Foundation and the man who saw my friend through both her surgery and recovery, asked me to be patron of the Melanoma Foundation. I told him I was not very good at speech making. However, he felt that if I could help publicise the danger of taking the sun I would fill my role.

I had heard about one of his patients, Mark Marcelis, and the brave battle he was fighting. The hideous thing about melanomas is that they often strike young people in the prime of their lives. This man was in his late twenties. As a young child he had migrated from England and taken to the Aussie sun, sea and surf with a vengeance. By the time the Prof examined an enlarged, dark and angry mole on his back it was unfortunately too late for Mark. He put up a great fight and courageously volunteered to have his story told. I rang Gerald Stone, then Executive Producer of '60 Minutes' and a friend. They filmed Mark's story. The reaction around Australia was incredible. People poured in to have spots, dots and moles diagnosed. The Prof estimated the coverage saved hundreds of lives. Sadly not Mark's. Gerald Stone, years later, recalled it as one of the most powerful stories he ever put to air. Like most Australians I'd spent a life getting sunburnt, but from that time on I became a fifteen-plus blockout person.

RICHARD AND I both loved travelling: short breaks interstate, racing and seeing his family in Melbourne, up to Queensland to visit my old friend Ross or stay in our favourite Noosa and, at least once a year, Europe. Although Richard was jealous of my relationship with my kids, particularly Amanda, he enjoyed our times with her and Sergio in the impossibly beautiful Positano, on Italy's Amalfi Coast. Visiting them there, it seemed, placed less strain than when they visited us in Australia.

In 1987 we planned an extensive trip to Europe. First England for some racing, Richard's new passion, then down to Rome, our favourite city in the world, and on to Positano late September. Amanda and Sergio were about to shut the restaurant for the season so they joined us in Florence. Amanda had lived and worked there, so she knew it well. I had loved it since Ettore took me there years before. Together we enjoyed introducing Richard to this beautiful, gentle city. The kids stayed for three days, we then kissed them goodbye and prepared to move on to France the next day. But back at the hotel Richard received a message to phone Christopher Skase in London.

Skase had recently bought the Seven Network. Richard had known him briefly back in his early Melbourne journalistic days and they had met at the station a few times since his takeover. But why was he phoning from London? We sat on the rock-hard beds, as they all seem to be in Italy, and looked at each other. I don't know how, but I just knew that Skase was going to offer Richard the evening news. I told Richard that if I was right he would have to think very seriously about it. The fact was that topping Brian Henderson on the Nine Network would be a big ask. Richard's work on 'Eleven AM' was relatively stress free as ratings in that slot were never going to be vital to the network. But the news was a different thing.

We discussed it thoroughly. I could see his mounting excitement. I desperately wanted Richard to be successful because that's what he wanted. However, I was realistic, and I knew this would not be an easy assignment. Those critics who were slipping the knife into Richard and 'Eleven AM' from time to time would be even more aggressive if he was reading the prime-time news. I found it difficult to explain this to Richard. I didn't want him to lose confidence but I did want him to acknowledge that taking this position would mean hard work, concentration and dedication. Early in our relationship Richard had said to me, 'Maggie, you learnt to work before you learnt to relax. I learnt to relax before I learnt to work.' His sister Amanda used to say he didn't really know what hard work was.

When Richard phoned, Skase asked if we could put our holiday on hold and fly to London to discuss something important.

Arrangements for tickets, car and hotel came through, along with a tap on our door later that evening. I answered it to a tree! Well, it looked like a tree. A diminutive porter stood struggling under a huge floral arrangement of lavish and ridiculous proportions. The card read: 'So sorry to interrupt your holiday. Regards, Christopher.' What a waste, I thought. After all, we were leaving the following day.

We arrived in London and spent a quiet evening speculating. Then the next morning I kissed Richard goodbye, wished him all the luck in the world and went to have my nails manicured to stop me biting them. I'll never forget the flushed and excited look on his face when he bounded in after the meeting. Yes, it was the news. Yes, Christopher had faith in him. Richard had never made a secret of the fact that he longed to be famous. I guess we both felt this was the first step. We packed and flew to the south of France, elated and in love.

We hired a car and drove up toward Paris. Before we had left Australia, Richard had told me I would have to do all the driving. He refused to drive in Europe. I didn't mind, it was tiring but in fact I preferred it.

THE REST of the year seemed to evaporate, but not before we were on the move again. My friends Alfredo Bouret and Lex Aitken had returned to Australia and were dining with us in the white house. I loved that little house but it wasn't really the best house to share with Richard. Women clean up as they go, men rarely, Richard never. I was spending a lot of time keeping that white house white! During dinner Lex mentioned that he knew of a house for sale in Hampden Avenue, Darling Point. It was federation style with a pool, gorgeous gardens and breathtaking harbour views. We abandoned dinner and drove around, not that we could see much. Like kids we were jumping up trying to look over the fence and into the front room. We made an appointment to see it.

The house did have a nice feel. It was also considerably larger and less hard edged and minimalist than the white house. Richard would be able to have his own study and bathroom. The pool was a plus and the view spectacular. On the down side, every room was wallpapered in a different fancy pattern and the floors were carpeted. But I knew that white paint and sisal floor coverings would make a difference. The one thing I couldn't afford to consider changing was the master bathroom. It was quite bizarre, with high-tech Italian fittings that included a round shower capsule. After I bought the house I never once stepped into the shower without saying, 'Beam me up, Scotty.'

As we moved the painters in and the fluffy carpet out, I prepared to sell the dear little white house. This was not without some heartache — I loved that house. It represented some important things in my life, such as taking charge. However, I sold it for more than I bought it, which was pleasing and it went to a nice man, a friend, Bani McSpeddon, the advertising whiz. Richard had no emotional ties with the white house. However, he was very excited about Hampden Avenue and he couldn't wait to move in. While it was being renovated we would often take a pizza and some wine and go around to sit on the top balcony, admire the view and eat our picnic dinner.

Sadly, it proved to be a difficult house to live in. It was three storeys high, I seemed endlessly to be running up or down stairs, having forgotten something I needed on another level. The day we moved in Barb and I began to arrange the furniture in the living room. Now we are both pretty skilled at this and it had never been a problem in the past. In each new house we always knew where each piece should go. But this long, skinny room had us beaten. 'Dear God, it looks like a bloody railway carriage,' I said, and promptly burst into tears.

We spent Christmas 1987 at Hampden Avenue, with friends and family seated around the pool for lunch. I lost about five kilos, zipping up and down those damn stairs to the kitchen. In the New Year Richard began to read the news on prime-time television for the Seven Network, with the beautiful Ann Sanders as his co-host. It was to prove very stressful. In my time on television I had always been fortunate, I had never really had a bad review. But I felt every negative review the critics gave Richard as if it were my own.

Two things he had in his favour were his looks and his tailor. He was voted by some visiting American matrons as the most handsome man on Australian television. However, the serious business of the daily news required something more. He would always expect me to watch the programme and tell him what I thought. Should I have lied and said, 'You were wonderful, darling'? No, what help is that? I believed he wanted to improve and grow in the business so I was honest. I did try to encourage him. Sometimes he would phone just before he went on air, and I'd say, 'Darling, you can really do this, it's just a matter of focus. Just focus, Richard, focus.' And he would for a couple of nights and I'd be full of praise. Then the next week he would drift back and do one of his disinterested reads. It was hard for both of us. In retrospect I probably should have kicked him in the bum and thrown down the challenge.

IN MARCH 1988, Harry Miller rang to see if I would accept an invitation from the French Cognac Information Centre to be their Australian ambassador. 'What would it entail?' I asked.

'Oh well,' he drawled, 'it would mean a first class trip to France, a guided tour of all the top Cognac houses, a couple of days at the positively splendid Hotel Crillion in Paris, and to do a bit of publicity when you get back.'

'When do I leave?' I said.

Then I broke the news to Richard. As my dear friend Georgie Swift was also to be in Paris, I arranged for her to accompany me to the Cognac region. It was a fantastic trip, educational, fun and unfortunately fattening! We spent four days going from one grand Cognac house to another and never left without a couple of bottles of their best. I have total recall of arriving at the train station to head back to Paris and watching a diminutive Georgie staggering up the platform loaded down with bottles of fine French Cognac.

We met her husband Snow in Paris and decided we would have to drink at least half our stock. Customs would never have let us take so much alcohol back into Australia. Leaving the Crillion one evening, after a few sample nips, we met a man in the corridor walking hand in hand with a chimp. It turned out to be Michael Jackson and his pet, but for a moment the three of us certainly wondered just how much we had consumed!

Shortly after this we received an invitation to Christopher Skase's fortieth birthday party to be held in his luxurious Brisbane mansion. You entered from street level then took an elevator up into the house, which was built around a courtyard and a glittering pool. A grand marquee was set off to one side and everything was lavish and totally over the top. The who's who of Sydney, Melbourne and Brisbane all danced attention, and the glowing, polished and perfect Skases were gracious hosts. A few token American movie stars had been wheeled in, including George Hamilton with that impossible and ever-present tan and Loretta Switt, the blonde who played the original Hot Lips Houlihan. John Farnham, an old mate, entertained with zest and style. It seemed the perfect party.

Late in the evening Richard and I bumped into Christopher by the pool. During our conversation he assured Richard that Channel Seven would stick with the Zachariah–Sanders combination. Christopher was committed to giving them a chance and that meant giving them time. But then he looked at Richard and said, 'But you have to work harder, Richard, work, work, work.' And he punched his fist in the air for emphasis. Richard nodded, reassured. I felt uneasy.

When Richard completed his news season in early December we both let out a sigh of relief. No more scanning the TV columns, thank God. As we had some free time we decided to celebrate my birthday with a holiday in New Zealand. We were going to look at studs and horses and have my birthday dinner at Huka Lodge. Richard's interest in thoroughbreds had reached plague proportions. He had a phenomenal memory, honed by long sessions reading breeding books and then having me test him. 'Who's the sire of …?' We had started to dream that one day we might own a thoroughbred stud. I love New Zealand. The people are generous, wonderful hosts, the land is breathtakingly beautiful, and the studs picture-book perfect, home to some of the finest breeding stock in the world.

Within days of returning home we were packing again. This time for Hawaii, where we would stay at one of my favourite hotels, the Halekulani on Waikiki, then out to the island of Kauai where Derryn Hinch had lent us his house. Derryn was then with the Seven Network and had struck up a friendship with Richard. Amanda, Sergio and Brooke were flying in for Christmas and my cousin Dr Lyndon Wester, son of my favourite aunt Thelma, who is with the University of Hawaii, was to join us for Christmas lunch.

On our first night at the Halekulani the phone rang. Richard answered and I heard him say, 'Oh hi, Bob.' He listened for some time then said, 'I demand to talk to Christopher.' I glanced up, he looked shaken. His voice choked and I knew in an instant Christopher Skase had not kept his word, he was not going to give the time he had promised. It was Bob Johnson, the news director at Seven. Richard had just been sacked. How cruel to let him go on holiday then cut him down. Why not tell him before he left Australia? I put my arms around him and held him tight. I felt his pain. My chest hurt. I felt sick.

I don't know how we got through the next few hours. He was terribly distressed and I felt helpless. Richard tried to fight back but his calls to Skase were refused. Skase was never to speak to Richard again. Much later when the Skase castle crumbled I know Richard felt some sweet revenge. At the time I was torn by the conflict I felt between my head and my heart. My heart ached for Richard, for his humiliation and disappointment. But he hadn't achieved a following. It was a bitter reality. I loved him so very much. I cast about for words of comfort but there was really little I could do.

The kids arrived and were wonderful as they tried to chivvy Richard out of his gloom. Amanda, regardless of the way Richard had treated her in the past, felt great sympathy for him. She turned cartwheels coming up with ideas to cheer him up: 'Let's horse ride'; 'bike ride'; 'go for a swim'; 'play tennis'. Then the weather turned foul. I should have known, a sign at the airport arrival gate said: 'Welcome to Kauai, the wettest spot on earth.' Let me tell you, they are not joking. We struggled through Christmas, all trying too hard to be too cheerful.

Back home we had to review our life. Richard was without a job. There was even more disappointment when he realised that Ann Sanders had not been similarly sacrificed. She was to head up the news with Roger Climpson. It had been announced on the eve of Richard's sacking, which means it had been in train for some time. Television politics is not for wimps. At the dawn of 1989 I found myself refusing offers of work. I didn't want to be away from Richard. We grew even closer, and without the restrictions of an evening news bulletin to read we enjoyed more time at the farm and more travel.

IN APRIL I had one of those calls we all dread, my dear friend Rob Palmer had died suddenly. Big Rob had a talent the size of his frame. He was the one who came up with the Maggie T concept and convinced Carl Dowd he needed my name. He had acted as a negotiator for both Carl and me in the initial discussions, and I always marvelled at his ability to see both sides as he guided us so skilfully toward our eventual partnership.

Richard and I flew down for his funeral. Adele, his gorgeous wife, and his kids were all naturally distraught, but I've never seen so many friends stunned by a loss. I guess Rob was such a powerful character that his presence in our lives was huge. It was unthinkable that he would never again wrap me in one of his bear hugs, make me laugh and grace me with one of his outrageously generous acts. Once I walked into his splendid Melbourne offices to find him wearing a bright blue jacket made from soft sweatshirt fabric but tailored like a normal double-breasted jacket. I raved about it. It was so innovative. He took it off, draped it over my shoulders and said, 'Wear it with joy, darling.' That was Rob, generous and joyous. I still miss him.

By the time we flew home from Melbourne I wasn't feeling very well. Possibly because of Rob's death I knew I couldn't ignore the chest pains I was experiencing. They would wake me in the night and my anxiety increased. My doctor recommended a heart specialist and I went off to St Vincent's Hospital to take a stress test. The result showed enough to make them recommend an angiogram. Richard was terrified and for once I wasn't as stoic as usual. I kept thinking, I can't die, I've got too much to do and I love this man and my kids too much to leave them.

A few days later when I went into hospital, I was comforted when the anaesthetist bowled into my room, took one look at me, and said, 'Don't worry, you don't look like a heart patient, it's probably hormonal.' The next morning, after a restless, anxious night, I was trundled along to the theatre where the procedure was explained. I remember the doctor telling me I could watch on the monitor the catheter travelling from my groin through my artery. 'Eeerr, no thanks,' I said. 'I'll wait until it comes out on video.' It got a laugh. They sat me up quickly as the catheter found its mark and released dye into my heart's plumbing system, a strange feeling, like boiling oil being poured over your head! When it was all over, the doctor kept extreme pressure on my groin to the point where I thought I might bop him. Eventually I was taken back to my room.

Richard and Brooke were anxiously pacing the floor when I arrived. Then we sat and waited for the diagnosis. And waited and waited. By the time the doctor came there was a lot of anxiety floating around the room. 'The verdict,' he said — we held our breath — 'is that everything is fine, no problem with the heart.' Richard let out a whoop of joy and jumped three feet into the air. The anaesthetist had been right, it was hormonal. Hugs and kisses, the relief was intense. I looked at my man and my daughter and thought, thank you Lord, thank you for giving me time.

The Home
Show

I THOUGHT I had put my television days behind me. I was
still doing TV commercials but I had recently turned down
the offer to host a daily programme for the Ten Network — too
hard, too demanding. Then in late 1989 Richard's sister Amanda
rang from Melbourne to say a friend of hers, a producer, Ted
Dunn, was anxious to talk about a new television concept that
would involve both of us. Richard was immediately keen. And
me? Well, if it meant an opportunity for Richard I would have
to listen. He hadn't worked for months and we both knew that
wasn't good for him or our relationship. It didn't help that I was
mainly supporting us. Although this didn't worry me, I'd paid in
my first marriage, I'd paid in my second marriage. In fact, when
Richard came home with his first pay packet from Channel
Seven and said, 'I'm going to give you four hundred dollars a
week,' I nearly died of shock. And he did until he lost his job.
Funny thing though, when he resumed work he never went
back to paying the faithful four hundred.

So we began to talk with Ted Dunn about a home show. Ted
had taken his concept to the ABC, which had expressed interest
in it. Deep down I really didn't want to go back to television.

I worried about how I'd cope with the extra workload and being older I knew I would have to practise some discipline to look good on camera. I also wondered how Richard and I would fare working together. But overriding all that was the reality that Richard needed to work. I agreed to do a pilot. We knew it would still have to be approved by the ABC. Perhaps it might all go away, I thought. Well, it didn't.

The pilot was to be shot in Melbourne. Ted would direct, along with an ABC producer. The house chosen as the key feature for the pilot was not my idea of a great 'show' house. Architecturally it was a mish-mash of styles. There were two overstuffed, over-the-top white satin couches in the living room, alongside a two-metre high ceramic cheetah. I know taste is an individual thing but I have a strong sense of style and while I appreciated the show would need to appeal to a broad market, there are certain levels of taste I require. Others were to think differently. Overall, however, I loved Ted's enthusiasm, so we ploughed on despite some maddening interference from the ABC guy. A taxing period was to follow. Ted would tender to the ABC a show format, an item by item rundown. The ABC producer would then question some niggly little thing and the whole show would be pulled to bits and we'd start all over again. I could see Ted's frustration and more times than I care to recall I felt my own.

When the pilot was finally delivered, the ABC engaged Ted as a consultant and appointed John Eastway to handle the production. John Eastway proved to be both efficient and fun to work with. Although I think even John would have to admit he spent a lot of time encouraging Richard, whose confidence was like the tide — high then low. This could sound egotistical but I had spent many years in television and I'd made a lot of commercials. The *Women's Weekly* film crew used to call me

'One-take Tabs'. Generally I didn't have a problem with my lines and I could nip a second or two off the read as the director required. I was efficient at the 'business'. However, recording the openers and closers of the 'Home Show', where Richard and I worked together, caused problems, take after take.

And Richard would often argue about the script and who would deliver which line. I came to dread those openers and closers days. The tension was tangible and as it increased it became difficult for both of us. I could feel Richard's resentment and I don't think I was able to hide my tension any longer. At the same time, John Eastway had constant battles raging with the ABC, but with his good humour he managed us all.

The 'Home Show' was an original, the first of the infotainment housing programmes. Its format developed over time, but essentially it was a programme about houses and everything in them and around them: architectural design, decor, colour, finishes, furniture, appliances, heating, lighting, cooling. We also gave handy hints on a range of things, from cleaning the silver to removing candle wax from that beloved table. It was informative and entertaining. During the course of the series I met many talented people and I learnt a hell of a lot.

Just prior to filming the first ten shows we had an opportunity to visit Tasmania. The Tasmanian Tourist Bureau asked if I would present its Annual Awards for Tourism in Hobart. I was offered a car and a week's accommodation around the highlight spots of the island. After the weeks of fiddle faddle concerning the 'Home Show' this would be a terrific break. Our friend Quentin Madden joined us. The Awards night went smoothly and the next day we piled into the car and headed out to discover Tasmania. It was late one afternoon, driving to Cradle Mountain Lodge, that we had a strange encounter.

We were all besotted with the superb Georgian houses we

had passed. If a 'For Sale' sign came into view we would fantasise about selling up and moving to Tassie. It was such a sign that found us driving up a narrow road 'just to see' when we realised we were, in fact, in a private drive. With some considerable manoeuvring we managed to turn the car around, and were heading back to the main road when our path was blocked by another car. It stopped and out jumped a young woman, entirely wrapped in an American flag. She bounded up and cheerfully answered all our questions about the adjacent property which was for sale. Encouraged by Richard, she proceeded to tell us her life story. That's when our collective jaws dropped. We were talking to Gene Autrey's daughter. Yep! Her dad was the famous Hollywood cowboy. It launched me back to my childhood days at the Unley Odeon and my favourite Saturday matinee westerns. I didn't mention that I really preferred Hopalong Cassidy. It was only as we drove away that it dawned on us it was 4 July, American Independence Day, hence the American flag dress.

My friend Quentin is a most stylish lady, and I say 'lady' in the true sense of the word, so it was something of a surprise when she blew her stack at Richard. One evening we had arrived at our destination, a small lodge, and I was as usual lugging our bags out of the car boot. Richard always held back, and I guess I'm naturally impatient. But this offended Quentin: 'Richard, if you let Maggie carry those bags one more time I'll …!' He muttered something about my impatience and said, 'But if she would only wait.' However, he did carry the bags and for the rest of the trip made an effort. It didn't last long after we came back from Tasmania.

WE FOUND ourselves looking forward to working on the twenty-part 'Home Show' series. However, sometimes the television machine moves in slow motion, and it was not until a few months later that we started filming again. We continued to have friends most weekends to stay at Borees. Jill Robb flew from Melbourne one weekend, arriving with a very stylish all-white wardrobe. Not exactly ideal rig for a bush weekend but she looked gorgeous. She bounded out of the bathroom one morning in top to toe white, announcing she was going for a walk along the river. I dispatched her with my usual warning: 'Watch out for the Joe Blakes.' An hour later I looked out to see this bedraggled figure making her way up the drive. Jill had stepped too close to the edge of the river and the bank had collapsed beneath her. She was covered in mud and the whites were no longer white. We all roared with laughter but none more than Jill whose energetic sense of humour had her crying with laughter.

I often reflected on how much Boree Bills had changed me. I now coped with mice, snakes, our resident goannas, a series of unidentified but seriously nasty looking creepy crawlies, numerous flies and blowflies, the odd bushfire, the often flooded river and never-ending dramas with cattle or horses. And I loved it all.

After spending a stinking hot and very wet Christmas at Borees, Richard and I decided to look for another property. We had battled the river too many times, getting flooded in or flooded out. Risking our lives crossing a swollen river had finally lost its charm. Richard was lobbying also for a better property. By this time he was deeply involved in learning more about breeding thoroughbreds. It was his dream. So whenever we were flooded out we drove great distances in search of an alternative property; one with the potential to be a good stud. It was a sort of game. Most were too far away or too expensive and it seemed that if the house was wonderful the land was poor, or the reverse.

By looking at what was available we finally came up with a profile of the type of place we wanted. After I'd crawled through a dozen creepy old houses I knew I didn't want some draughty, ancient joint, no matter how grand it looked. No, it should be single-storey with modern bathrooms and a big, efficient eat-in kitchen, and there should be sufficient bedrooms to accommodate family and friends for weekend stays. Well, that was my side of the equation. Richard's desire to breed thoroughbreds meant he was more interested in stables, decent fencing and room to run some cattle. We were in agreement that the property should be no more than a two-hour drive from Sydney. After all, we had signed a contract to work in Sydney and we didn't want to waste our lives driving long distances.

We had almost given up hope of finding our dream when Greenville found us, or I should say Barb found Greenville for us. It had been raining for a week, there was no chance of getting into Borees for the weekend. We were at home in Darling Point on a seedy Saturday when she phoned. An avid Saturday paper reader, she had spotted an ad in the *Sydney Morning Herald* with a small photograph of a rotunda-fronted house in the beautiful Southern Highlands on one hundred and sixty acres. It looked like an old house, rather like the famous historic Fern Hill in Mulgoa, New South Wales. But in the ad we read that it had just been built by Heather Buttrose, a young contemporary designer known for building very large modern houses in the Mosman area. She was married to Ita Buttrose's brother. I rang the Bowral agent. He didn't have any photographs but he did have a floor plan. 'Fax it please, now.' Then I rang Barb and she came over for lunch. I'll never forget the fax spilling out with this fantastic floor plan. We opened a bottle of wine, rang the agent back and arranged to drive down and see the place the next day. Then we sat down and played fantasy. 'If I buy it where will we place the furniture?' By mid-afternoon we had fitted all my furniture from Boree Bills and the Hampden Avenue house into

Greenville and by cocktail time we knew all that stood between us and our new dream was probably about two million dollars. It gave us a lot to laugh about.

Despite the mass opinion that I was rather rich, I wasn't. I had come out of a twenty-six year marriage with my furniture and just enough dollars to buy the white house. Ettore had handled all my money and while I'd earnt a lot I guess I hadn't learnt to manage it or hang onto it. But since our break-up I'd worked hard, paid cash for the white house and later Boree Bills and Hampden Avenue. Now I had property but little cash.

The next day we drove to Bowral. After a gentle amble along an unsealed road through densely timbered bushland we came to a steep rise in the road and suddenly, there below, was Greenville. We gasped. Greenville sits perfectly into the landscape. In front of the large house were two lakes, some handsome tall old trees and some new plantings. Off to one side was a new tennis court and further again a picturesque little timber manager's cottage, which had been the property's original homestead. At the rear, near a fine new set of cattleyards, sat a huge new shed. Above all, Greenville lived up to its name. It was picture-postcard green, securely private, surrounded by Water Board protected bushland.

We stopped, took it in and then we laughed. 'Dear God, I'll never be able to afford this, even if I sell everything I own,' I said. As we approached the property a car coming in the other direction stopped. I recognised a former neighbour from Hampden Avenue. While she and her husband had completely renovated their house we had uncomplainingly put up with the long and noisy procedure. We wanted to be good neighbours as we believed they were going to be living there for a long time. Only once had I called to ask her husband to refrain from stacking bricks at four-thirty in the morning! When they completed the renovations they immediately put the house on the market, made a small fortune from the sale and disappeared to live in Tuscany for a year. Now I marvelled at the strangeness of life. Here we were both interested in the same property and they were obviously well ahead, being cashed up. My heart sank.

I can't really explain to you how I felt about Greenville. We had started this search because of the access problems in and out of Borees but mainly because Richard desperately wanted to breed horses. I came to know that he had an insatiable thirst for bigger, better, more. I confess I spoilt him. But his character is such that the best is never good enough, and enough is never enough. This goes from the quality of a bottle of wine to his comfort in a chair to, as in this case, poor old Borees. But the moment I saw Greenville it wrapped me in its spell. All these years later as I write this book I'm still here, inexplicably bound by its magic, its big, generous rooms, four-metre high ceilings, its light, grace and the wonderful vistas from every room. As you've probably gathered, I'm passionate about my home.

But back in early 1990, we drove slowly up Greenville's drive and slowly into months of tension and negotiations. This is what then happened. I desperately wanted this property but could I afford it? I called on my solicitor and friend Lyndon Sayer Jones and my accountant at Moores, Phillip Donnelly, and they 'crunched' some figures. Harry M. gave them estimates of my future earnings and they crunched some more. Ian Robinson valued Boree Bills, the real estate agent, Billy Bridges, did the same with Hampden Avenue. Finally Lyndon rang with good news — if I sold both my existing properties at his conservative estimates, yes I could purchase Greenville. We were exhilarated.

In the middle of the night I woke Richard: 'Darling, what if Borees sells first and I can't sell Hampden, then we won't have Greenville or Borees?' I was indifferent about the city house but

I adored Borees. Life without it, if I couldn't buy Greenville, was untenable. Early the next morning I phoned Lyndon with my dilemma and, God bless him, he found the solution. I would sell Borees on the condition that I could sell Hampden Avenue. And I would endeavour to buy Greenville, on the condition that I sold both my properties — Borees and Hampden. After months of anxiety, stressful auctions and negotiations, that's exactly what happened. And to this day I believe it was meant to happen. I've loved many of my houses, but none as much or as passionately as Greenville.

Having bought Greenville we now had to consider where we would live in Sydney. Regardless of where we went, I faced an awesome move. I had the untiring support of my best mate Barb, and Brooke was wonderful at organising cupboards. Richard would simply vanish.

He had met Theo Onisfuro, a lawyer who later went on to develop some interesting apartment complexes in Sydney with James Packer. Theo had bought in Paddington on an investment basis. He believed in the area and encouraged Richard to consider buying there. Because I'd largely financed our lives Richard had been able to put some funds aside, and he had enough for a deposit. With Theo's help he found a house in Elizabeth Place, a diminutive terrace, about seven feet wide. I felt it had potential and wholeheartedly supported Richard buying something of his own. For his personal self-esteem he needed to contribute in this way to our lives. I assured him we would be comfortable and happy in the little house.

It was a bit like playing doll's house when you consider the entire Paddo house would fit into the garage at Greenville and there would still be room to park two cars! We used to laugh about how we would have to adjust to the Paddo house; to comfortably fit one large person would be an 'ask' and for two rather tall and well-proportioned people like us it was really taxing. But I wanted the place to look good so I helped fund the renovations. He put on a new roof. I had the entire place painted white and fitted sisal matting in the small bedroom and dressing room. I put in better lighting and then took on the task of trying to furnish this minuscule space. Minimalist was definitely the way to go.

Packing up Boree Bills was an emotional business. We'd had some wonderful times there and I knew we would miss our neighbours, Peter and Eve Slaney, Walter and Jenny Cavill. But I had no qualms about leaving Hampden Avenue, nor our next-door neighbour. She and her husband were pruners *par excellence*. Not a twig or a blade of grass, let alone a tree, was left to grow free and full. Oh no! It had to be manicured into submission, and at one stage that caused a huge ruckus between us. They had lobbied us numerous times to chop back our trees on their side of the fence. I agreed to a trim but it was never enough to satisfy them. When we took a short holiday they had slaughtered the trees with the most brutal chop extending way over our side of the fence. It left the poor trees out of balance and in shock. I arrived home and went into a rage. Richard tried to calm me down but I was furious. The next morning as we were about to leave the house I saw her. I gave her both barrels. This woman was a small blonde who wore pale dimity print floral dresses. I was wearing tan boots and a khaki shirt and skirt. Richard later related the encounter to friends and said I looked like Idi Amin bearing down on a pygmy! I was very angry and probably over the top but I was also outraged at the sneaky way they had slaughtered my trees, and I wasn't having it happen again. Mind you, it did. The day after we moved out they did it again before the new owner could move in.

So out of Borees, out of Hampden, into Paddo and into Greenville. I devised a sticker system for the furniture and boxes so the poor removalists knew what went where. Green dots for Greenville, blue dots for Paddo and white dots for storage. It worked a treat. I got our removalists', China Bear, gold stamp of approval for organisation.

From day one Greenville was almost too magical. I'd stop and look out at the lakes, watch a flock of ducks zooming in to land or a pair of swans gliding gracefully by. It would take my breath away. Waking up in our big bedroom to watch the mists roll out of the bush, the tall roos grazing in the far paddock or the white frost come in at dawn was overwhelming. I was in love with Greenville and every day I'd pinch myself. I couldn't believe it. I'd say to Richard, 'Aren't we lucky, darling, we are living our dream.' When we walked along the top road on our morning hikes Richard would stop, wrap me in his arms and say, 'Look, Maggie, do you believe it's yours?'

I'd always answer, 'No, I don't, and anyway it's only on loan from God.'

It was an enchanting time. We had this amazing house, we had a terrific job and we were about to make Richard's dream a reality and set up our small thoroughbred stud. Over the next couple of years I bought our mares. All greys. I used to call them the 'Greenville Greys'. It was wonderful to see their bellies grow fat with their foals. I loved it as much as Richard did when they came back from the stallions at various studs, confirmed in foal and then to watch them with their new gangly-legged progeny at their sides.

It should have made Richard blissfully happy, but for all that he still had his 'blacks' or as he called them, his melancholic Welsh moods. They were increasingly difficult for me to handle and I found myself dancing around his bad days trying to chivvy him along. But I was still in love and when you're in love? Well, you know what I mean.

The Paddington house, for all its diminutive size, was convenient. We would come home exhausted from filming, take a quick shower and walk to any one of four good restaurants close by for dinner. We settled into a new life. We had hired a manager, John Conners, for the farm and while he didn't have any cattle or horse experience, he and his wife Caroline were intelligent and eager to learn. Richard's time on the land, ten years in Victoria working on his father-in-law's farm, had given him good cattle experience.

Just when things were looking great life went terribly wrong for me. In the previous couple of months I had felt extremely tired. I put it down to work, buying and selling properties, organising the move and just my rather hectic lifestyle, but gradually it worried me and I went off to see my favourite GP. He ordered a blood test then rang and requested I go in to see him — he wouldn't discuss it on the phone. I drove to town with a thumping heart. Dear God, what could it be? It was diabetes. I was stunned. Why? How? What? My doctor assured me it could be controlled with diet and medication. Diet! 'Oh great,' I said. 'You know how good I am about diets!' But I was so alarmed I went to a dietitian and to some extent changed my lifestyle.

I hated pricking my finger for the blood tests and I hated the diet, but I soon discovered if I broke out I paid for it by feeling foul the next day. Eventually I found some discipline and asked the 'Home Show' caterers to accommodate me with a simple sando lunch. I would try not to look while the crew tucked into enormous lavish lunches. 'Shit!' I said. 'Shit! Shit! Shit!' Well, it happens, doesn't it? I also vowed to keep this news very quiet — only my family, closest friends and those I worked with knew of my condition and they kept my counsel.

With filming the 'Home Show' two days a week and another day doing voice-overs, production meetings and publicity, plus running both houses and attending to my other work commitments I was extremely busy. One of the great pains about working week to week on television is what to wear. I had some things from Maggie T. My dear friends, Inge Fonagy of Simona, George Gross, Harry Who, Lizzie Collins and Carla Zampatti made me others, and I bought knits from Wendy Heather and Weiss Pringle. I kept a diary of what I wore each week, but it was difficult. It was impossible not to double-up sometimes in one show. And at other times I wore a different garment for almost every story, like I was in some demented fashion parade. It was of constant interest to the press. At one stage some rat at the ABC leaked my contract details to the media, which wrongly reported I was paid eight thousand dollars a week wardrobe allowance! Bullshit! For the record, it was eight thousand dollars over a series of twenty shows. I rang Harry M. who insisted I ignore it and not demand that the press correct the matter. 'Just leave it,' was his advice. Well, I did and it needled me for ever after. It simply went into history and was frequently referred to as a fact. But I'll never forget one letter from a viewer. She wrote: 'You always look like a million dollars so I don't know how you manage on a lousy eight thousand a show!' I fell about laughing and it put the whole silly press thing in perspective.

By September the 'Home Show' series was completed and in the 'can'. Then we set about the business of publicity and promotion in Sydney and Melbourne. One Melbourne journo, who shall remain nameless because he deserves to be, came to the interview session wearing a suit that would have disintegrated if it hadn't been held up by so much grime and a large safety pin clearly visible securing the hem of his trousers. I'm sorry but filth offends me. My mother used to say, 'Soap and water costs little enough.' He was offensive in more ways than just his sloppy hygiene. He wrote a too-smart-by-half interview piece anyway.

I vowed I'd never be put in that situation again, publicity or no publicity.

For the most, the press have always been very kind to me, and they were about the 'Home Show'. Richard, on the other hand, used to say, 'Any publicity is good publicity, and I'd rather they talked bad about me than not at all.' This attitude would stun me, particularly as he was so thin-skinned about any negative press review. A much more pleasant experience was being guests on Ray Martin's 'Midday Show', unprecedented when you think that there we were on the Nine Network plugging a programme for the ABC.

During our recess from the 'Home Show' Richard did a stint on radio at 2UE, headed up by the delightful John Brennan. It was a phone-in evening show and Richard said he found it difficult to handle the light conversation required by both the audience and the timeslot. What I could never fathom was where was the ratbag larrikin Richard I knew? He would have been great on that show.

To try to get it moving one evening, a dear friend phoned in calling himself 'Ken from the city'. I fell about laughing when I heard him say, deliberately baiting a reaction, 'I reckon all women should be barefoot and pregnant and in the kitchen.' The 2UE switchboard lit up in protest. Sadly it didn't light up enough. Richard would have loved to do more radio. Mind you, I was never any better on radio.

Way back in my 'Beauty and the Beast' days I did a stint on ABC Radio with Ellis Blain who was married to another of the 'Beauties', Anne Deveson. He did a morning show called 'Leave it to the Girls' and had a different woman on each day to co-compere. I became the Monday girl. But my irreverent style, I knew, didn't fit with either Ellis or the ABC. After some months I gave it away, quite happily. I felt more comfortable on television. An expression can speak a million words but only if it's seen. For ever after I had radio offers, but I also had a keen sense of survival. I think I know what I'm good at and radio isn't one of 'em.

Finally, 1990 was at an end and we looked forward to Christmas at Greenville with great joy.

First
Christmas at
Greenville

I ADORE Christmas. I've never understood why people moan and groan about the shopping, the food preparation, the tree, the decorations, the gifts, and wrapping them. To me it's a great pleasure, to be shared with loved family and friends. Maybe I'm part of a dying race. My family are constantly begging me not to go to so much trouble, but I know they always have a fabulous time. Given the choice they would probably opt for a Club Med Christmas on a tropical island, if just to get out of doing the dishes!

We bought a generous tree for Greenville's living room, which I spent hours decorating. And I had a new dining room table — a huge kauri pine piece — delivered in time for Christmas Eve. I'd met Stephen Gibson on a segment of the 'Home Show' in his tiny recycled furniture shop, The Original Finish, in Newtown. He had made a handsome serving table for Boree Bills and I went back to him to find a dining table. After some weeks he called and said, 'Come and see your table.' In high excitement I visited his shop. He took me out the back and I climbed over piles of old furniture until there, standing against the wall, towering to the ceiling were two vast planks of almost black timber. My heart sank.

'Oh no, Stephen, I want a pale table.'

'Maggie, it's kauri pine. It came from a Newcastle tannery, the timber is hundreds of years old and when I finish it will be the colour of warm honey.' I paid him half the price there and then, and made him promise I'd have it installed for our Christmas Eve supper. It was. Almost five feet wide and twelve feet long, it was beautiful, honourably marked with its history. And, as promised, it was the colour of warm honey. My God, it's had some great dinner parties around its handsome frame since it came to live at Greenville.

The kids arrived from Italy. I had my suspicions from various phone conversations with Amanda that she might have some special news, and she did. She was pregnant. I was overjoyed and she looked wonderful, even though she was still experiencing morning sickness. It reminded me of my own pregnancies and I felt for her. Sergio was obviously pleased and was tender with her. We spent a lot of the holidays playing 'name the baby'. Christmas Day arrived, Barb, her kids, Matt and Ash, her dear mother, Alvina Turnbull, and old mates Alfredo Bouret and Lex Aitken, Hall Ludlow and my darling Brooke, Nicolas, Amanda, Sergio, Richard and I sat down for our first traditional Christmas lunch at Greenville. It was magic!

Over the holiday break we enjoyed a terrific lunch at Doyles Seaside Restaurant in Sydney. Peter Doyle, God bless the man, had tolerated our noisy bunch of friends. After lunch, at Richard's urging, we went off to the Ingliss horse sales. I sat on the terrace having yet another drink when a very merry Mike Willesee came into view. He joined us for a drink then stunned the party when he leant toward me and said loud and clear, 'Hey, Mags, show us your tits.' For a nanosecond I paused. Then I looked at his gorgeous face, knew he was somewhat under the weather, I mean we all were, and I chose to roar with laughter.

The long end of this short story is that, in our cups, the friends and I all put in with Richard and bought the horse he believed had something going for it. Sadly little Avalanche never did win but we had some fun with her. Incidentally, I've always been a Willesee fan. The man who dared to use the long, drawn-out pause in television interviews will never be surpassed as far as I'm concerned. He won even more Brownie points from me years later when I heard him give the eulogy for our mutual and dear mate, Noel McGurkin. He was brilliant, warm, funny, witty. Everything our dear Noel was too. As we left the church I said, 'Hey, Mike, can I book you to do mine?' I've since been to enough funerals to know that for the most, eulogies, even given with the best intentions such as love and respect, can be as boring as hell. And for the most, emotions get in the way of truth. So how about it, Mike. Will you? If you do I'll show …! Just kidding folks.

Early in the New Year, Amanda and Sergio decided that their child should be born in Australia. I was thrilled but it was a distressing period for me personally. I desperately wanted to spend as much time with my daughter as I could. I wanted to watch her belly grow round with my grandchild and I wanted to help her, but she and Richard shared an uneasy relationship. Occasionally it flared. I knew she made great allowances for Richard's hurtful comments and moods because she loved me and she knew I loved him. Amanda tried really hard, but Richard didn't want to share me with anyone, least of all my much loved younger daughter. It's painful when those you love don't measure up to your expectations. It was very disturbing but somehow we found a path around the situation.

The kids moved in with Ettore, who by now was divorced and living alone in Sydney. He loved their company. They also came to the farm for three or four-day stints. We muddled on as I juggled my attention between those I loved. Eventually I begged Richard to come with me to see the shrink, who I hoped could help sort out this jealousy thing. At last he agreed and while the doctor's advice never really dispelled the angst, at least it brought about a sort of truce for a while. Richard would try to understand he had nothing to fear from my love for my daughter, it wasn't a competition. I, on the other hand, realised he needed me to himself. I agreed that the kids' visits to the farm would be broken up with short stays back in Sydney. They generously understood.

In April 1991 we started filming the next series of the 'Home Show' again with John Eastway and still with considerable, and in our opinion, unwarranted interference from the ABC guy. Also my once a week voice-over sessions at the ABC took on nightmare proportions. They were scheduled for seven-thirty in the morning. I am always ridiculously on time. I drive friends to distraction because if they say dinner at eight, I'm there at eight. As one remarked, 'Who, Maggie, is ever on time today?' Well, let me tell you, I am. I believe it's good manners and, in a work situation, professional. However, at the ABC I rarely got into the studio till after the appointed hour, because of frustrations — the headsets were missing, the operator was late, the mike wasn't working. Bum, bum, bum! I complained loud and clear. It was as though it were a deliberate plot. I would be nauseous with anxiety because I would be scheduled to meet my film crew on location, but because the ABC were late I was late. And the whole day would disintegrate. As an outside production we knew we were treated with some disdain by the ABC diehards. That wasn't my only frustration.

During that winter the little Paddo house was snug, but it just wasn't big enough. I'd crawl out of bed about five-thirty on filming days, fumble my way in the dark, so as not to wake Richard, to the diminutive dressing room and try to sort my clothes in the cramped little wardrobe for the week's shoot. Then I'd do the same for Richard — shirts, ties, trousers, jackets or sweaters. By the time I packed them into their hanging wardrobes and carried them down the miniature staircase I was already pooped and faced a thirteen-hour day. Then we had the battle of the bathroom, the pygmy-sized bathroom. There simply wasn't room for us both to stand. If one was at the basin the other either had to be on the loo or under the shower.

Then my makeup artist Richard Sharah would arrive, begging for coffee. Sharah is a huge man. While he did my face I used to look down at his enormous feet and think, my God, they take up one half of our dining-room floor space! Paddo was starting to wear very thin. We began to talk of yet another house. In our comparatively short relationship we were already on number five. Oh well, I thought, why not? Richard was earning good money and I felt it was the perfect time for him to upgrade his investment. As it was, we were just too busy so we stashed the idea for a few months, but I religiously scanned *The Wentworth Courier* each week.

Meanwhile, Amanda's tummy grew and grew. She was in radiant health. We loved shopping for my grandchild together. David Jones loved us shopping for my grandchild, too. We certainly did some damage. But what excitement. Occasionally when I popped into see Amanda and Sergio in the city I'd run into Ettore. We were friendly but I sensed he was embarrassed. The marriage he'd abandoned ours for had failed, and that was very difficult for him to come to terms with. Maybe it was even harder for him because by contrast it seemed my life was now so full and happy.

As Amanda's confinement day came closer I grew more anxious. I prayed all would be well, her delivery safe, the baby safe. I knew it was a deep fear from the loss of my own baby son all those years before, and as a mother I don't think it's unusual to go through those anxieties. I often thought of my dear Mummy and how she must have felt when her four daughters had numerous children. Perhaps she got used to it. Or did she? I wished I could ask her. I still missed her terribly.

I had been filming the 'Home Show' all day and had just walked into the little Paddo house when the phone rang. It was Sergio. I asked how he was feeling. He'd had surgery that day on his jaw, a painful but necessary process. He mumbled through his stitches that he was OK, but Amanda had gone into labour and they were on the way to the hospital. In an instant I went through a whole range of emotions: excitement, fear, joy, panic! Much earlier we had discussed whether I should be there for the birth. I wanted to support Amanda but I didn't want to encroach on their 'special time'. They agreed I'd be welcome so I had made the commitment. Now I felt a slight hesitation. I knew I had to be strong and calm, Amanda had a big job in front of her, she needed support, not some hysterical mother.

I phoned Richard, who was heading back to Greenville, then Brooke who was going to be 'second' in the support team, then Barb, whom we felt should support the support team. Amanda would need time to settle into the hospital so Sergio urged me not to rush. Barb decided we needed dinner. She, Brooke and I met at our local Italian restaurant, and the waiters all got involved in the excitement of the impending birth. There was great celebration in the air. It was only when we left to drive to the hospital that I realised I was not exactly dressed for the part. I still had my rather elaborate television Sharah face on, I was wearing very high heels, dark stockings, a very short skirt and a big black sweater. What the hell, I was anxious to see my daughter.

Amanda had been prepared for the birth and was spending time on the hospital verandah walking her way through the early contractions. Poor Sergio looked shocking, his lower face swathed in bandages. He was obviously not feeling too well but courageously he didn't utter a word of complaint. He would take Amanda's arm and they would walk. Later when she moved into the delivery room Sergio and I took up our positions on either side of the bed. Barb came in, kissed her good luck and left. Brooke popped in and out of the room tendering encouragement and love. My dear daughters, they had gone through all the teen-age battles with one another but there was great love between them now. I could see it clearly. And so we got down to business.

The clock on the wall dragged at snail's pace through the hours. At one stage Amanda said, 'Mummy, I need some mineral water.' Right, I sprang to attention, 'I'll get it.' The nurse informed me I had to go down and out of the building, across the road to the main Prince Alfred Hospital and up to the first floor where I would find a vending machine. Frankly, I thought it was extraordinary they didn't have their own. Was mine the only daughter who wanted mineral water during labour? Anyway in the high heels and my ridiculous makeup and outfit I tottered down and out and across to the main hospital, up in the elevator, only to find an 'Out of Order' sign on the vending machine. Damn! Another nurse suggested I try the pub a block down on the other side of the road. Oh no, I groaned but I was a woman on a mission. So I tottered along the dark road and into the rowdy main bar of the pub. You could have heard a pin drop in the sudden silence.

'Jeez, it's Maggie,' said one guy. Then after a second there were lots of 'G'day, Maggie, let's buy you a drink.' They were adorable.

'Sorry fellas, my grandchild is about to be born and my daughter needs mineral water.'

'G'arn take her a bottle of bubbly,' shouted a wag.

I staggered out with several bottles of mineral water to shouts of 'Best of luck Maggie' and 'Come back when it's born and we'll celebrate.' God I love Aussies!

Back at the hospital I raced into the delivery room and offered Amanda a glass of mineral water. She took a sip then, 'Phaw! Oh Mum it's got gas. You know I only drink flat mineral water!'

'Amanda, DRINK IT!'

She did, for there was no way I was going back to the pub, and anyway things were speeding up. I didn't want to miss the final act. Amanda's doctor had encouraged her in her desire to have a natural birth but as the delivery started to get tough she asked for some help. Too late. My grandchild had at least partially appeared, Amanda was asked to go the extra mile. I loved her so much at that moment, her courage was fantastic. When it really got bad I wanted to scream, 'Darling, just get out of the bed, I'll do it for you.' If only I'd been able to.

Then a dark little head came fully into view and a push, a shove and prayer later, Marco Tabberer Bella was born, on 25 May 1991. The joy, the absolute joy and flood of love in that room was fantastic. We were all crying and laughing at once. Brooke took photographs like some crazed paparazzo. I don't know if Amanda has ever forgiven her for a couple of close-ups! Amongst all the elation there was a sudden tension. Amanda haemorrhaged. Anxious minutes dragged by, my heart was pounding with fear, but finally the doctor assured us all was well. I cradled my grandson then reluctantly handed him to the nurse. I kissed my beautiful daughter and told her how much

I loved her and admired her courage. She was already nodding off into a well-earned sleep. I embraced Sergio, who was equally exhausted but so elated at the arrival of his son, and then Brooke and I drove home.

Back in the little Paddo house as the first rays of dawn appeared I rang Richard at the farm. I started to tell him about the birth and I just broke down in tears and I sobbed and sobbed. With joy? With relief? I don't know but I couldn't stop. I washed the remnants of my tellie face off and crawled into bed, and as I drifted off to sleep I thought of my new grandson, Marco. What a gift. Thank you God.

The next days were spent racing between my work commitments and visiting Amanda and Marco. It wasn't all plain sailing. This tiny boy developed jaundice. At first they wrapped him in a special treatment blanket. It glowed bright green in the dark and had a sort of tail attached. Amanda said she frightened the hell out of some late-night visitors as she took him for a walk along the corridor, he looked like a little alien. Eventually he went to intensive care for thirty-six hours. When we visited him there we realised how lucky we were. The tiny premature babies and their anxious parents were distressing to witness.

Amanda and Marco were cleared to go home, and after they had a few days with Ettore I moved them to the farm. I often felt inadequate. Amanda would ask me about how to care for the baby if this or that happened. I found it hard to recall. I'd been a mother at eighteen, it seemed such a long time ago but we muddled along. Marco survived our joint care and settled into a routine. Whenever the kids were in town Ettore would spend hours sitting looking at Marco in his bassinette. The day Marco actually held onto one of his fingers he almost melted. Amanda said it was very touching to see.

A couple of weeks later we had a big splash-up lunch at

Greenville. We called it Marco's 'Name Day'. It was a family celebration with dear friends. Snow Swift gave the toast to Marco and his new godfather, Tony Potts, gave a witty address. It was a gorgeous day. *Women's Weekly* had asked to photograph the new family along with the new Nonna (although Marco now calls me Nanna). We didn't know at the time that Jenny Rowe, my editor, would make Marco a cover boy at four weeks of age. It was a great shot.

Finally the day arrived for them to return home to Italy. A tearful farewell and Greenville was suddenly very, very quiet. I went back to washing laundry once a week instead of once a day. Will you believe me when I tell you I missed it? But most of all I missed them. Of course Richard was happy to be back as Numero Uno again, the centre of my universe.

In September we took off to Europe. Richard and I had enjoyed some great overseas holidays together but this one was special. To Rome first, where we stayed at the Inghilterra Hotel, near the Piazza di Spagna and dangerously situated amongst the best shopping in Rome. We ate our way through Othellos, Il Tovla, Ninos, Giggi and Le Trescalini. I went mad and bought Richard a silver Hermes watch, then went madder and bought myself a gold one. We walked miles and fell even more in love with our favourite city. Then down for a week with the kids and the late summer sun in Positano. Marco went to the beach each day in his nanny's backpack wearing a bright bandanna on his head. He was a good baby, much adored by the entire village. We then flew to London and saw our friends Libby Reeves Purdy, her great love John Chalk and Edwina and Andrew Clark, who took us to stay with the Queen's trainer, Lord Huntington, William Hastings-Bass and his beautiful wife Sue.

I'll never forget Sue's great courage. We had gone to the races at Newmarket. Sue was seeing William's horses onto the course as he was in Germany for the day. Halfway through a race one of his horses fell. In a flash Sue was out on the track and it was she who had to agree to the vet's painful decision to put the horse down. In stoic British fashion she returned to her guests and simply carried on. She's quite a lady. She's also barmy about her dogs. We had gathered in her big beautiful kitchen to dine one night. Afterwards as she stacked the dishwasher one of her beloved Aussie Blue Heelers happily licked each dinner plate clean as she stacked them. I tried not to think about it at breakfast the next morning.

We spent a lot of 'horse time' in England including visiting the trainer John Dunlop. On his spectacular runs early one morning one of the lads took quite a tumble. We jumped into John's Japanese Land Rover, as he referred to it, and headed out to see if horse and rider were alright. I was in the back seat and moved across to make room for the boy. I mean, clearly John was going to pick up the lad, who by now was limping toward us. John stopped, had a few sharp words and then seeing that one of the other riders had captured his horse, said something like, 'Right lad, get yourself back now and on with the job.' Then we drove off, leaving the diminutive rider to hobble to God knows where. They're tough in England.

In Zurich we watched white swans glide along the river, dined in the amazing Hofbrau House and bought Richard a superb Armani jacket. Then on to Hong Kong to see my old friend Gerald Godfrey who runs Charlotte Horsemann Antiques. His home, high in the mountains of the New Territories, contains his amazing collection of rare jade. It also has one of the most glorious gardens in the world, with huge stands of vivid yellow bamboo. His immaculate staff served us a steady flow of delicious nibbles. It was a spectacular final night of what had been a marvellous trip. We came home high with happiness. But there is nothing in the world to beat Greenville, I thought, as we drove over the rise and saw it clearly in the morning light.

While we had been away I'd drawn up a list of what we should look for in an apartment. It should be in a very good location, preferably in the eastern suburbs. It didn't matter what the building looked like from the outside, after all, you live inside. It should be a small building without an elevator, they add to maintenance costs. It could be old and in need of renovation. We knew all about renovation, or so we thought. But it had to have at least two or three bedrooms and room for Richard to have a study. It should be light and sunny with tall ceilings.

Two weeks back home and Barb and I found it, in Fullerton Street, Woollahra. A deceased estate, it needed a total refurbish. It had been done up in the seventies and was a monster. Every room had a different floral wallpaper, in electric hues — orange in the kitchen, lime-green in the living room, iridescent blue in the bedroom. It was in a word, perfect. Richard was hesitant, he confessed he couldn't visualise how it could be salvaged. But Barb and I persuaded him it would look wonderful and it would be a good investment.

We had great fun planning the renovations and John Eastway suggested we film the transformation for the next series of the 'Home Show'. We hired an architectural engineer, then submitted plans to council. This was necessary as we wanted to remove a wall between the living and dining rooms, opening it up into one generous space, and install a new kitchen and pantry. However, despite the fact that it was really quite a simple renovation, as is Woollahra Council's way, it took weeks. But inch by inch we got there, having hired a most obliging builder, Jim Rennie, recommended by friends, Eve and Peter Slaney.

Richard had sold Paddington to buy the new apartment.

He had also taken on a mortgage so I contributed a considerable amount for the renovations, at the time quite happily because I really wanted to help him. Richard had bought the new apartment for a good price and later, after our separation, sold it for double. I didn't expect to get my dollars back.

It was to be another busy Christmas. Marco and his beautiful parents arrived. By now he was a round and robust baby, a joy with a big happy grin and the odd temper tantrum. We decorated tables, trimmed the tree, wrapped gifts. Our family and friends arrived for our second Greenville Christmas. A tradition had been started. We spent a frantic holiday period driving into Sydney, checking on the apartment renovations, then zooming back to Greenville.

I started to think about furnishing Richard's new apartment. I bought a couple of fine English antique pieces, discovered some amazing coconut-fibre chairs and had a new couch and chair covered in honey linen piped in white. I found a fine old armoire for our bedroom. We painted all the walls and ceilings white, stripped and bleached all the dark doors, laid sisal flooring throughout, tiled the bathrooms in snow white, paved the balconies in a new sand tile and fitted security doors and grills. The apartment looked wonderful — light and airy in the right street in the right suburb. We were both thrilled with it and in March 1992 we moved in. Our sixth house together.

In May I had news that my dear sister Betty had suffered a stroke. She was in intensive care. Betty had so bravely built a new life after losing her husband Ern to a painful cancer death. A woman who had totally devoted her life to her six kids and her husband, she had since learnt to drive a car and had taken up golf, a sport she became proficient at and enjoyed enormously. She had walked onto the course to tee off and collapsed. I spoke with her kids and arranged to fly to Adelaide the next day.

Nothing prepared me for the shock of seeing my vibrant sister connected to all the frightening apparatus that goes with intensive care. She looked so pale and so vulnerable.

Her kids were remarkable. My nieces and nephews drew up a roster, and for the many weeks of her battle at least one of them was constantly by her side. I'm convinced this outstanding show of love helped her to finally pull through. Today she leads a contented life, in care, but sees her family and friends frequently and continues to astonish us with her good humour and lateral wit.

It was shortly after this that I decided to stop drinking. I rarely drank hard liquor but I adored my white wine. I knew that often with the stress of filming and our frantic lifestyle I could overindulge, and I had started to have brutal hangovers. Previously, at the beginning of the day I would pledge to give up drinking, but by six o'clock in the evening I would have taken it up again. I remember we had gone down to Melbourne for the Logies, and everyone always drinks too much at the Logies, it's such a long night. Actually some of the highlights over the years have been caused by tipsy presenters or tipsy award recipients. Of course some of the lowlights have also come from them too. That year as we left the awards dinner I had a quick little dance with Magda Szubanski! So I was obviously feeling no pain but I was almost upright and sober compared to one well-known personality. She was legless and not an attractive sight.

The next morning when a waiter delivered breakfast, Panadol and Berocca to our room, Richard asked him how the hotel had survived the function. He told us the sad story of the personality who had been discovered collapsed against a wall with her legs spreadeagled and her knickers on view. Oh God, I thought, how humiliating and how many more drinks am I away from that fate? I looked at Richard and I said, 'Right! That's it, darling. I'm giving up the drink.'

'Oh sure,' he said, in disbelief.

But you know what? I did. It wasn't easy on me and it certainly wasn't easy on Richard. I was scratchy, but I hung in and eventually didn't miss it at all. Although Richard complained dinner was over very quickly because we no longer hung out at the table, lingering over a bottle of wine, or worse, two bottles of wine. I didn't drink for three and a half years. The stress of our relationship, I believe, saw me take it up again but certainly in a more tempered manner. The opinion amongst my friends is that I'm more relaxed and happier now than I was when I didn't drink at all. I mean, who wants to be miserable and mealy-mouthed? Anyway, Barb says I was 'bloody boring' when I gave up the vino. And I'm sure I was too bloody righteous for words. Cheers!

While we were renovating Richard's apartment there were constant negotiations between John Eastway and the ABC. Both wanted to proceed with another series of the 'Home Show' but there appeared to be a conflict looming. John finally told us he couldn't deliver what the ABC expected. The ABC informed us they were looking for an alternative production house. It was upsetting, Richard and I believed in John.

Finally the ABC appointed David Flatman Productions to the 'Home Show'. Our first meeting with David was not exactly compatible. We may have seemed defensive, we thought he was too aggressive. But Harry Miller and the ABC sorted out a truce, and we came to realise it was in all our interests to bridge our differences. David backed down a bit, we gave a bit. Gradually we sorted it out, with the considerable help of David's wife and partner Sue, who had the ability to see all sides. She was tested many times over the next two years. We started filming the third series of the 'Home Show' in July 1992.

At this time I began to experience some mood swings and strange anxieties, usually in the middle of the night. At first I thought it was just tension, I was unhappy with a lot of things on the 'Home Show'. I seemed to have a different director each week and I didn't like it. I enjoy working with a set team, you get to know each other and find a sort of shorthand as you work. But there were lots of changes around me and I found it disruptive. Then I started to experience hot flushes and knew I was at last into menopause.

Richard was not all that sympathetic. I was not exactly easy to live with, my hormones were rioting. It's a bitch. I went to my doctor, took some tests and started on HRT. After a time it settled down and I managed, but women do need support at this time. Richard found that difficult. I found it more difficult.

We had just come in from filming one evening when my sister Nancy called from Wales in the UK. She and her husband Lew had finally taken their first big trip overseas. I used to tease Lewis. He was what I called a dubious eater. Anything apart from a baked dinner he eyed with suspicion. I'd ragged him before they left on the trip, suggesting he pack a large jar of Vegemite just in case he couldn't cope with the foreign food. I was so excited to hear from Nancy that I babbled on for a couple of minutes asking her, 'Where are you, how's the trip, how's Lewis, is he eating?'

There was a silence of seconds and then she said, so calmly, 'Darling, Lewis died this morning.'

'Oh Nancy, no. Where? How? Why?'

They were staying in a small hotel in Wales owned by their daughter-in-law's brother. Lewis had got up quite early, gone to the bathroom and collapsed. He was dead by the time Nancy got to him. I couldn't imagine how it was for her, her husband of so many years, the father of her four fine children, the only man she had ever been with, suddenly snatched so cruelly on their dream trip.

'Darling, what can I do? Should I come?'

Unselfishly she said, 'No.' She already had the arrangements underway. She would fly Lewis home, she didn't know when. The red tape would take some time. We talked every few hours for the next couple of days. I marvelled at her courage, her coolness. 'She's got to crack,' I said to Richard. But she never did. Those Trigar girls certainly have backbone. I flew down to Adelaide for the funeral. I managed to get through the service, beautifully arranged by their children, holding Nan's hand. But when Lew's two sons joined by four strapping young cousins came to bear the coffin out of the chapel I disintegrated.

Lew had been a fine golfer, he adored playing with his sons and nephews. When he first started courting my sister I was a skinny little kid. He used to help me with my homework and best of all take me for a ride on his Harley Davidson. He'd worked hard all his life, he was a good father and husband, he had just retired, he loved life. It's not fair. It's just not fair, I thought. But then, I guess death rarely is.

WHEN I look back at my diary of 1992 it's as though it were written by a mad woman. Perhaps it was. I was ridiculously overworked, filming videos of the corporate wardrobes for ANZ and AMP, shooting brochures for both, and Maggie T. There were my pages and monthly commercials for *Women's Weekly* plus the 'Home Show' with its ongoing ABC push and shove, but somehow I managed to have weekend guests at our beloved Greenville. Both Richard and I looked forward to that so there were always long shopping lists each Friday. I loved to cook but I loathed the shopping.

One of the nicest things that happened to me that year was

to be invited to judge the NSW Architectural Awards. It proved a perfect opportunity for the 'Home Show' to film the latest and best of the state's architectural designs. I met some amazingly talented people and I really enjoyed working with the panel. The next year I went on to judge the National Awards and had the great pleasure of working with and getting to know my fellow judge, Glenn Murcutt. Glenn's a remarkable man, an internationally acclaimed and awarded architect. His work is exemplary and I had long been an admirer. Some months earlier I had nervously interviewed him for the 'Home Show' in one of his brilliant houses, and I wasn't prepared for his warmth and his wit. He took great delight in sending me up. He was amazed at how I was recognised around the country and quickly got into the habit of saying, 'Get Maggie to ask, they do anything for her.' We had a lot of fun.

At Greenville we had some ten acres of lawn to mow around the house. In spring it's a bit like painting the Harbour Bridge: you finish at one end and it's time to start again at the other. John usually cut it with the large ride-on mower, but he was taking a few days break so Richard decided he'd cut it. I heard him scream with pain and raced out. Somehow he had cut in under one of the big twisted willow trees, put the mower into reverse and backed into the tree trunk, sandwiching himself between the tree and the steering wheel. He was deathly pale. I got him into the house and into bed. The next day in Sydney the doctor said he had bruised four ribs. I understood it was extremely painful but Richard really was an impatient patient. To get him in and out of bed, he would wrap his arms around my neck while I'd struggle to manoeuvre this enormous man. After a couple of days my back was feeling the strain.

When I reluctantly had to leave him to fly to Melbourne for the Architectural Awards I prepared everything for him — a meal, special drinks. However, when he couldn't get out of bed without help he rang Brooke at some ungodly hour of the morning and she went around and filled in for her mum.

On another occasion at Greenville, I made a pot of coffee. I was in a rush and tried to force the plunger down. The pot exploded and boiling coffee splashed up over my forearm. The pain was excruciating. I quickly ran cold water over my arm, then somehow managed to empty an ice tray into a tea towel and wrap my arm. I took a couple of painkillers and alternated the ice wrap with the cold water from the tap. Finally Richard came in. He was grumpy with me, almost abusive, and totally without sympathy. I went to bed with my arm wrapped in ice and I got up every couple of hours to replace the melting ice.

The next day it was still brutally painful. We were to fly to Adelaide for Harry Watt's birthday party. As the plane climbed to its cruising height I watched in horror as the burnt skin on my arm turned black. During a stopover in Melbourne we went to the Chairman's Lounge where the attendant was so concerned she called a doctor. He examined my arm and said I was lucky there appeared to be no infection. It seemed the antibiotic I was taking for a minor ear infection had saved me. I was hurt by Richard's uncaring manner. He expected sympathy but he didn't know how to give it. Finally we wound up the year and prepared for another Christmas at Greenville.

During their 1993 New Year holidays in Australia, Amanda, Sergio and Marco spent a lot of time in Sydney staying with Barb as Richard was frequently moody. It was a strain. So when he announced he was going away with the boys for a week at Sanctuary Cove and the Magic Millions horse sale I didn't protest. He would be doing what he liked, messing around with his mates and seeing a lot of horses. Later, after our split, I read that he and the blonde had 'met at the Magic Millions'. I have since wondered how soon after that they started their affair? Was it that year? Had he lived a lie for the last two or three years of our relationship? But I guess he still needed me. We had signed for a fourth series of the 'Home Show' and we had also signed a lucrative commercial contract to endorse Luxaflex Blinds.

Nothing, it seems, was going to come between Richard and a quid. Yet he hated spending *his* money. For all that, I can't say we were desperately unhappy. All couples have differences and we had ours but for the most, particularly when he had me all to himself, he was warm and loving. Although increasingly his flashes of anger and temper, and his selfishness worried me. I saw a side emerging I'd perhaps chosen to ignore in the past.

More and more Richard took himself off to the races and horse sales without me. To be truthful it wasn't possible for me to be with him. I had to give the staff at the farm a break at the weekends and I have a rule that the property, because of the animals and for security, is never left unattended. But when I did go to the races with Richard I felt I was something of a burden. He once said to me, 'I'll dump you in the committee room.' Dump me! Charming, I thought. So rather than be a burden I opted not to go.

Halfway through the year we inexplicably started to move apart. When he was at Greenville he spent hours on the phone, mainly chatting to mates about horses or just gossiping. I found our previously cosy nights by the fire in the study were now strained. The lively conversation we had always enjoyed disappeared, replaced by an uneasy silence. How often had I sat in restaurants around the world and watched couples locked in that silence? It was sad. Increasingly I thought, he's physically here, he's not mentally here. The only time he showed any enthusiasm was when we talked about the horses, matching stallions with mares, but even this became difficult. I have no head for breeding lines. I would get confused and Richard would become impatient and scornful. He had been studying the horse business for years. I'd invested a considerable amount in them to please him, and although I loved the horses it just wasn't my game. My world had been fashion and I didn't expect him to be knowledgeable about that. When I first met Richard he didn't know who Armani, Hermes or Max Mara were. Mind you, he quickly developed a taste for labels, particularly Armani.

In July of that year I first met with the book publisher Allen & Unwin. For years various publishing companies had been after me to write 'the book'. At one stage Richard suggested he would write it, then he would add, 'No, I'd only get cross when I had to write about your ex-lovers.' But meeting with Patrick Gallagher, the company's Managing Director, for the first time I started to think, Perhaps I should do this. My close friend and successful writer Susie Mitchell encouraged me and scared the hell out of me by adding, 'If you don't, someone else will and they'll get it all wrong.' But I refused to sign a contract. I just wasn't ready. I asked Patrick to give me time. He was to prove to be more than patient.

We finished a difficult year with the 'Home Show'. We felt the ABC had fallen down on the publicity front. Also, they frequently asked David to make last-minute changes to the final cut of the show. Why was it always my favourite *fun* bits that got dumped? Then a couple of ratbag journos in provincial towns put the boot into the show a few times, and other copy-cat commercial programmes were popping up. For all that, I think in that last series we made a couple of the best shows in the entire four years. We also made some pretty average ones. I was working with Jeff Sims as my director and I really enjoyed that. He was witty, easy, laid-back and Mr Cool, even when he had to direct the dreaded openers and closers with Richard and me.

Richard continually wanted to alter the script, or he'd complain about people standing in his eye line. It's hard to ask people to move out of your eye line, particularly if you're filming in their house for God's sake. If you must, then ask with some charm. Richard didn't. I would cringe.

We knew that David Flatman was having trouble renewing the series. Finally the ABC decided not to proceed. They felt the format, now picked up by the other networks, was too commercial. Months earlier, Channel Nine had approached us through Harry Miller to move over to Nine. But we had our ABC contract in train and I've never walked away from a contract, ever. We gambled that Channel Nine might wait till the end of the year when we'd be free. They didn't. That's life!

That year a dispute broke out with respect to the rights to the 'Home Show', which attracted all the usual media innuendo. Ted Dunn sued the ABC, but fortunately the case was settled out of court early the following year.

When the show ended we took off on our annual trip, in high excitement. We went to Paris for the Prix de l'Arc de Triomphe, meeting Richard's old friend Nic Columb for lunch on the course. It was a spectacular day. I was fascinated with the chic French and the eccentric British. Their dress styles were worlds apart. An old friend who lived in Paris, the beautiful Wendy Rowe, had joined us. I had first met Wendy when Jan Geary grabbed her out of a department store crowd and we persuaded her to enter the Miss Maglia Quest back in the 1970s. She won, incidentally.

In the stampede for taxis and hire cars at the end of the day we missed out and had to travel back into Paris, straphanging in a bus, feeling a bit foolish dressed to the nines, me sandwiched between two Gypsy women, one breast-feeding her baby, the other seriously eyeing my Broome pearl earrings. Richard and

I both loved Paris and dined out in the most wonderful spots.

Our friends Libby Reeves Purdy and John Chalk flew over from London just to take us out to dinner in the Eiffel Tower Restaurant. Richard freaked on the way up in the elevator. He has no head for heights. Although I noted that after a good meal he wasn't at all disturbed on the way down. We walked miles during the day, it was cold and clear, perfect weather for sight-seeing. We crawled through the Louvre and the Musée d'Orsay, although at the Musée d'Orsay I find a conflict. I want to look at the paintings but I'm so blown away by the architecture.

Our plan was that Richard would go on to see the studs in Ireland, I would spend time with the kids in Positano, and we would meet back in Paris. So we went our individual ways and then met back at Orly Airport. Richard's flight came in about thirty minutes ahead of mine. He was there grinning at me as I came off the plane and wrapped me in a huge bear hug. I felt all his warmth and knew he had missed me terribly, just as I had missed him. I felt confident that things were going to be alright, that perhaps absence does make the heart grow fonder.

We hired a car and somehow I drove us out of the very con-fusing airport carpark. Richard was so 'charged' about Ireland, the studs and horses he'd seen. He was dying to tell me every-thing. At one stage I had to say, 'Darling, help me, I'm trying to drive on the wrong side of the road and I desperately need a navigator.' Finally we found the freeway to Deauville, headed off and he told me all about his trip. We stayed in a marvellous old hotel right by the sea. We shopped, walked the city squares and the foreshore, and found the best restaurant in town with a charming owner who thankfully spoke English as neither Richard nor I has an ear for French. And we went to the races.

Deauville's racecourse is delightful, surrounded with huge, magnificent trees. I love people-watching and there were a lot of well-heeled, well-dressed and very aristocratic French to observe. I remember we were looking at the horses as they came out for race three, I always bet on the third in the third. Don't laugh, you'd be amazed how many times it comes home. A big grey horse came into view. Richard and I love greys but as it came closer Richard said, 'Darling, that horse is lame.' And it was. We watched it circle the saddling paddock and there was no doubt it had a very distinct limp. No one else seemed at all amazed that a horse with a limp was about to go out and run a race. To our surprise it not only ran the race, it bloody well won.

It was perhaps the happiest of our trips. By the time we arrived back I had convinced Richard that he should lease his Woollahra apartment and use the rent to pay off his mortgage. He was, and had been for some time, writing a racing column for the *Sun-Herald*, but now that the 'Home Show' had finished his income was savagely reduced. I suggested I buy a small pad in Sydney. We only needed somewhere to crash as we were really living at Greenville. Barb and I set out to find something, and we did: a cute, one-bedroom apartment with a big sunny terrace in a newly and cleverly renovated building in Curlewis Street, Bondi.

Richard liked the prospect of being able to walk to the beach in the morning. He quickly leased his apartment for a handsome rental. Then he paid me a small rent on the Bondi apartment, as we had agreed providing a city residence was his responsibility. Once again I was packing up with a sticker system: blue dots for Bondi, white dots for storage. Quite a lot had to go into storage because the Bondi apartment was very small but it looked great when I had finished, with a sharp black and white decor. And Richard was happy there. We walked on Bondi Beach every morning and he would plunge into the surf. We were close to a number of good restaurants so it was fun, for a while.

Gradually, however, I came to the conclusion that while

Bondi may eventually 'happen', it just wasn't going to 'happen' in my lifetime. The beach was beautiful, the foreshore disgusting and the whole area suffered neglect. One morning we walked out to go to the beach and someone had dumped an old refrigerator right in front of our gate. By the time we came back an hour later it had given birth. There were three old refrigerators in front of our gate. The itinerant occupants of the apartments that surrounded ours would move out and just dump their old furnishings on the street. I was constantly picking up trash thrown over the fence into our neat little garden. Once some people who were renting in our building moved out and cheerfully took with them a console table and mirror from the building's foyer. And often the delinquent teenager in the building next door would abuse his parents so loudly that we had to turn the music up full bore. I started to hate Bondi.

LATE IN December Susan Duncan, Editor of *The Australian Women's Weekly*, was unceremoniously dismissed. Susan had been a very talented writer with the *Weekly* and had taken over as Editor when sadly the previous Editor, Jenny Rowe, was forced to resign by management. It was cruel timing. Susan's husband was dying tragically and painfully of a brain tumour. Nene King took over as Editor-in-Chief, handling both the *Weekly* and *Woman's Day*. Nene called me into her office, made flattering comments about my pages and said, 'Your fashion pages are the only ones in the entire magazine I don't want to change.' However, it didn't turn out that way.

Over the next two years she would often request specific stories. I didn't always agree with them but I bowed to her wishes. After all, she was the Editor, but it was the first time in my many years at the *Weekly* that I'd had an editor dictate my material. It was frustrating and confusing, probably for both of us. But first there was another Christmas at Greenville and by now the ranks had swollen. We had a lot of visitors from overseas. It was, as always, noisy, busy, wonderful.

Each January since moving to Greenville, we had held the 'Greenville Cup'. It was a fun tennis day with about forty friends. Some could play good tennis but for the most, it was a hit, miss and giggle sort of day; an excuse to get together and have a good lunch. It started as a way for our friends to say goodbye to Amanda and Sergio before they returned to Italy, but it grew into a real production. I designed T-shirts and had them printed. We also gave out caps and headbands. Partners in the mixed doubles were drawn and we were fiercely honest about this. The Cup, retained at Greenville, was inscribed each year with the winners' names, and smaller versions were given to winners.

I hadn't played tennis for yonks but the first year I drew a good partner, David Welsh, and we won. Richard was a bit po-faced about it. He could play well but his temper usually got the better of him. This year it got the better of both of us. It was a glorious day, our friends had all arrived, and Richard and I had been drawn as partners. We survived the first round. In the second, I think I blew a shot at the net and he became furious. He then deliberately threw the match, hitting a deciding point into the net, and for once I got really mad at him. I kept it pretty much to myself until he went to the other end of the house to shower. I followed and asked him why he had thrown the match? He said, 'You were hopeless. We were going to lose anyway.' I exploded.

'Richard, that's the big difference between you and me,' I said. 'I hang in until the end, I never give up, not until the fat lady sings. You, on the other hand, give up before the fight's half over. You're pathetic and embarrassing.' I also pointed out that at least I'd won the Greenville Cup once, something he hadn't done. He sulked in the study, I went and joined our guests, smiling a lot but probably fooling no one. Richard's sister Amanda put her arm around me, often she and I had an unspoken understanding of how difficult Richard could be. A week later he took off to New Zealand to cover the horse sales. He rang every day and we somehow got over the crisis. I always forgave him.

Before the kids took Marco home to Italy I realised he had developed a fetish for his mama's breasts. He's very Italian. If he was upset or tired he wanted to cuddle his mama and would invariably let a hand stray to caress her breasts and comfort himself. Amanda was steadily and gently easing him out of the habit, but he obviously still had a healthy interest in all bosoms. He called them 'diddle diddles'. He sprang me in the bathroom one morning as I was cleaning my teeth, naked, at the basin. I noted his keen interest but we've never been coy in our family, so I just went on with what I was doing. Finally I couldn't cope with his penetrating gaze any longer. 'What is it, Marco?' I asked.

He gazed up at me, gave a rapturous smile and said, '*Bella* diddle diddles, Nanna!'

'Marco,' I replied, 'that's the nicest thing a man's said to me for a long, long time.'

A few days later, as they were packing to leave Marco looked at me and said, 'Don't cry little baby Nanna.' I melted and I did cry. It had always been hard to say goodbye to Amanda and Sergio but Marco made it even more so.

In March I was scheduled to go to New Zealand with a bunch of the other *Women's Weekly* editors for the *Weekly*'s tea parties. This had begun some years before. It was an annual event where the editors met with readers who had been selected through a draw in the magazine. The editors would each sit at a table for ten minutes answering questions and then move on to the next table. It was for the most part fun, sometimes embarrassing. You'd be amazed what people can ask!

This year Nene generously asked if I'd like to take Richard along for company. He was thrilled. There was a fine old stallion standing in Dunedin, we would have an opportunity to visit him. We went over a few days ahead of the tea parties. Flying into Christchurch the weather was soupy, but an hour later when we were due to fly on to Dunedin it had turned fierce. We boarded the aircraft and the captain announced, 'Well, the weather is pretty awful, however, we are going to try to get into Dunedin. We have a fifty-fifty chance of making it.'

Fifty-fifty chance! I looked at Richard and said, 'I'm out of here, I don't like the odds.' Air New Zealand were very good about taking the baggage off, and I placated Richard by telling him I would drive him to Dunedin the next day. We found a good hotel, had a good dinner and made love. The next morning dawned with torrential rain but I figured a promise is a promise, so I hired a car and we set off, down over the Canterbury Plains. Mind you, we could hardly see them, the weather had really closed in. It was difficult driving. After about an hour and a half we stopped for a coffee. 'Where are you headed?' asked the cafe proprietor.

'To Dunedin,' Richard answered.

'Oh no, you're not,' she said cheerfully. 'The road's cut. Worst flood in years.'

We drove back to the city in almost dead silence after Richard berated me that we should have stayed on the plane. He never forgave me, particularly when the stallion he so wanted to see died a few months later. He'd had a free trip and he got to see several other studs. But he was to bring it up again and again.

At *Women's Weekly* things were not so easy. I'd had good relationships with all my previous four editors and I wanted to please Nene. My pages had not altered — the formula had proved successful. I strenuously endeavoured to cover different age groups, styles and budgets, but it's hard to please all the readers all the time. The odd letter of complaint upset her. The writers seemed to focus on either budget or age. I covered *real* budget fashion at least three times a year, out of twelve issues, which seemed a good balance, and most other issues covered medium-priced merchandise. But a letter that began, 'I'm sixty-five, I'd like to see fashion for my age group', didn't wash with me. I firmly believed the general fashion merchandise I covered for the *Weekly* was ageless. So I'd reply, 'Dear so and so, I'm a grandmother. I don't go out and buy a grandmother's dress and neither should you,' and I certainly wasn't going to put them in my pages! Happy readers usually don't correspond, they just continue to buy the magazine. Only the unhappy ones feel inspired to take up a pen with their complaints. Nene wanted more and more budget fashion.

Midway through the year I was forced to do the only reshoot I've ever done in my fashion career. Nene hated the location of one of the shots. It was clean, stark and I thought captured the mood of the minimalist garments. I was rather rattled by the incident and I started to think, maybe I won't last long here. For all that I admired Nene, she's a gutsy woman. She would come into my office on a good day and we'd discuss HRT and what a shitty, unfair thing menopause was, laugh and compare our symptoms. Often I felt I'd touched base with her, that I'd broken through a sort of defensive barrier. A day later she'd silently pass me in the corridor. I knew she was under enormous pressure. Pleasing the power brokers upstairs couldn't have been easy but increasingly I found it unsettling. If only we'd been able to really talk it out.

I was also having trouble filming *Women's Weekly* commercials.

I'd been doing them for years. If the director asked I could cut a second off the rapid-fire reads, even more when required. But the commercials were repeatedly overwritten in an effort to promote more of the magazine's content. The reads became speed gabbles. I started to sound like a Disney chipmunk in fast forward. The ad agency was also having trouble pleasing the *Weekly*. Finally they were sacked. Then we went through three or four different agencies in a very short time. All had great difficulty with the account. I hated the changes.

One director was so intent on covering his own butt in every possible way that my normal half-day shoots became full-day marathons. I'd do take after take so that he had speed reads of different fractions of a second and alternative inflections on every grab. I didn't even sound like me! There was no room to use an expressive glance to camera or even a telling pause. I think the commercials suffered because of that. They became flat strap, wall to wall gabble. We started to call it *Women's Weekly* Speak. When I came to do other commercials for Luxaflex or Black & Decker the directors had trouble slowing me down to human speak. I was going home from filming days feeling like a limp rag. I complained to Harry Miller who in turn discussed it with the *Weekly*, but it was never to get back to its previous sanity. Even though eventually they appointed a terrific director, David Lewis, we were constantly battling unworkable script times.

ONE DAY at Greenville, Richard and I had taken a long walk with my beloved dog Bronson, who had been a birthday gift to me from John and Caroline Conners, the farm managers. A fluffy white ball, he had grown into a handsome big golden retriever. His best mate was the Conners' dog, Magnum or Mags as we called him. Mags was very old and was having trouble with his back legs. He spent a lot of time over at my house and when the Conners were away I fed him. Despite his age he had a healthy appetite but he no longer came on our long walks and could barely manage to get to the end of the drive.

Richard and I were discussing the inevitable. How sad it would be for John, Caroline and us when Mags finally went and how lonely Bronson would be without his old mate. Richard floored me by saying, 'I'll buy you another dog.' He was not normally given to such acts, he was never a gift giver. I knew that all my birthday gifts, bar one, had been bought at the last minute and on advice from either Barb or Brooke, and my Christmas gifts were the same each year — a thin gold bangle.

We rang the breeder who had bred Bronson. Yes, he had a male dog, six weeks old. With almost indecent speed this adorable puppy was delivered. Wallis came into my life. He became a great joy, the other dogs loved him instantly and tolerated his sometimes rough play. Within a couple of weeks he could take himself to and from the manager's cottage and he settled in well. That is until he had grown enough to wander further. I had noted that he had developed a slight limp and took him to Jane, our Bowral vet. She confirmed he had a genetic problem with his front legs. I rang the breeder, distressed. They offered to pay for half the operation. I never took them up on it but a thousand dollars later Wallis had straight legs.

Then he took to running off with Bronson. They were monsters, haring out into the bush for hours, coming home exhausted and covered in mud like two naughty schoolboys. It wasn't what Wallis needed and I loathed tying him up. He fretted. Eventually, sadly, I had to listen to the vet. 'Maggie, one golden retriever will be your best friend. Two and they will be each other's best friend.' She was also concerned that Wallis' legs were never going to heal properly and grow strong with such extreme exercise.

So we found him a good home with a young family with a small backyard in Bowral, and I cried my heart out.

I've often wondered if Wallis was a conscience gift from Richard. There was an incident with Wallis that I will never forget. Richard had taken off on his morning run, I had stopped going with him, perhaps to avoid more of his silences. He had just come through the gate onto the road when I noticed Wallis heading out after him. I called to Richard to ask him to bring Wallis back to the house. He was recovering from his leg operation and wasn't supposed to go on long walks. I was still in my dressing gown, standing on the verandah. Richard stopped halfway up the hill, turned, then screamed at the top of his lungs, 'Fuck you!'

His vile words and all the anger behind them sped over the beautiful green paddocks, past the tranquil lakes in the early light and hit me with an impact I can't describe. I felt the blood drain from my face. He came back with my poor little dog and I just looked at him. I couldn't speak. I took Wallis in my arms and Richard stormed off to take a shower, yelling more abuse. John wandered over from the cottage, looked at me searchingly and said gently, 'You OK, Maggie?' I think if Richard had been there John might have punched him.

'I'm fine, John, just not a good morning.' I sat on the verandah for a while. I felt the tears sting my eyes. The savagery, the hostility of that 'Fuck you' had stunned me. Surely there was more behind that than just the inconvenience of having his run interrupted. But what? It would be another year before I found out. Another whole valuable year of life. Damn it.

In July we took off on our annual trip, first to London, seeing old friends, lunch at Harry's Bar with Libby Reeves Purdy, Di Jagleman and Ros Packer, drinks at the Dorchester and lunch at Cicios with Bernard Leser. We went racing at Goodwood in freezing drizzly conditions. 'A typical English summer,' we remarked, and then took off to Positano where we stayed in the sensational private villa Nuvolari.

Friends had taken the villa for a month and generously hosted various mates from around the world. We were a merry gang until Richard and the English actor, Nigel Havers, joined forces. Like larrikin boys they formed a liaison, drank too much, laughed at their own jokes and generally misbehaved, often ignoring the rest of the party. One day they idly started to throw lemons that had fallen on the terrace over the cliff. Richard aimed and threw a large lemon a considerable distance down the mountain to where the girls were sunbaking on the rocks. It hit Nigel's beautiful wife Polly on the ankle, which immediately turned navy blue. I was livid with him. Our diminutive hostess grabbed Richard and gave him a stern talking to. Richard, as usual, just laughed it off. Nigel, who participated in the juvenile lemon throwing, got the cold shoulder from his good wife and spent an uncomfortable night on the living-room couch.

The villa, with its big cool rooms, spacious terraces and sensational views hangs on a cliff overlooking the impossibly blue Mediterranean with Positano to the right, Praiano to the left a stone's throw from the Zefferellis' impressive villa. Elena, the cook, prepared wonderful lunches taken under an arbour of lemons on the big terrace. Sometimes Sergio would send the boat for us and we'd go out to his restaurant Da Adolfo and lunch with him, Amanda and Marco. Somehow Richard got on with Amanda when we visited Positano. He even expressed admiration for the way she could organise anything required by our hosts or the other guests. In the evenings we would take a water taxi into Positano to dine in one of the numerous excellent restaurants. It was a stinking hot August and the endless Positano stairs often got the better of us but our hosts were remarkable and I, at least, felt very privileged to be there.

Troubled
Times

BACK HOME Richard whinged about what he felt the property manager had failed to do while we were away. I reminded him it's not easy to ask staff to look after the property twenty-four hours a day for four weeks. But he was fast to point out other people's failings and even faster to forget his own. It had been a problem for some time. John and Richard had a tense relationship and every now and then it flared. I'd tried to discuss this with Richard, pointing out that the best way to get things done his way was if he and John worked together rather than criticising him. Every time Richard tried this he'd come into the house elated and say how much had been achieved. But then he'd go back to his old pattern and just disappear to Sydney and return to criticise.

I felt I was constantly trying to maintain calm. It didn't always work. I was not always witness to their spats but I certainly heard about them from Richard. The Conners endeavoured to keep any unpleasantness from me but Caroline's body language toward Richard started to show. She would come into the house, talk to me and ignore Richard. I can't say I blamed her. He was fiercely vocal about what he perceived to be her rudeness.

'But Richard, you can't abuse her husband and then expect her to be your best friend.'

Our five mares grew fat with their pregnancies, then their foals at foot were a constant joy. In November we were in Sydney for a few days and John phoned, distraught. During a sudden thunderstorm a filly from our best mare Top Dance had gone up on her hind legs, twisted and crashed to the ground. John had the vet on the way but it didn't look good. We kept in touch by phone and headed back to Greenville. Shortly after this they had to put her down. She had smashed her shoulder. We both loved that filly, she was correct in her formation and full of promise. I'd invested a lot of dollars buying her mother and we anticipated that she was going to balance the books for us at the yearling sales. She was flashy, had a spirited temperament and Richard believed she had all the right ingredients to be able to run. She never had a chance after that thunderstorm. Breeding horses, I came to the conclusion, was a bloody cruel business and more than once I asked myself what I was doing. Pleasing Richard was always the answer. And for what? The pain was twofold, emotional and financial, and the dream was turning sour. No matter how I tried I was never going to be able to put it together again.

A few days after my birthday in December 1994, Harry M. rang with the news that the *Weekly* had decided to go with a different format for their commercials. Given the difficulties I'd had filming in the past months I suppose I should have been thrilled, but of course I wasn't. My pride was hurt. I had fronted the *Weekly* commercials for fourteen years. I felt rejected. My difficulties with Richard only highlighted all my fears. Was I too old? Was my career about to dissolve? My confidence and self-respect took a massive dive but finally I just had to set it aside. There was another Greenville Christmas, the family arrived from Italy, there were chores to be done. I got on with my responsibilities, the joy of Marco eased a lot of the hurt and confusion I was feeling, and we somehow managed to enjoy Christmas.

I felt it was critical that the news about the commercials had to be delicately announced. Harry had assurances from Consolidated Press management that it would be. It wasn't. Given their expertise in handling the press I could only assume it was neglectful. But it illustrated that there was little concern for my feelings. One press piece said: 'The *Weekly* dumps Maggie.' I was devastated.

Finally I had to face the reality of my position at *Women's Weekly*. Deep in my heart I felt it best to resign. I was saddened at their treatment of me. Also, I could see that no matter what I did, which was what I'd always done for sixteen years, I was having difficulty pleasing my editor. Kerry Packer had personally hired me. It had been good for both of us for a long time. Now I needed to talk to him. Should I stay or would it be cleaner if I resigned? I felt he would help me make the right decision. I would pay him the courtesy of asking his advice. I called, I faxed, I badgered his secretary, all I really needed was a few seconds of his time. I didn't hear back.

After a few more stressful days I tendered my resignation through Harry to Richard Walsh, the Chief Executive of ACP. Within hours flowers had arrived from Nene and Richard and cards asking me to stay as Fashion Editor of the *Weekly*, to please reconsider. In retrospect I should have stuck to my guns and made a clean break. But then when your ego gets in the way you'll clutch at any straw. I reached out and withdrew my resignation. A couple of days later Kerry faxed me at the farm. He agreed the whole thing had been badly handled. He apologised but pointed out he was no longer involved in the day-to-day running of Consolidated Press. It was of some comfort but it was really too late. I resumed my fashion pages for the *Weekly* but I felt hurt by the past events and uneasy about my future at the magazine.

Early in the New Year Barb rang to say that mutual friends, Tony and Sandra McGrath, had offered her their wonderful house in Fiji. 'How about we gather up all the family and take off?' After my recent stressful time she felt it would do me good. The kids were all for it. Richard shrank from the prospect of a family holiday but urged me to go (I now know why). So early in February Barb, her son Matt and daughter Ash, Brooke, Amanda, Sergio, Marco and I all boarded Qantas for Fiji. We spent the night in Nadi and the next morning raided the local supermarket and wine merchant to stock up with supplies, then took a small aircraft over to the McGraths' house on a tiny island. The complex, which consisted of a group of three large farés, traditional thatched-roof houses, exceeded our expectations with its beauty. The farés were set high on a hill with a breath-taking view that embraced both the island and the clear blue tropical sea. We were in heaven.

Sergio and Matt quickly made friends with the local fishermen and we looked forward to their calls each day. One memorable evening they delivered three enormous crayfish. The boys had them on the barbecue in a flash and we sat down to a candle-lit feast. It was an easy, relaxed holiday with a lot of laughter and joking going on. I swam each day, achieved a safe tan and felt happy. One morning I woke to realise that the tension I constantly felt in my neck had evaporated. At the time I didn't really analyse why, but I've since wondered was it being away from the stress at the *Weekly* or the stress of Richard? There was no phone at the house but I called him every couple of days from the village store. He rarely seemed to be home. He was always out having a 'bite with a mate'.

The kids all adored Fiji. Marco swam happily in the pool, secure in his floaties, and he spent hours trying to catch one of the zillion little frogs that covered the lawn at dusk. He christened them 'Watermelon'. This one was Watermelon, that one was Watermelon. They were all named Watermelon.

Most nights we'd barbecue fish or make a big pasta but occasionally we would wander down to dine at the resort by the sea and watch the locals sing and dance. We struck up a friendship with a handsome Italian who, with his girlfriend, was sailing around the islands. He'd been sailing for something like five years, a real adventurer. He took us for a sail one day and we invited him to join us the following night for dinner. He would only come, he said, if he could bring the pasta. How he made pumpkin ravioli for nine people in his tiny galley on the yacht was beyond me. He served the pasta with a fine herb sauce, ladled out with great style from a huge hollowed-out pumpkin. Those Italians, I love 'em. When it comes to food nothing is too much trouble.

Back home I gave Richard and our friend Andrew Clark a joint birthday lunch at Greenville. It was March. I picked huge branches of autumn leaves and set a lavish table with claret-coloured lacquered plates, crisp white table napkins and the mountain of autumn leaves set in a big wooden bowl. Andrew looked at the table and said, 'Oh Mags, I'm glad to see you didn't go to any trouble.' It was a pleasure. I wanted it to be very special, and we had a very happy day. But apart from those occasions when we had guests, the silences grew longer between Richard and me. I was shattered. I'd walk away from him in his study to the kitchen and try to think of conversation. I had never before been lost for words. In the past, Richard and I had always had heaps to discuss. Our relationship was slowly unravelling and I felt powerless to stop it. He was frequently less than nice to me. He also started to stay in town after the races.

He was still writing a racing column for the *Sun-Herald* where Andrew Clark was Editor. I came to loathe column days. Richard would sit in the study at the lovely old desk I had bought for him and pound away on his ancient typewriter. He would type a few words, then rip the paper out and start again on a new sheet. The paper basket would overflow with his discards then the floor would be scattered with more. I hated the waste. I suggested he learn to use my new word processor. He said he couldn't. Occasionally I'd contribute a thought or some words. At first he welcomed this, he'd tell me how clever I was. But later it became clear he resented my suggestions so I backed off.

Probably due to his column, he was offered a job with Foxtel to consult on the racing industry. Foxtel were eager to set up a racing channel and Richard was to lobby the industry. This may not be a totally accurate job description but it's how I understood it. When he came home after his first day at the lavish new Foxtel offices in Darling Harbour he was exhilarated. If he said to me once how *exciting* he found the *young* people in the office, he said it a thousand times. I was happy for him having found a job he enjoyed but I started to feel threatened by his continued raving about the young staff, and why did they all have girls' names? I'd often said to my family, 'I'm getting old,' but I never really believed it. I didn't feel old. I didn't think I looked old, well as old as my years anyway.

Thinking about that period now, I was obviously mentally in worse condition than I acknowledged. I felt depressed and anxious a lot of the time, to the point that finally I went to my doctor. Dr David Walker had seen me through numerous crises in my life. Usually I found a good talk with him set me straight, but this time he suggested that I consult a psychologist. I dreaded going to those rooms in Macquarie Street. I feared being seen and I hated it when I passed other patients in the waiting room.

I heard one ask the receptionist in a stage whisper, 'Is that who I think it is?' However, the psychologist I liked a lot, she was a no-nonsense sort of woman. It took me three or four visits to realise I was covering up my real feelings. I just couldn't tell her truthfully about Richard's behaviour and about my fears. I focused on my work-related problems.

It was ridiculous to see her and to avoid discussing what I knew were my real anxieties. I don't know why I kept going but I did. Perhaps I thought one day I'd find 'the voice' to tell her the truth, or perhaps one day she would somehow, miraculously, discover it. I'm sure she was aware of my ruse. Several times she questioned me about Richard and to my surprise I heard myself defend him. 'No, he's wonderful.' Or 'No, there's no real problem there.' I did, however, tell her about his difficulties with my family, his jealousy of Amanda and Brooke, but nothing more. Who did I think I was kidding? I must have been mad. Well, perhaps I was, a little.

Richard knew I was seeing the shrink. However, he was not very interested in hearing about my visits so I avoided discussing them with him. Increasingly he criticised me. I was hopeless because I didn't grasp the intricacies of horse breeding. I was idiotic because I occasionally wanted to watch something on television that he considered to be trash. One morning, lying in bed, we were discussing how we would celebrate his fiftieth birthday when we went to Positano in a few weeks time. His friends, Tony Hartnell and his wife Mary-Ed, had said they would join us for the celebration. Somehow the conversation turned to my age and I innocently said, 'God where does time go? I'll be fifty-nine next birthday.' Richard cringed.

'My God, that means you'll be sixty the year after!'

I looked at him, he almost recoiled. I bit my lip, got out of bed and went to take a shower. I realised all too clearly that

Richard had a problem with my age, and therefore I had a problem with my age. All my fears had been realised with those few cruel words. Richard hated turning fifty but he hated more the prospect of me turning sixty. I had committed the cardinal sin of getting old.

Somehow our trips overseas had always provided joy, a diversion from real life. In June we took off for Italy, England and Ireland. In Rome this time we changed hotels and stayed at the Hotel De Le Ville, next to the Hassler at the top of the Spanish Steps. We had an enormous terrace room with magical views over the Rome rooftops. We shopped, took the sun on the terrace and dined in our favourite restaurants and discovered the culinary delights of the hotel's restaurant. One night I looked up from the menu to see Sean Connery enter. My God, I thought, now there's a man. Richard and I were fascinated with his companion, a rather strange looking woman who sat down, opened her mouth and didn't shut up for the next hour and a half. Poor Sean just worked his way through a fine bottle of red. The following morning we bumped into him toting his golf clubs coming out of the room right next to ours. I remarked to Richard that I could now say, 'I've slept next to Sean Connery.'

From Rome we drove down to Positano. Richard's papa, Harry, was to join us for the birthday celebration. At the last minute, however, it was decided the many steps of Positano would be too arduous for a knee problem he was experiencing. So Harry would meet us in London, in the two-bedroom apartment we had booked in a delightful boutique hotel.

Amanda and Sergio went to great lengths to provide a happy scene for Richard's fiftieth. Nene had asked us to take shots for a piece for the *Weekly*. Amanda found a local photographer, a friend Raphaella, who did the job beautifully. For all the guests Amanda provided navy and white-striped T-shirts printed with a big red squid design. Tony and Mary-Ed Hartnell flew in and took the room next to ours in our favourite little pensione, Le Fenice. Wendy Rowe came from Paris. I bought big colourful kerchiefs as napkins for the table and the waiters picked fresh wild flowers from the hill and placed them in hand-painted pottery jugs. Sergio generously provided some beautiful local wines, fine French champers and an exceptionally lavish birthday cake.

We had a really great day, but I wonder why we all tried so hard to please Richard. I knew I still loved him, despite some unpleasant times, but the kids really knocked themselves out. It was a sterling effort given his indifference to their feelings over the years. I loved seeing Marco. He had grown so much and now chatted freely, switching from English to Italian mid-sentence if he got confused about which language you spoke.

Next we went to London. Harry Zachariah had arrived earlier in the day from Australia. I had called the management of the hotel from Italy to explain that Harry was elderly and we would appreciate their caring for him. They had welcomed him and made him comfortable. Harry was happily ensconced in the apartment watching cricket on the tellie when we arrived. We phoned our friend Vicki Jones who was also visiting London and she came in to have dinner with us in the hotel restaurant, which had a reputation for serving some of the finest food in London. It should have, it cost a couple of gold bricks but it was superb.

We had just taken our seats when the maître d came to welcome us. He was immensely proud of the restaurant's new decor, which included hand-turned wooden objects made by Viscount Linley, Princess Margaret and Lord Snowdon's son. These objects were displayed on small wooden shelves fixed in a pyramid shape into mirrored walls at either end of the room. As our rather impressive entrées were set before us there came a loud crash, followed by another. We watched in horror as one object and shelf collapsed, skittled another object and shelf, which in turn collapsed and fell, to wipe out another and another until the entire display lay in a heap on the deep-piled carpet. Much like the dismantling of a relationship.

The London apartment was beautifully situated just behind Harrods. I would trot off to buy lunch, simple things such as salmon or ham and a fresh salad and baguette. The only thing about shopping at Harrods is the price. I never seemed to get out of there for under 'Ninety-eight pounds please'! It was outrageous. I remember one day standing before the pâté counter. Immediately in front of me there must have been twenty-something different pâtés. I was reading the tags, trying to make up my mind when my eye travelled further along the glass display counter. It seemed to go for a mile, all pâtés. There must have been over a hundred. I suddenly felt sickened by the excess. It was retail gone stark, raving mad! I left the store and never went back, choosing to shop for our lunches at Harvey Nicolls down the road, where the food hall was smaller and on a saner scale.

Richard's sister Jane, who is a teacher in Scotland, came to London to stay with us for a few days. I had organised Richard's measurements to be faxed to Moss Bros in London prior to our departure from Australia so he would have the right gear for Ascot — morning suit, waistcoat, top hat. The 'works' as they say. We went off to his fitting together. I loved watching the Poms come in to be fitted. Tall, short, fat, thin and oh so pukka! It was better than 'Candid Camera'. Richard looked handsome in his gear but I thought at the time he could have done with a larger hat. He only tried it on for a second and assured me he would probably just carry it.

Back at the apartment Richard dressed and strode out to show Harry and Jane. Jane looked up, laughed and made a light remark about Richard looking a little like Sir John Kerr. The image of Sir John at the Melbourne Cup in that ridiculously undersized top hat perched atop his massive head of snow-white hair flashed before my eyes. There was a resemblance of sorts. I laughed too, so did Harry. Richard hurled some savage words in Jane's direction and stormed back into the bedroom, his vanity sorely dented. Jane's eyes filled with tears, shocked at his reaction. I assured her he would get over it and went to make all the right cooing noises to him.

In London the weather was less than wonderful, cold and bleak. We were both forced to buy raincoats. I bought Harry a handsome warm jacket, and he and Jane took off for Scotland. Richard and I drove to Windsor where we stayed in a picturesque little hotel within sight of the castle. The Queen's Guards marched with pipe band by our window each morning, their bright red jackets decked in gold, topped with those incredible black bearskin hats. We were caught in the pomp of Ascot week in Merry Ol' England. We spent three magic days racing and lunching with friends in their splendid marquee, set amongst the trees in a park opposite the main gates of Ascot, meeting interesting new people such as Andrew Lloyd Webber and renewing old friendships with Sir David Frost and Clive James. Then Richard and I went on to Ireland.

Since Richard's first visit two years before he had often mentioned how he would love to show me Ireland. Until then, on most of our travels, I'd been 'tour leader'. I had travelled for years and knew my way around but I'd never been to Ireland, so it was a role reversal, one I looked forward to. We flew into Dublin. Richard had phoned ahead to our hotel, which was an hour's drive out of Dublin, to request a television set be in our room. England and Australia were to lock horns in a Rugby final that afternoon. We anticipated arriving just in time to catch the match. The hotel was a huge old mansion surrounded by a picturesque stud. When we arrived the manager was having a screaming match with one of the maids in the foyer. It was, I thought, very 'Fawlty Towers'. We both laughed.

In our large room I discovered enough furniture for the entire mansion. We squeezed between overstuffed chairs, assorted tables and an enormous four-poster bed, plus sufficient bric-a-brac to stock a stall at Paddy's Market. I politely asked the management to remove half the cluttered furniture, which they did reluctantly. I then went around with a basket I'd found in the bathroom and removed all the silly dried flower arrangements and knick-knacks, and tucked them behind a door for the four days of our stay. The staff never got the message. We'd come back to find every boring little object back in its place. I'd gather them up and stash them behind the door. The next day we'd go through the whole business again.

One morning we went down to breakfast to discover the dining room in a blue haze of cigarette smoke. Two big tables of Japanese tourists were ensconced. We took a seat by the window and opened it to let in the fresh air. We watched fascinated as the jolly, roly-poly lady who ran the dining room kept up a lively conversation with the non-English-speaking guests. 'Now then you'd be wanting a full Irish breakfast. Right, darlin' won't be long, help yourselves to tea.' They'd blink and she'd disappear, then return with plates piled with eggs, bacon, sausages, potatoes, mushrooms and tomatoes. The Japanese eyed them in horror. Both Richard and I were highly amused. The phone rang and our waitress answered. She then went to the table where the Japanese sat in stony silence, nervously shoving their enormous breakfasts from one side of the plate to the other. 'Phone for Mr McGuire,' she announced. No one at the table could possibly be a 'McGuire', but undaunted she went around asking each confused Japanese if they were 'McGuire'. Then she went back to the phone and informed the party there was no McGuire. A few minutes later the phone rang again. She answered and very positively headed in our direction. 'It's for you,' she said to Richard. He went to the phone and I watched as he doubled up with laughter. Richard said the caller had asked loud and clear, 'Mr Tamassito?' We were convulsed. Oh the Irish!

On his previous visit, Richard had struck up an acquaintance with a local taxi driver, a gentle man who drove him around the studs he wanted to visit. After getting lost numerous times and listening to Richard's cursing when we first endeavoured to locate our hotel, I agreed it might be simpler to leave the car and have his taxi friend take us out to the studs. The thing about Ireland is that the road signs are totally inadequate. There would be a signpost with only two town directions on a four-road crossing. Then at another there would be five town directions and only two roads. It's deliciously mad but you can waste a lot of time getting lost then unlost.

Richard met up with a crew as he was to film some 'horse pieces' for Channel Ten to roll into their all-day coverage of the Melbourne Cup later in the year. He loved it and I felt at last he may have found his perfect TV niche. Perhaps, just perhaps, it would lead to something more permanent for him. He had endeavoured to cover Ascot in England but it was impossible. The English television had securely tied up the rights. Now in Ireland he wanted to cover a small country race meeting and also visit some of the studs. They were good stories. We moved on to another hotel further into stud country, another grand old house that had certainly seen better days. However, our room under the rafters had such a spectacular view that even the lumpy bed didn't worry me, although the plumbing was hazardous.

I developed a sore throat and overnight came down with a

horrible virus. I sneezed, coughed, my head pounded, every bone ached and I ran a high temperature. I took to the lumpy bed, and Richard asked the staff to bring me soup and check on me while he went off filming. I felt like hell. I was also aware that his producer was a stunning young woman who'd already announced to us her marriage wasn't working. I was surprised that I worried about her. I'd never before feared another woman. As a close friend used to say to me, 'The one thing you'll never have to worry about is Richard straying.' I liked to think that she believed he was madly in love with me, but deep down I realised that she really meant he knew he was on, what some would call, a 'good wicket'. I never acknowledged that I knew what she meant. I suppose it was too painful. Now here I was feeling like hell and worrying about Richard and the pretty producer spending jolly days together. I scolded myself, took an Aspro and tried to sleep.

When Richard had started to follow the races he became obsessive about his appearance, his hair and his wardrobe. I'd try to joke him out of his vanity and say things like, 'Now listen Dick, don't you go running off with a big-titted blonde.' At the time I didn't realise it was prophetic. She was by then waiting in the wings. Back home race days came close to the horror of column days. I always took pride in pressing Richard's shirts to perfection. He would select his shirt and tie, check with me to see if I liked them, then a minute later he'd be back in a different shirt and a different tie, again asking my opinion. He would get cross if I didn't give him my full attention. This could sometimes happen three times before he went out. It was manic. I found myself walking to the other end of the house one day and realised I had clenched my hands into such tight fists, my fingernails had made indents in my palms. I was also biting my tongue in an effort not to blow up. I considered his behaviour pathetic, not made easier by discovering that all the freshly pressed shirts had been haphazardly rammed back into his wardrobe, or worse, dumped in a hurried heap on top of the clothes basket. All needed re-pressing.

Melbourne Cup time came around in November 1995, and Richard was asked to MC the four-day presentation for the Victorian Racing Club and the Channel Ten broadcast. He was ecstatic and I was truly thrilled for him. Maybe this would be his big break. He went ahead to Melbourne a couple of days before me to hire his morning suit. I reminded him to get a bigger hat and black, not grey. Black is chic. We stayed, as usual, at the Regent Hotel. They were always kind and upgraded me to a suite, and again we found ourselves in luxury on the fiftieth floor. Richard always adored the special treatment I was given. I reminded him it was one of the suites we'd spent a lot of our courting days and nights in. We made love, saw old friends, had his family in for dinner and generally seemed to be having a happy time. Perhaps we had just travelled a rough patch, I thought. All relationships have them, don't they?

Melbourne Cup Day dawned bleak and wet. I opted for a black Simona pantsuit and a Jane Lambert large black hat with a white gardenia. Simple, comfortable. Richard was absolutely handsome. Some men don't wear morning suits well, Richard looked as though he'd been born in one. He was nervous and more than once reminded me he'd be busy and I'd have to look after myself. What in the hell did he think? That I couldn't? Of course I knew he would have to concentrate on the job, but it only involved introducing winning jockeys, trainers, owners and presenters. There would be race breaks in between the pre- sentations, ample time to check the next piece to camera. It was hardly wall-to-wall intensive broadcasting. I couldn't understand what he was on about but I didn't say a word.

He 'dumped' me in the committee room where dear Reg Ingliss kindly took me under his wing, made sure I had lunch companions and saw that my champers was topped. Reg came from the famous Ingliss family, auctioneers of the best horseflesh in the country. He had observed our first tentative steps into the breeding business, and I had bought all our mares from his auction ring. Occasionally Richard would appear briefly then dash off again. I watched him on the monitor. I wished he'd smile more. This was supposed to be a day of fun, a celebration of racing.

After the Cup was run I went down with Annita Keating, wife of the Prime Minister, to watch the winners come in. We stood chatting together, Richard came over and quietly said, 'Go back up to the committee room, don't stand down here.' I was stunned and insulted. When I asked why, he muttered something about me making him nervous. In a blinding instant I realised he was lying. He didn't want me there, but for what reason? I walked with Annita and her entourage back along in front of the members' stand. We were talking and somehow, because of the crowd, got separated. Suddenly there was a large man between Annita and me. I could see she was still talking, thinking I was right behind her. I put my hands up, sort of under the guy's arms to ease him to one side. 'Excuse me,' I said. He leapt into the air and spun around. I don't know which of us got the bigger shock. He was Annita's personal security guard and I'd touched his gun in its holster under his arm — a 'piece' I believe it's called. Annita twigged in a flash and we all laughed. I said goodbye and, like a dutiful girl, went back up to the committee room to wait for Richard and drink a lonely glass of champagne.

I thought, something's going on, but what? I was hurt and confused by Richard's words. Then a few minutes later he was by my side. He felt he'd done well in the broadcast. I told him he'd looked handsome on camera and avoided other comment.

He dragged me off to the Channel Ten hospitality tent for a drink. I didn't go to the races the next day. Some time later, after my world had fallen in a heap, I learnt that indeed the 'other woman' had been at the races that chilly November day. Richard wasn't asked to MC the Melbourne Cup the following year.

Back home at Greenville a strange thing occurred. Richard was dressing for the races, we were in the bedroom. I don't know why but I reached up and wrapped him in my arms. I looked deep into those big hazel eyes of his and I heard myself say, 'Darling, please don't ever humiliate me.' Seconds ticked by. I had shocked myself. Where had that come from? What did it mean? Did my subconscious know something I hadn't wanted to admit? He looked uncomfortable, kissed my cheek and pulled away. Cold fear rose in my throat.

BROOKE WAS turning forty. She hadn't had a twenty-first party so I'd promised her a slap-up lunch for fifty at Greenville. I spent the next couple of weeks finalising the party. Invitations went out along with a list of hotels and motels and taxis in the area. As the party was to be on a Saturday, most of the guests would stay in the area rather than drive back to Sydney. I planned the menu with the caterers, we bought special wines. The day before John helped me clear all the furniture out of the living room. We moved in four big round tables set for ten and set my long table for another ten. The tables were dressed in snowy white linen to the floor with white chair covers. My local florist, Christine, did as I asked and built huge displays of various rich green foliage for the living room and front hall. Brooke loves colour, so I steered away from my favourite white flowers for the tables and Christine arranged beautiful bowls of brightly coloured spring blooms.

The room looked sensational. The party was a great success.

There were funny speeches. Brooke sang, she has a sensational voice. Lots of good wine was downed. Richard floored me by making a flattering speech about Brooke's great mother. It was a complete surprise. Friends had stayed over at various hotels so the next day I got up early, shoved the house into shape and glazed a large ham. I had no idea how many might pop in for lunch so the ham and various side dishes was a good idea. Brooke's birthday had been a perfect day with clear blue skies, but the day after it was bleak and misting with rain. As the morning wore on the weather closed in. I was just setting the table when I heard a thunderous noise. The next thing Richard raced into the kitchen and said, 'There's a bloody great helicopter landing in our paddock.' We all ran out to watch it land.

The rotors stopped and a slight figure jumped out in the blinding rain and headed for the house, nimbly leaping a fence on the way. He strode up the lawn then stopped and hooted with laughter, as I did. It was my old friend Dick Smith. 'Sorry about this, Maggie,' he said. 'I had no idea this was your place but the weather turned foul and I thought it better to land.' His wife Pip joined us, and we all sat down to an amusing lunch with Dick regaling us about his near misses around the world in his chopper, confirming my opinion that the wretched things are not to be trusted. After lunch the weather cleared, Dick apologised for not helping with the dishes and he and Pip jumped aboard and flew away. A few days later I received some gorgeous aerial shots of Greenville with a thank-you note from Dick. He's a nice man, Dick Smith.

It Gets
Worse

THE DAY after Brooke's party Richard left for Sydney. Later that night he rang to say he was going out for dinner with some friends from the office. I told him to have a good time and went to watch television. Then much later he rang again. He said, 'Hi, darling, I'm in the car and on my way home.' Wait a minute, I thought, he's not in the car. I know what the car phone sounds like. Alarm bells went off in my head.

'OK, darling, sleep tight,' I said and hung up. But I couldn't let it be. I rang his car phone number.

A voice said, 'This number is out of range or switched off.' I waited a minute then called his mobile. He answered.

'What's going on, Richard?' I asked. 'Where are you really?' There was a silence. A long silence. I could almost hear his brain ticking over.

'Oh, Maggie, I'm at the pub still having a drink.'

'Then why lie about where you are? Why, Richard?'

'Oh stop it,' he said. 'You're so bloody suspicious.'

Then I heard it, a dull click. I knew it was a door being closed and don't ask me how, but I knew it was a bathroom door. Richard was in a hotel room and someone had just walked out.

I don't remember the conversation that followed, I was in deep shock. All the past suspicions crowded my mind. I felt a tightness in my chest. I couldn't breathe. I hung up and sat very still at the study desk. A short time later Richard rang again, this time I knew he was in the car. Why had he lied? He muttered some piss weak excuse.

'Well, I was with a nice girl from the office. I knew you would be upset, it's innocent. Don't go on, Maggie.' I didn't believe a word. Later still he rang me from the Bondi apartment.

'Richard, we have to talk, I know something is going on,' I said. Again he denied it.

The following day Barb and Brooke left. I hadn't said a word to them about Richard's call. I don't know how I got through those days, but I was determined that until I knew the truth I wouldn't discuss it, not even with them. For the next two days I wandered around the house in a blank daze. Richard rang often. He said he had work commitments and would come back to Greenville the following weekend to talk. He also diligently rang me each evening to assure me he was home. Alone? I wondered.

I couldn't sleep. I spent the nights reading a book but I couldn't recall what I'd read. I forced myself to appear normal to John and Caroline, but I looked so shocking I finally fibbed and said I thought I was coming down with a cold. On the fourth day I found myself weeping uncontrollably. Barb rang and suddenly I needed to confide in my old mate. I told her everything. She said Richard and I needed to have a long and honest talk. Fifteen minutes after I'd hung up she rang back to tell me she'd be on the eleven-thirty train. She was coming back to Greenville to hold my hand.

Barb's consensus was that I was not imagining things, it sounded as though Richard certainly was lying. He rang that night. I told him Barb was with me. 'Good,' he said, but he sounded nervous. He would be back the following evening, he thought it a good idea if Barb would adjudicate our talk.

I don't know what I expected. Would he rush through the door and convince me it was all in my imagination? Would there be a legitimate excuse? Could I hold onto this relationship? I willed it with all my strength. There was obviously an uneasy air as we sat down to dinner. Richard pulled the corks on two or maybe three bottles. We were all tense. When we got down to discussing the situation Richard insisted I was being silly, nothing was going on. He just wanted some 'space'. The word reached back from over the years and walloped me between the eyes. 'Space.' Ettore had wanted 'space'. His space had turned out to be a redhead. From that second on I knew we were doomed. Richard and I drank too much wine, went to bed and made furious, angry, hungry love. Exhausted, we fell into a fitful sleep.

Over the next few days I found it difficult to hide what was happening from close friends. I confided in a few. Susie Mitchell heard me weepily describe all that had happened and said, 'Maggie, write a diary. Keep a record of what happens.' The next day I started that diary. I labelled it 'The break-up file'. I'm sure it will be familiar reading to many who have been through this.

RICHARD LEFT this morning saying he would see me in Sydney on Thursday. We have more or less agreed to a 'time out' until the end of January, two months. Oh God! Today I shopped in Bowral and bought one small round of fillet steak. Is this my future? I'm consumed by pain. I'm certain he has had an affair, is having an affair. But I don't want to admit it. It's so final. But then maybe final is better than this pain and these horrible, horrible thoughts. He is a selfish bastard. He is bloody difficult. OK, I'm not perfect but really we had it all as close to perfect as we could get, I mean who or what is perfect? And where do we go from here?

From tears in the butcher's buying my lonely little steak to tears on the phone. My darling Matt rang. His mother, Barb, had told him, he was upset and so concerned for me. He told me he loves me and to call if there is anything I need. How about a new heart, Matt? How about some steel in my soul? How about taking away the fear, the real fear? For me. For Richard. For us. For the rest of what's laughingly called my life.

This week I moved all my personal things from the Bondi apartment and spent two hours unpacking Richard's clothes, tidying his drawers and generally fixing his wardrobe for him. Bloody mad! I must be bloody mad! The weekend went up and down, lots of discussion. I still don't believe him. I'm not proud of being a snoop but when he left for Sydney to go to the cricket I knew I had to find out. I went to his file and took out his car phone bills. It didn't take long. A mobile number leapt off the page. There it was again and again and again. Sometimes two and three times within an hour. I couldn't help but think of Richard courting me. He'd often phone several times in one hour. 'I love you. I love you. I love you.' Where was that love now? I took a deep breath and dialled the number. A woman's voice answered. I pretended some confusion. She said, 'This is Louise.' I hung up. Louise. Louise who?

When Richard rang after he'd got home to Bondi I told him what I'd done. At first stunned, then angry and defensive, he screamed a string of denials and finished with, 'How dare you go through my personal papers?' I reminded him that his lies and deceit had caused my actions. We hung up. I waited a minute then dialled his number. Busy. I dialled Louise's number. Busy. God, how could he be so stupid? He was stupid, stupid. I went to the bathroom and vomited.

Sometime later I rang him at Bondi. 'Richard, we have to stop this, you have to come clean with me.'

'Well, Maggie, you've done this search and destroy mission. Just when I thought we were working things out. I really enjoyed being

with you at Greenville last weekend. This other thing is not a rela-
tionship that's threatening to us.' At last he had admitted there was
another relationship. I held my breath.

'Well, Richard, I've got news for you!' I hung up.

I TOOK steps to find out just who she was: two small children,
worked as a rock star promoter on the Gold Coast, was involved
in racing, something to do with publicity for the Magic Millions.
Aha, the Magic Millions. It all fell into place. I drank for Australia
that night. It didn't help. I sobbed into my pillow and my feelings
of rage and anger turned to self-pity and desperation. It was over,
this relationship I had given my all to was lost.

I called Brooke, she was devastated. 'I'll come down, Mummy.'

'No, darling, you have your work commitments,' I said. 'I just
have to work through this.'

Amanda, Sergio and Marco were to arrive in ten days. I had a
lot to do for Christmas. I said, 'I'll be fine.' Brave words for a
woman who was fractured into a thousand pieces. I was exhausted.
I phoned Louise. The essence of our conversation was that I
needed to know how serious her relationship was with the man
I'd lived with for ten years.

She replied, 'Maggie, you don't have a problem with me. Your
problem is with Richard.'

I suppose that was true, but it takes two to tango. I went back
to crying myself to sleep, short unsatisfactory sleeps that saw me
wake suddenly and in panic, sweating and shaking. For the
first time I was spooked in the house. Beautiful Greenville — it
was to have been our dream home. Then why was I living this
nightmare in it?

I looked like hell, a thousand years old, I thought, as I eyed
myself in the mirror. The stress and not sleeping were certainly
taking their toll. I finally had to tell John and Caroline that

Richard and I were having problems. With wry amusement I noted that had to be the understatement of the year! They were sympathetic, caring and supportive. Amanda, Sergio and Marco arrived, tears, hugs, joy. I waited until they had settled in then told them as bravely as I could. They were shocked. Amanda burst into tears, threw her arms around me. 'Oh, Mummy, no. The silly bastard,' she said. That was the second understatement of the year!

Richard had declared he wanted to move back into his apartment. The lease was up in late January, could he stay on in my Bondi apartment until then? I agreed, God knows why. In bed that night I recalled how some weeks ago he had mentioned he should sell his apartment. He said we'd have to put all my furniture back in to make it look terrific and get a good price. He was to mention this many times. I now knew why. My God! Had he seriously wanted me to furnish his apartment, make it look beautiful for him and his mistress? In the lonely hours of the night I had to face the reality that the answer was yes!

Harry M. was wonderful. He moved into his counselling role and I was grateful. I had real fears about my financial situation. I had lost on my first marriage, I had lost a lot more through my second. God, was it going to happen again? Harry and my solicitor, Lyndon Sayer Jones, agreed we needed to get a document ready. In the next couple of days there was a lot of debate. At first Richard was happy to sign. Richard's solicitor and friend, Tony Hartnell, told my solicitor that Richard believed we'd get back together anyway. I knew it couldn't be. A quick death was better than a long illness, which was how it would be, seeing him drive out of Greenville and wondering where he was going, who he was with. I couldn't live like that. When trust is lost, it's lost. I'd lived through a marriage like that before. You finish up hating yourself as much as the others involved.

My emotions ranged from a cold, blinding fury to a fragile, bloody mess. I couldn't stop vomiting. My kids were wonderful, Marco a diversion. When he first arrived he asked where Richard was. I replied he was 'away'. From that day on he never mentioned his name. He started wandering along from the nursery in the middle of the night, bringing his favourite book, his teddy bear and his frog clock. He would place these on Richard's side table and crawl into my bed, wrap me in his little arms and legs and sleep soundly, while I cried quietly.

THE ELEVENTH of December, my birthday. I drove to the city on a sad, final mission. Richard's solicitor had finally drawn up an agreement. We would sign at Harry's. I arrived and went into Harry's office, determined I wasn't going to weep in front of everyone. Bloody hard. Richard and my solicitor arrived a little later. When Richard came into the office I couldn't trust myself to look at him, so I didn't. I sat stiffly on the couch while he, Harry and Lyndon discussed the fact that Tony Hartnell was locked in some meeting and this might take some time. God, no, I thought. All I wanted to do was get out of there. I was staggered to hear Richard suggest to Harry that he couldn't see why our joint Luxaflex contract couldn't continue! Now I looked at him. With a withering stare I said, 'You have got to be joking.' Quickly after that, Lyndon and Harry manoeuvred us into different rooms. I think they believed I was about to either explode or crack open.

After three and a half hours of fiddle faddle between Tony Hartnell, Richard and my solicitor, the wording of both the document and a press release was agreed. We signed. A condition had been added that I could never disclose the details of the settlement. I felt sick. As we left the office Richard came to my car. 'Maggie, I — .'

'Richard, here are my keys to your Woollahra apartment, here is your passport and here are the bracelets you gave me.'

He protested that he didn't want to take them but I shoved them in his hand. 'You don't have to do this,' he said.

'Yes I do,' I replied. 'Yes I do.' I drove away. I was sobbing so much I couldn't see the road. It was over, ten years squandered. Friends had tried to remind me that we had had our 'good times'. But I couldn't recall one. I was so consumed with pain.

HARRY'S PRESS release went out late that afternoon. The Channel Nine News announced our split and the *Daily Telegraph* ran a huge front-page piece by Dorian Wild with a giant colour photograph. There was no mention of another woman but now the world knew. The gossip had probably been confined to the eastern suburbs rumour mill until then. I went to stay with Brooke, my beautiful, sympathetic daughter. She cared for me tenderly. That night my family and lots of friends descended on her apartment and we made a pretence of celebrating my fifty-ninth birthday. Knowing how Richard felt about my ageing and given the day I'd spent, it was a hard road.

The next day I was in a local shop and, because of the press, embarrassed about being seen. I kept telling myself I hadn't done anything wrong, but I knew I looked like a victim. A little tough workman came into the shop, eyed me and said, 'Well, how are you doing?'

I couldn't help myself, my response was natural. 'You have got to be joking!' I said.

He looked at me for a second then said, 'Listen, it's shit. I know, I've been there myself, but hang in there, you'll be alright, Maggie.'

I was so touched by this concern from a total stranger I burst into tears, much to the discomfort of the shopkeeper. In the following weeks I was constantly moved by the kindness of strangers who took pains to show their concern for me. It's something I will never forget.

Back at Greenville I had a call from a friend of Richard's who said Louise had been in town the week before and Richard had introduced her to him. I rang Harry. He had warned Richard that the press would be sniffing around, the whole thing could blow up in his face if he wasn't more cautious. When Richard confessed he'd collected Louise from the airport Harry really blew his stack. It was in all our interests that we keep this affair quiet.

During the next days after the *Telegraph* front-page story, my phone and fax went berserk. I had calls from old friends, new friends, acquaintances, some of the hardest to cope with came from Richard's family. His dear papa Harry was devastated. He and his daughter Susie were sure we would work it out. Of course they didn't know about the other woman. His sister Amanda rang. She was furious with him. I told her about his affair. She said he had emphatically denied it. How painful to have to tell her it was true. Richard had constantly lied to his family, even to his good mate Billy Bridges and our mutual confidante Peter Weiss. I knew that eventually it would have to come out.

I HEAR via Harry that Woman's Day *has discovered the rumour about Louise and Richard. They are going to run a piece. I feel humiliated. Despite my pledge not to call Richard I do. All the pent-up rage, anger, hurt and pain poured out. It is not pretty. I finish with, 'You have been very difficult to love at times, Richard, but, let me tell you, you are very easy to hate!'*

Who is this person? It's not me. I hate it. He accused me of not stopping the Woman's Day *piece going to press. Apart from the fact that I have no power in that direction, why should I? Now it will be truly out in the open, I won't have to answer that flood of questions about 'What went wrong?' Everyone would know about his deceit. It's best, I tried to tell myself.*

THE MAGAZINE ran a photograph of Louise and a profile of her life with a strong statement in quotes from Louise that she was *not* the other woman. 'Bullshit!' I said and tossed the magazine on the fire.

DEAR WAGGERS rang that night. 'Darling Mags,' he said, 'I wish I could be the one but we'd laugh too much.' I adore him. He also asked if he should send me another door and brick, a reference to what happened when Pross left. My God, I have to face the reality that I've had two husbands and a de facto and they have all left me! Is it me? I was falling in a heap until Barb rang and told me to 'take hold' of myself and pointed out some parallels about mid-life crises in the male of the species. It's true. I'd slowly watched it happen with Richard. I knew the all-out obsession with his appearance and the fixation on the 'young people' in his office had exceeded normal behaviour, but it seemed I was powerless to bring him back to earth. Now it was too late.

SOME DAYS later Richard called to discuss my decision to sell the mares. 'Let me handle the sales for you,' he said. 'You don't know anything about the business.' I declined his offer.

I HAD hoped that having organised the sale of the horses, there would be no further need of bitter exchanges with Richard, but it wasn't to be. Today we had another. He said, 'I can't understand why you are so angry.'

'Oh Richard, pleeeease.'

'Maggie, this is not a relationship that should threaten ours.'

'Richard, I've got news for you.'

'This is the nineties.'

'Richard, if the situation was reversed and I'd been screwing around, tell me how you'd feel?'

Peter Weiss commissioned Greg Barrett to shoot a portrait collection of famous Australians from diverse professions. Initially used for a David Jones/Weiss Pringle promotion, Peter then generously gave the collection to the National Portrait Gallery. Here are Richard and me.

A Greg Barrett photo of the Tabberer girls — Brooke, me and Amanda in about 1983. Rickie Quesada did our makeup.

David McNicoll on board Snow Swift's yacht, tied alongside my boat the *Maggie T,* where I'm showing off my surprise birthday cake. Just what I needed!

An advertising shot for Maggie T Expressions sunglasses. Greg Barrett has photographed me for more than twenty-five years, and he's so good he should be bottled. (Courtesy Bausch & Lomb)

One of the great Christmas holiday gatherings at Boree Bills. *From left:* Peter Slaney, Vicki Jones, me, Richard, Eve Harmen-Slaney, Sam Slaney and a little friend, Brooke, John Chalk, Libby Reeves Purdy and Ken Stevens, photographed by Anthony Browell.

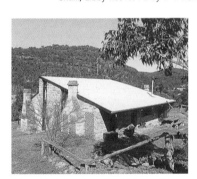

Above: My beloved, rustic, old Boree Bills, my first farm, where my family, friends, Richard and I had many a magic time. (Courtesy *Belle*)

Right: With Sarah and Henry Crawford at their stunning home in Woollahra, celebrating my fiftieth birthday.

Covering the royal wedding of Fergie and Andrew for the Nine Network, with Ray Martin and Dame Edna Everage. Richard said to me, 'If your hat blows off, don't chase it!' (Courtesy Nine Network)

Christmas 1995 at Greenville, It was my first there without Richard, but I was surrounded by the love and support of my family and closest friends: Amanda, Sergio, Marco, Ashley, Barbara, Matthew and Brooke.

My sixtieth birthday, complete with stunning views, fabulous food, fireworks, family and friends at Vicki Jones and Ken Stevens' splendid apartment.
(Chris Chen, courtesy *Vogue* Australia)

Richard and me at Greenville in happier times.

'This Is Your Life' (again!) in 1997. With some of my favourite men: Peter Weiss, John Laws, Marco, Nicolas, Leo Schofield and Stuart Wagstaff. (Courtesy 'This Is Your Life', Nine Network)

On the same night, with the most important people in my life: Brooke, Marco and Amanda. (Courtesy 'This Is Your Life', Nine Network)

Above: With my best mate Barb.
(Greg Barrett)

Right: Marco and me on the Da Adolfo
boat coming back from Sergio's
restaurant in Positano.

With my adorable Bronson at Greenville, after being named a recipient of a Member of the Order of Australia in the Queen's Birthday Honours, 1998. (Courtesy *The Australian*)

There was a long silence, then, 'Maggie, have I blown it?'
'Richard, you sure as hell have.' And I hung up, again in tears.

TODAY A *fax from Richard finalising where I should send his horse and his possessions, then, 'And now I will disappear from your life, or as the Buddhists would have said it, "a spray on the ocean".' And at the end of the fax, a poem:*

The beach
Walking on it
The sand imprints
Washed away in an instant
Your print now a spray on the ocean
Just walking on it.
      Zachariah, Dec '95

I sat at the desk and thought, after ten years of love, concern, help and care, and all the other things, was I just a spray on the ocean? Oh Richard, how cruel. How really cruel. Then I got mad and fired off a fax saying, 'You're no Auden.'

He replied, 'No, but I'm alive and he ain't.'

I'm stunned at the bitterness of our exchanges. Love gone wrong, so very wrong.

I prepared the stuffing for the turkey and another Christmas at Greenville. The first without Richard. The kids have been wonderful and Barb, Matt and Ash arrived and we had a great Christmas Eve. John and Caroline and some of their friends came over from the cottage for a glass of champers. They had planned a surprise for Marco, a visit from Father Christmas. He appeared on the bright green lawn, out from behind the big oak tree, came staggering up to the house on bandy legs in his brilliant red suit, flowing white beard, the lot. Marco screamed with joy and danced around in circles. He was so excited. Then Father Christmas gave us all little gifts and he sang a special song for Maggie. 'Single bells, single bells, single all the way.' I laughed aloud but my gut churned. Single all the way. How long and lonely will that be? But I looked around at my friends and family showering me with great warmth and love and I thought, this is how this house should be, no tension, no bad vibes, no nerves about callous comments. I have to hang onto that thought. 'Keep remembering, Maggie,' I tell myself, it has to help.

Graham Kennedy rang tonight just to say, 'I love you, this is my number if you need me.' I'm so touched, reaching back over all those years to show me his concern.

Thursday dawned and I knew I had to pack Richard's things. I started with his clothes meticulously labelling the boxes with content descriptions, packing everything beautifully. Deep down I figure that might 'hurt' more than if I just chuck them in, but he's such a selfish bugger he probably won't even notice. I then very methodically go through our rather extensive book collection and open every flyleaf to check if it was Richard's or mine, and again packed them carefully. Richard was never a gift giver but he did frequently buy me books and he always wrote a message in each. It's hard to read those loving inscriptions, so painful. Finally it's done. John carries all the boxes out to the garage for the removalist and I once again burst into tears.

THE PHONE went and a voice said, 'This is Ansett, is this the contact number for Mr Zachariah?'

'Not any more,' I said.

'Well, would you have a number for him? It's about his return flight from the Gold·Coast.'

I couldn't help myself. 'Try his girlfriend,' then I gave them her number. I put down the phone and started to shake. Uncontrollably shake. Then in a blind rage I rang Louise.

'Louise, tell Richard to get off his arse and call Ansett and change *his contact numbers and while I have you on the phone let me tell you!'*

I'm not proud of what I said, I'm too embarrassed to write it but all the rage and pain exploded. I can fight dirty. Despite his constant calls to me that 'it's all over with Louise and, darling, I know given time we can work this out,' he was still seeing her and despite her Woman's Day *proclamation that she was not the other woman, she very definitely was.*

The next morning Richard rang. 'Maggie, I went to the Gold Coast on the spur of the moment. The Telegraph *was chasing me.'*

'Oh Richard, how bloody pathetic, why not leave a paper trail.' I hung up and thought, it's only a matter of time, this thing is going to blow up in his face. Oh well, he always said any publicity is better than none. Hang onto your hat, Richard.

I'm cheered by a touching call from Ros Packer. She and the Boss have invited me to spend New Year's Eve with them at Palm Beach. I've accepted. The Sun-Herald *rang this morning. 'Would you like to talk to us?'*

Damn it.

'No, thank you.'

'Oh well, I guess I understand,' the reporter said.

Later another call from a different reporter at the Sun-Herald. *'Miss Tabberer, I know someone rang you earlier today but this is regarding another matter. We understand Mr Zachariah is no longer going to be doing the Luxaflex commercials. Can you comment?'*

'No I can't. I suggest you contact Harry Miller.'

I call Harry at his farm, he assures me he won't be commenting either. I wonder if Richard really understands the cost of his affair. I know Luxaflex have decided to go with me alone on an ongoing contract. I suppose I should feel some sort of satisfaction, but I don't, I just feel sad, then mad. And I'm so damn tired, so very, very tired.

1 JANUARY 1996: Enough! Maggie May, enough. He's not worth my tears and certainly not my concern. It's the New Year and I have to start a new life and a good one at that.

I RETURNED to Greenville after spending three days at Palm Beach with special friends Peter and Doris Weiss. It was nice, cosy, and New Year's Eve with the Packers very funny and jolly. We laughed a lot. Afterwards my old friend David Shmith suggested he drive me back to the Weiss' but the Boss said firmly, 'No you've had a few drinks. I'll drive Maggie.' We arrived at Peter's house in two minutes flat. As I was getting out of the car a youth driving a souped-up bomb stopped and started to abuse Kerry Packer, who he said had his lights on high beam. I heard him say, 'You silly old bastard!' I glanced up just in time to see the sudden shock of recognition hit his face. K.P. was so cool. They exchanged some more subdued words and both drove away.

I KEEP telling myself, 'Look, I'm better than I was a month ago, a week ago, I am growing stronger every day.' But I guess the real test is not when I'm surrounded by family and love of friends but when I'm all alone, living alone at Greenville.

4 JANUARY: I had a call from Nene King. Seems Richard has been holidaying with Louise on Vanuatu. She had calls from the island and was told when they were coming back. She had a photographer at the airport and he sprang them. They were not pleased. Nene said she wanted to tell me she was going to run a piece in Woman's Day *but was gracious and said, 'Maggie will it hurt you? I will pull the story if you want me to.'*

I simply said, 'I'm already hurt, Nene.'

Well, I guess this will definitely put a full stop to all the speculation. The humiliation will be total and very public, but then dear God

*let that be the finish. I wonder if Richard cares? I understand Richard
phoned Nene and tried to get her to stop the article. He said to her
it would hurt me further and added in a threatening tone, 'I have
to tell you, I'm on Mr Packer's payroll.'*

*To which Nene replied, 'Then I suggest, Richard, you phone
Mr Packer.'*

*Wrong move Richard, wrong move. And not the only wrong move
you've made. Mixed emotions. Normal I guess. Later the same day
the phone goes. 'This is Richard Zachariah calling.'*

'Really?' I said.

'Have you heard from Nene King?'

'Yes,' I replied.

'Are you going to do anything to stop this publication?'

'No, Richard.'

'Why not?'

'Why should I?' Then so on and so on.

Finally, 'Maggie, how could you do this?'

*'Richard, I've done nothing. You're the one having an affair.
You're the one who ran off on an island holiday. You're the one who
has shown no discretion and now you're the one who is going to
have to wear it.'*

*Harry M. rang to say Richard had called to ask Jane in the office
if she really thought* Woman's Day *would run the story? She said,
'Unless Fergie's having another toe sucked, yes Richard, I do.'*

*6 JANUARY: Two old mates came for lunch. Their calm is infectious.
They mentioned that last October, just before our break-up in
November, when Richard and I had visited them they were concerned about some of the things Richard had said to them while
they walked along the beach one morning. I had to screw it out of
them but it appears he said, 'Well, the problem is Maggie's career
is finishing and mine is just really starting.' I am appalled. Was his*

concern that he might have to one day support me? Was that all I'd been, a meal ticket? We also discussed Richard's temper the night he had booked us into dinner at a busy restaurant. We arrived to be shown a table near the loo. Richard was furious and said with venom, 'I should have booked the bloody table in Maggie's name, then we would have got the best in the house.'

AFTER THE press broke 'the news' of Richard and my split Pross had phoned me and said genuinely, 'Maggie, I'm sorry for your troubles. All I can say is that he will be sorry. I was.' I cried for the rest of the day. Cried for what might have been, I suppose. I'd lost two men I loved very much.

Pross more or less invited himself to lunch at the farm one day. What could I say? The girls adored him, he was mad about Marco and I still had a lot of deep affection for the old devil. He walked into Greenville, said, '*Christo*' three or four times and then, 'Not bad for a little girl from Adelaide.'

I had to keep reminding myself about what I have achieved. My self-esteem had been battered, I needed to prop myself up. Pross stayed for hours, we all reminisced, laughed and even cried a little.

14 JANUARY: The removalist arrives to take Richard's boxes. I feel shattered. This really is so final I also embarrass myself by bursting into tears in front of the guys.

18 JANUARY: Woman's Day hit the streets and it blew me apart. I felt destroyed, ashamed, humiliated. I was teary on and off for three days.

I found Richard had left in my Bondi apartment a bag of dirty shirts. I phoned him. 'Richard, I know you've been washing your dirty linen in public but do you seriously expect me to wash this bag of shirts for you?' He then said he would come and get them. I don't want him here. I said I'd drop them at his front door. I'd give him two rings on the phone on approach, which I did. By the time I turned into his street he was already on the footpath. He opened the door to my car. 'Darling, we have to talk, we have to be friends.'

'Ye Gods! Richard, I have friends, wonderful friends of real calibre and after what you've done I am no longer your friend.'

'Maggie, if only you had left all this alone.'

'What, so you could have your mistress down here in Sydney and leave me tucked up on the farm serving up all the fringe benefits you've become accustomed to? Forget it Richard, I know you don't hold me in any real esteem, but you know what? I do!' I can't recall exactly what was then said but I started to shake and I was fighting back the tears again. I just wanted to get away, I hated how he looked. I shoved his dirty shirt bag out of the car and said, 'Shut the door, please.'

As he turned to go I put the window down. 'Richard.' He stopped, turned. 'As it said in Woman's Day, *you are now known as Maggie Tabberer's ex, and you know what? That's all you'll ever be.' I gunned the engine and drove away. I've become a bitch.*

19 JANUARY: The Bowral dry-cleaners mention that Richard hasn't picked up his sweaters. I told him weeks ago they were there. They asked for his address, then said how do you spell Zachariah? I spelt it out for them: B-A-S-T-A-R-D. The girls cracked up.

31 JANUARY: In flight back from Noumea. We've had ten days at Club Med. Such a happy holiday for the kids. Sergio played every sport going, Amanda and Ash not far behind. Even Barb and Brooke did water aerobics each day and Marco adored Mini Club. I did little but swim, walk the beach, eat and drink, and value the love of my family, my best friends and, yes, strangers. One day by the pool a gorgeous grandmother asked me to be photographed with her and her two-month-old grandchild. We set up the shot and she leant close to me and said in a low voice, 'Maggie, meeting you has been the highlight of my holiday. I've admired you for years.' I almost burst into tears, I was so moved. The fact is I feel old and rejected. I have to summon up my self-esteem.

I've sold three of the mares and their foals. Ken and Vicki turned up at the sale for support. I love their thoughtfulness. The Financial Review ran a piece about me 'offloading' the horses and said, 'Mr Zachariah had fancied himself a studmaster.' He won't like that.

14 FEBRUARY: Valentine's Day and my dear Mummy's birthday. Thank God she's not here to witness this mess. Richard went to see Harry M., having been told by phone, then sent a letter, that Luxaflex were not going to pick up his contract and, yes, they were going to continue with me. The conversation, Harry says, went like this:

R: *How much damage do you think leaving Maggie has done me?*

H: *Lots.*

R: *What do you think people think of me?*

H: *That you're a bastard.*

R: *How long will it take to go away?*

H: *Richard, people who think you're a bastard will always think you're a bastard.*

R: *What should I do?*

H: *Keep your head down, don't be seen with cheap blondes, see them in private if you must, but if you have to go out then go out with someone respectable.*

R: *Do you have anyone in mind?*

H: *Richard, I'm not in that business.*

R: *Well, if you need an extra man for a dinner party call me.*

H: *Goodbye Richard!*

ANOTHER CALL from Richard to me.
   'Darling, please let's talk.'
   'About what?'
   'About being mates, friendship.'
   'You know I can't, Richard, I can't.'
   So sadly I can't.
   The next day Bronson and I go for a long walk over Greenville. The kookaburras work the lawn. There're about fifty ducks on the lake, the horses look shiny and strong, the cows fat and healthy. I'm a lucky woman. Now for God's sake Margaret get on with it.

14 APRIL: Oh hell, the Sun-Herald *ran a full-page piece on Richard. 'Not just a Beach Boy,' says the headline. Then all the old Maggie–Richard 'Love affair of the decade' bit. It's sickening. He's still 'Maggie T's ex' I note. 'While he's positive about the future, "That's one thing Maggie taught me," he says.' That's wry! Why didn't I teach myself? The article goes on to say he wants to be 'taken seriously'. Seriously? Is that what troubled Richard? The article rambles on about his passions, Bondi, horses (no mention of blondes?). And then they print that bloody awful poem he sent me about Bondi sand and sea spray. I could cheerfully puke. I don't. Is this a good sign? The article finishes with Richard saying he believes he will probably 'finish up back on the land. In a broken-down cottage with a couple of broken-down dogs.' Oh God, Richard. Still playing that old tune.*

5 SEPTEMBER: It's Francescino's birthday. He would have been twenty-nine. I was in town and went to shop in Queen Street. I went to have a coffee in Nosimos. It was packed. I found a table at the back of the room and was reading the paper. I didn't see him come in, just a pair of long legs at my table. 'Can I join you?' I looked up. How can I describe that feeling? The inevitable had finally happened.

'Are you OK?' he said.

'I'm fine,' I replied.

He sat down. I glanced around the room and nearly laughed out loud. One hundred eyes were glued on us. Coffees stopped mid-air, toasts caught halfway to mouths, silence. Perhaps the humour of all that helped. I took a deep breath.

'Well, Richard, how are things with you?'

And so we talked of friends. 'How was Ascot?' (He knew I'd been over to Europe in June and July.) 'What's happening at the farm?' He started to tell me how to run it again.

'Richard, don't do that please.' I felt my hackles rise. But I couldn't look into his eyes, I really didn't trust myself, my heart was thumping.

Finally, 'Maggie, can't we talk more?'

'We really don't have anything to talk about.'

'Not true. Look at the last half an hour. Will you at least take my calls?'

'Don't do this, Richard. It's too hard.'

'No, just to talk.'

Then out of the restaurant, at my car, he said, 'You're the best looking thing I've seen in a long time.'

Now I looked into his eyes. We were both sad. It was painful for both of us. I wanted to say, 'You silly, silly bastard. Look what you've done to us.' But I couldn't, my mouth was dry. I moved to go.

'Maggie, will you take my calls?'

I couldn't help myself. 'What would your girlfriend say, Richard?'

'There's nothing there, Maggie, I've told you that.'

'Then it was a very expensive exercise, wasn't it, Richard?'

'You were right, it was a mid-life crisis.'

I don't recall the last words. He reached out and kissed me. I was aware of heads popping out of shops. I drove away. More tears, more pain. God, will it ever stop?

I HAD gone to Europe with Barb in June. Nene King had generously given me an overseas trip for two. We went to the races at Ascot then travelled to Spain where we met our old mates Rickie Quesada and Ray Freeman and met with Elsa Peretti, the famous jewellery designer, in Barcelona. She invited us to her village of San Martivel Girona, where we stayed in her ancient home, restored over twenty years at countless cost. So very, very beautiful. Then to Italy and ten wonderful and lazy days with the kids. Positano, as always, was glorious.

I had felt at last some sort of demarcation had occurred, a separation from the past. But this meeting with Richard made me realise I would never ever be truly separated from the past. At that time, John and Caroline were having thoughts about leaving Greenville. The Conners had been with me for six years, now it was just time for a change. But it was painful, emotional, a tough goodbye. My sister Nan and her partner Peter Reedman came to stay and helped to sort me out. The new manager, Steve Jessop, his wife Di and teenage son and daughter moved into Greenville and we set about a new maintenance programme. Steve had the place looking a picture in no time.

My mother always said 'things come in threes', good and bad. My situation at the *Weekly* had become difficult. It seemed Nene King and I had a lot of differences. I understood her stress, her job was a monster. Then tragically she lost her husband in a diving accident at sea. Her grief was total. I admired Nene's efforts to keep working but it certainly affected those around her. We all tried to understand but I was tired, suddenly too tired.

I phoned Harry Miller. 'I want to resign,' I said. This time he didn't try to talk me out of it. I wrote to Nene saying I hoped she'd understand. I felt I wasn't pleasing her and she didn't need any more stress in her life. It would be better if I went. She agreed. Richard Walsh wrote a charming letter having received mine of resignation. He said I'd had an 'amazing run', the Donald Bradman of the fashion world. I'd also written to K.P. but I was never to hear back from him personally. It hurt. Fifteen years is fifteen years. Perhaps he's just not good at that sort of thing. All this wasn't without a lot of pain and stress, and again sleepless nights. I was highly emotional. Perhaps Richard had been right, my career was coming to an end.

Harry rang. The *Weekly* wanted to give me a goodbye party. 'No, Harry, no parties. I'd hate it.' The next day he rang again. 'Just lunch at Forty One for a few key people. You've got to do this, Maggie.' I tried to argue, I really just wanted to fade away. But he insisted. 'They really want to do something nice for you. I'll be there,' he said.

The day arrived. I was nervous and emotional. The one thing I didn't want to do was fall into a tearful heap. James Packer came, Nene, Richard Walsh and some other senior management people. At the close of lunch Nene produced a huge blue Tiffany box. I stumbled some words of thanks and said I'd open it later. Nene kindly said, 'Maggie, change it if it's not to your liking.' At home I opened it, it was a very large, cut crystal vase. The next day I wrote to thank Nene and to explain that I was going to exchange the vase. A couple of days later I went into Tiffany's and changed it for a silver Elsa Peretti bracelet.

I had been assured my successor would not be announced until I had left the *Weekly*. Unfortunately it was. The article was hurtful. The details are irrelevant. It was just another hurt on top of a hurt. Dear God, I'll be glad to see the end of this year, I thought.

'A Current Affair' asked for an interview about my leaving the *Weekly*. My old mate Mike Munro was doing the piece and experience had taught me that he was good. I had been with the *Weekly* for fifteen years, it was time to say goodbye and do it with some dignity. Mike came with the crew down to the farm. Bronson performed beautifully, slept at my feet as they filmed me at my desk, sat with a soulful head in my lap as we did the face to face interview, and cavorted handsomely as I took him for a walk by the lake for overlay film. It was a nice piece. I wanted to show a positive new me. I wish I'd been truly as positive as I sounded.

After selling my Bondi apartment I had bought a stunning New York loft-style unit in Rushcutters Bay. It was a Theo Onisfuro–James Packer project. Every week I picked up the newspapers, the real estate pages carried some item about my purchase. I was fascinated at their fascination, but I loved the apartment. It was just taking longer to complete than anticipated. Finally I was in and once again was shoving furniture around and decorating. I knew the kids would love staying there when they came out for Christmas and my sixtieth birthday.

Actually, I had almost made up my mind that I was going to ignore my sixtieth. It was a painful reminder of the 'age' thing I knew had affected Richard. But one day the phone rang. It was my dear mates Vicki Jones and Ken Stevens. Ken had developed and built a simply stunning apartment complex right on the water at McMahons Point with unparalleled views of the harbour, the Bridge, the Opera House and the city.

'Darling,' he said, 'Vicki and I want to give you a party. We are going to do everything to get the place finished on time for it.'

I was staggered by this generosity. We worked out we could seat fifty people. The invitation list was drawn up, redrawn and drawn again and again. It was hard work editing out friends but finally invitations went out, replies flooded back. Excitement built. Ken was working around the clock to finish the apartment, Vicki to furnish it. The kids came from Italy. Inge Fonagy made me a marvellous white gown. The florist and caterer were briefed and the day arrived. As a kid I never had parties, we simply couldn't afford them. Later, as I've told you, my kids were always giving me surprise parties and I'd given myself the memorable fiftieth. But my sixtieth was, in a word, sensational.

The night was clear, starry, warm. The apartment glowed with candles like a rare jewel. It was a jewel. The flowers were sensational — all white gardenias and lilies. Guests were bowled over by the breathtaking view. Everyone dressed in either black or white. Ken, as host, said a few gorgeous words of welcome. Then, before I could reply, he asked guests to take their drinks and go out onto the balcony. As we did fireworks exploded from a barge moored on the harbour just in front of the apartment. The display was awesome and went on for some twenty minutes, finishing with a grand finale. The entire side of the barge lit with the words 'Happy Birthday Maggie'. Passengers on a large ferry coming into the dock below sang 'Happy Birthday Maggie' joined by the patrons in the restaurant over the road who had all poured out onto the dock to watch the display.

Yes, you guessed it, I was in tears. This time tears of joy. Back inside I made a speech. I so wanted to thank all my friends, to let them all know how much I'd valued their love and support over the past year. I'm sure it was inadequate. Leo Schofield made a funny speech and then we partied. Oh boy, did we party! Vicki and Ken had given me the best birthday ever, and in the morning I thought I don't mind being sixty. Others might but I don't. So there!

Another Christmas came and went at Greenville. I'd heard Richard had gone to Europe. We had guests from Italy to stay. It was rowdy, fun, busy as hell. The dishwasher and stove did overtime.

19 JANUARY 1997: Oh God! No! No! No! The Sunday papers both carried large picture stories on Richard Zachariah and his new love, Tessa Dahl. The phones went wild. All my family is in Sydney, they're concerned for my state of mind. All my mates ring. Harry, Pete, Georgie, Barb, Glen Marie, Vicki, Ken, others. Everyone wants to know if I'm alright. I'm not alright! Over the next two weeks I hear all about Tessa and Richard. Woman's Day *carries photos of them walking on the beach. I believe Richard's 'Walking on the beach shots' have reached serial proportions. Walking on the beach with Louise. Then alone. Now with Tessa. Shit! Why, oh why does it still hurt? Fourteen months and I still feel pain. And I'm so sick of it, so very sick of it.*

I finally hear that Tessa has been dispatched back to England. Rumour has it that Louise is on the scene again. She can't have any pride. Later I bump into Richard in Sydney. He boasts about his ability to attract publicity. 'God, Richard, if you think that's good publicity you're sillier than I thought you were,' I say. He just laughs. Before I drive away I add, 'Richard, you may not miss me, but your shirts sure as hell do!' His face dropped, he panicked, touched his collar.

'Why, what's the matter?' I eyed his grey-white shirt. It said it all.

'I hope you're not paying someone to do that laundry,' I said and drove away. Smug bitch!

In May New Idea *carries a colour story on Richard and Louise and their wedding plans. (Another bloody walking on the beach shot.) I note he's still referred to as 'Maggie T's ex to marry'! But I cringe at the sub-headline: 'Louise is my future, Maggie was my past.' Oh Richard, was that necessary? They also lie about when their romance began: 'Christmas '95.' We broke up in November 1995. It seems someone can't count and it's not me! The next week there is coverage of their wedding. He who couldn't cope with my adult children professes he's 'looking forward to being a father to her two daughters'. Amazing! A month later Tessa Dahl's 'Richard broke my heart' dramatic tell-all tale appears in* Woman's Day. *How do I feel? Sick to my stomach. Will it ever end?*

This Is
Your Life...
Again!

I T WAS August 1997; for the past few weeks Harry Miller had been talking about an American cosmetic company that had made enquiries about me. He said he'd sent photographs, my CV and some of my television tapes off to the States, and one of their executives would be in Australia shortly and we would meet. Seems they had a skin-care range for mature skins and were considering asking me to endorse it.

'Mature skin! Sounds like me,' I admitted, reluctantly.

Finally Harry called: 'The meeting's set up for next Thursday, eleven-thirty. Meet me in the office and we will walk down to the factory together.' The factory is Harry's residence — a warehouse conversion of considerable scale and style. He only holds special meetings there. An encouraging sign, I thought.

It was late morning when I parked the car and walked into his office fifteen minutes early, as is my norm. An unusual scuffle was going on. People running frantically around the corridors. 'Harry's not ready,' said a harried staffer.

'That's OK,' I replied, and settled into a chair.

Minutes later Harry came out. I did notice that he was talking at double speed, but Harry often talks at double speed. We walked to the factory and, once in Harry's huge living room, he instructed me to sit in a certain place. Now Harry's couches are about two inches off the ground and I hate low chairs. 'No, Harry,' I said. 'I'll sit here.' Moving to a more upright chair.

'No, no, no,' he said. 'Sit here.'

'Harry, I hate low chairs,' I protested. Bossy bugger, I thought.

But he persisted, saying that before the American arrived he wanted to show me the plans of his penthouse in one of Sydney's newest highrises. He practically arm-wrestled me onto the low couch and before I could protest further, whipped out a huge set of plans and spread them across my lap.

Suddenly there was a rushing noise behind me. A pair of dark trousers strode into my line of vision, I was aware of a bright light, a cameraman, a microphone dangling, and I looked up straight into the beautiful baby blues of Mike Munro. Then he spoke the unthinkable line: 'Maggie Tabberer, this is your life.'

Stunned, I said, 'Oh no, *not again.*'

You see twenty years earlier I had had a similar surprise, when the then host Digby Wolf stepped out of the darkness in John Geary's office, where I'd been called with my partner Jan to another business meeting, and spoke the same line to me.

Can I be that old, I thought, that they're doing me again. It's a bloody serial!

Now I looked at Harry and Mike and realised I felt strangely elated. I'd just lived a rough couple of years and my self-esteem had been seriously dented — this was very flattering. I think we chatted for a few minutes while the crew packed up and Mike explained that Barb, along with Rickie Quesada and Ray Freeman were on their way to collect me. The rule of 'This Is Your Life' is that once surprised the victim is not allowed to speak to any family or friends until the programme is recorded that night. I would be guarded by my mates for the rest of the day in total isolation.

My mind was racing. God, who will they drag up? I wondered. And we laughed. Harry was being wired for sound when I'd arrived early to his office — hence the panic. He panicked again when he thought I might not sit in the right chair, with my back to the stairs where Mike and the crew were to enter and spring my surprise. I couldn't believe they had kept all this from me. I usually have a nose if something is going on. My friends duly gathered me up and we went back to my apartment. I paced the floor for the rest of the afternoon trying to screw some clues out of them about who was likely to be on the show. I so wanted to call Brooke.

'Do you think they will bring Amanda from Italy?' I asked more than once. Only to be met with, 'We know nothing.'

'Bullshit!' I said.

By four o'clock I felt I needed a stiff drink but resisted, it would be dangerous — I had to stay upright and very sober for whatever fate was to be mine.

Brooke had organised for Inge Fonagy to make me a black silk suit exactly the same as one she had recently designed for me. I had worn the first one to a gala dinner two nights earlier and Brooke said, knowing me, I would have spilt something on it! So a second garment solved my problem of what to wear. In the late afternoon John Adams arrived to do my hair, then I decided to wear my new little Jane Lambert evening hat anyhow. He was a darling about it.

By the time we stepped into the limo for the drive to Channel Nine I was seriously nervous. Mike was backstage to greet me. I met the research and production crew. Everyone seemed happy and very excited about this show. More than once I was touched by their enthusiasm, and then it was time to step through those doors tightly holding Mike's hand. I was truly amazed and delighted to see the audience stacked with my friends. They had all turned out for me, and suddenly I felt very teary and very emotional. And so there I was, doing Part Two of 'This Is *My* Life'.

First came my old mate John Laws, who told how he'd kissed me twenty-something years before. Then my darling sister Nan, who'd also appeared on my first 'This Is Your Life'. A real surprise was Judy Holmes. I hadn't seen her for forty years. As Adelaide teenagers we'd worked together at the Alaska Icecream Company. It was an enormous thrill. I loved Judy. My mind raced — how in the hell did they find out about all this stuff?

Then came my darling daughter Brooke. Later I was to learn she was largely responsible for directing much of the research. Next came Waggers, my old 'Beauty and the Beast' mate, grinning like a Cheshire cat. He dispelled the rumour that we had been lovers, but confirmed the fact that we were still great friends. Then it was Leo Schofield and Peter Weiss in tandem. We had worked together, played together, our friendships surviving the years.

My stepson Nico was next. He looked so like his father. I glanced at the monitor and there was a film clip of Pross and me on our wedding day. I had to bite back the tears. Mike, I realised, was suddenly talking about Amanda, Sergio and Marco. And there they were filling the screen, all looking so beautiful, filmed in Positano sitting on a rock on the beach where Sergio's restaurant stands. Well, of course, they couldn't get away to Australia, I scolded myself, this is the busiest season for them. I don't know if it was disappointment or just an overflow of emotion, but I was really crying now. I thought, to hell with the mascara! Dabbing the tears from my eyes with a tissue Mike had so sweetly handed me, I realised he was saying something more ... what?

No! 'Well, they're not really in Italy.'

The door opened and there was Amanda and my grandson, my beautiful grandson Marco, throwing himself into my arms, hugging me tight, tight, tight. I was absolutely bursting with joy.

It was a perfect night, the guests all crowded around. Everyone was laughing and crying. Marco tugged at my hand. I looked down, 'What is it, Marco?' A clever director had his camera on us in a flash, in time to catch a small boy look up at his nanna and say loud and clear, 'Did you miss me, Nanna?' What a scene stealer.

For weeks after the show, people came up and said how they'd cried with me. Marco had won a million hearts and the show had, as they say in the business, 'rated its tits off'. And it gave me the most enormous lift.

Peter Weiss generously threw a fabulous party for me at the Ritz Carlton with sixty friends the night before the taped show went to air. David Leckie, head honcho of Nine, made a charming speech. He said Nine thought it was the best 'This Is Your Life' show they had put together.

A few nights later my friend Amana Finley gave a cosy dinner party for me and close friends. I felt very spoilt and loved, as opposed to the rejection and despair I'd known those lonely days and nights when I had felt old and lost, my pride and dignity in tatters. In the following days I was inundated with mail from all over Australia. I couldn't go shopping without being stopped, everyone it seemed had seen the show. If I'm really honest 'This Is Your Life' Part Two helped me turn a corner. I appreciated how people felt, even those I didn't know really cared. I felt very privileged.

On reflection the only thing I'm still miffed about is that there was no cosmetic company deal — but as I've learnt, you can't have everything, can you?

The Last
Word.
Well, Almost

AND SO I wrote this book. At first it was just handwritten thoughts salvaged from my depression and scribbled onto a notepad. Then on holiday in Positano with my dear friend Barb I made my first real attempt to give those thoughts some order. I sat in the sun overlooking the Amalfi Coast and wrote about my friendships. It was healing. Back home it was winter in the Southern Highlands, and I holed up in my study at Greenville and worked on my word processor, the fire going and Bronson, my beloved Bronson at my feet. Stalled, I flew to Adelaide and stayed with Susan Mitchell and Mary Beasley. Susan gave up her desk and her computer for me to work on and the pages poured out. But back home I stumbled again. I didn't write every day and I didn't write with any real direction.

Susie encouraged me to go through all my old diaries (I had them dating back to 1974). They were business diaries but they noted every major hiccup of my emotional life. They provided a path — a path I sometimes found very painful and one that also proved very lonely. I've decided writing has to be the loneliest job in the world. As I gathered speed I found my word processor was too slow. I bought a Toshiba laptop and fumbled my way into a new era; a skill I'm proud of having accomplished. By now I had written from my childhood through to the heights of my television career, but then I felt intimidated by the realisation that up ahead were some very painful passages of my life I would have to revisit. Barb's advice was to 'get it over and done with', so I stopped writing in a chronological order, bit the bullet and tackled the most distressing periods of my life. I know that given time and distance from the break-up of my most recent relationship it would not loom so large — time does lend perspective. But, as anyone who has been through a similar experience will know, betrayal — no matter who you are — is hard, very hard, and in this case so publicly humiliating. At the time of writing this book my wounds were still raw. It wasn't easy but once done I was free and could double back and work my way through to this conclusion.

I've cried quiet tears as I've written and I've laughed out loud and heartily, and I guess that pretty much sums up my life. If one's had a balance of both then I don't suppose you can ask for anything more. Now I stop myself and say, 'Margaret, you know that's not telling the bloody truth. Of course you want more.' More of everything. I want to have more good years. I want to see my children achieve their goals and fulfil their ambitions. I want to see my grandson stand tall on his twenty-first birthday. I want to cherish my friends and family, give them the comfort and love they've always provided for me. And, if I'm really honest, I guess I want to know what it is to love again and be loved in return. And maybe next time, just maybe I'll be lucky and it will be forever.

Whatever forever really is.

Epilogue

ON 8 JUNE 1998, I was named a recipient of an AM — a Member of the Order of Australia — in the Queen's Birthday Honours. TV crews called at the farm, radio and press interviews were conducted by phone. The fax and email ran hot with congratulations. Late that night, in the quiet of Greenville, I thought how proud I felt as I cast back over my life and the other awards I'd received. And then it hit me, I'd been so lucky, so rewarded in my career. Sad I hadn't been able to achieve the same in my romantic relationships. But then I thought of my family, my friends, how rich they made my life.

A couple of days later, at the airport, a chap stepped up and said, 'Well, what do we call you now, Dame or Lady?'

I replied, 'I've always been a dame and I've never been a lady, so just keep calling me Maggie.'

It'll do.

—

Birthing a Book & Goodbye Greenville

I HAD been so focused for so long on finishing this book that I hadn't really given a great deal of thought to the aftermath.

There had been numerous meetings with my publishers as they planned the publicity tour of Australia and New Zealand. My fax at the farm had moved into overdrive coping with tour schedules and tour re-schedules, until finally a solid five-week programme was in place!

Somehow I grabbed a couple of weeks in Positano to catch my breath, and try to relax before the tour. I knew it was going to be tough and it was, but it was also the most exhilarating and moving experience.

Nothing could have prepared me for the overwhelming response to this book. The Australian media, for the most part, were extremely generous to me and it was awesome to be told there were waiting lists in every state for places at our literary lunches. Back home I was inundated with mail, letters from people from all walks of life and all ages; generous, warm letters. It took some time but eventually I managed to reply to each one with a handwritten note. I had been tempted to quote from some of those letters but I've decided I can't: they were after all private — for my eyes only. There is one, however, that gave me such a laugh I have to share it. It came from a witty young man about town, one William Petley, who wrote: 'Actually, Maggie, I think you should have called your book *I Should Have Married Barb*.' How we hooted when I rang to tell her.

Back at Greenville after the tour, I faced a new reality. The book had been all-consuming in my life for about two years and now the job was complete. Painfully, I came to the conclusion that it was time to make a change. I loved my Greenville but I now felt a need to be free — free of some of my responsibilities and the biggest was Greenville. As passionate as I felt about it, like a demanding lover it held me tight, committing me to its care, its growth, its maintenance, its staff and stock.

Sure, I'd been able to slip off to Italy for short breaks but now I wanted to be free to travel when I felt like it and more importantly to stay for as long as I liked, not just three weeks but maybe three months. My grandson was growing too fast too soon. I needed to share in more of his precious childhood. I had been working since I was fourteen years old, here I was facing my sixty-second birthday, and finally I could say now it's time for me. I wanted to cast off that bloody work ethic and sit in the sun for an entire day and read a book without feeling guilty. I discussed it with my family and close friends; they all endorsed the decision. It was difficult and emotional but I knew it was right.

After consulting with my real estate agent, we decided to wait until after Christmas to put Greenville on the market, but as it happened three private viewings took place. Two parties made offers, we danced around a bit but then agreed we were all busy, and would talk again in the New Year.

Christmas came and went; a nostalgic time because we all knew it would be our last at Greenville. A few days later the farm staff gave notice as they had suddenly decided to move on. It was terribly inconvenient and I wasn't quite sure what to do next, when my dear sister Nan rode in on her white charger, metaphorically speaking. She suggested her nephew and his son, both ex-farmers, may be able to fill in. They did, and Chris and Adam Uppill were also a godsend. They kept Greenville at its shiniest, neatest and best, and kept me calm throughout the ensuing weeks.

Early in the New Year we reopened sale negotiations and danced around a bit more. Finally, Greenville was sold to a nice couple with grown-up kids and an adorable dog. While all this had been going on, I had agonised about Bronson. There was no way I could take him to a city apartment. He was a country dog; he'd only ever known freedom. I shed a lot of tears at the thought of leaving him. Friends offered to take him, but one day when the new owners came to visit, they asked if they could keep him. In a flash I knew it was right. Bronson would stay at Greenville — his home. He could continue to swim in his lakes, sniff around his wombat holes, and chase those noisy plovers and silent roos and foxes across his paddocks. He also struck up an instant love for the new owners' bouncy little springer spaniel Micha; it was obvious they were going to be good mates. I found that very comforting.

In the following month I rarely left the property. I cleared out every cupboard and closet, sent hordes to the Salvation Army and distributed things amongst family and friends. I sold some furnishings and planned what to keep for my city apartment and what to store for my children if ever they want it.

Bronson with his new mate Micha on the steps of Greenville.

I wrote lists upon lists for the new owners about Greenville. Two pages were devoted to Bronson alone: his habits, his communication skills — like what means what, along with his diet, feeding habits and health regime. All the essential information. I have since discovered he's completely won his way into their hearts and is sleeping in his basket at the bottom of their bed. That's my boy!

As the days ticked on towards my departure, Greenville really turned it on — a full-blown orange moon and a breathtakingly beautiful, star-encrusted sky. Bronson and I spent hours sitting out in the evening air gazing up at it; his head in my lap as I lay back on the verandah, its stone still warm from the sunny day. Through the early mist one morning, nine kangaroos cheekily came down the drive to graze on my freshly cut green grass. The next day I woke to find a huge pelican on the lake, gobbling his way through fish after fish. He stayed the whole day until, at dusk, he swam to the far side of the lake, flapped his gigantic wings a few times and, like a jumbo jet with a full load, struggled to gain flight and was gone into the evening sky. He came back again and again over the next days, feeding his face non-stop then lumbering off. I am told he is still visiting Greenville on a regular basis.

All these beautiful things only made my leaving harder. Autumn had suddenly arrived, the trees were turning brilliant gold and red. As the leaves start to fall I'll be leaving. It seemed appropriate.

On the phone one evening I said to a friend, 'The packers are coming first thing in the morning.' 'Who? Kerry and James?' 'No, silly, Moss Vale removalists.' For three days they packed. I had everything marked with my sticker system again: green for my apartment in Sydney, orange for storage, yellow for the things I was giving my godson, and white for furnishings I had sold to the new owners. Alan, my removalist, said on the third day, 'Maggie, you've made it easy. We can have you out of here tomorrow.'

I'd counted on it taking at least two more days. Suddenly I wasn't prepared to leave. That last night I sat surrounded by a wall of boxes in the kitchen, just me, one chair, the tellie and Bronson. I had the television on but my mind was elsewhere. I thought back over the past nine and a half years, my time at Greenville. I relived all the good times, even found I could recall the tough times with a new tranquillity. I was sad, very sad, but fully resigned to the fact that this was the right thing to do.

Early the next morning I said a teary goodbye to Bronson. It was as if he understood. In the past he always stood in the drive to watch me as I left; this morning he gave me a long, loving look, turned as I started my car, and bounded alongside young Adam back to the manager's cottage. I felt a pang of jealousy but then a strange calm, because I knew this was the right decision for Bronson, too. He'd be fine.

I drove slowly out along the driveway. I'd planted plane trees on each side as saplings; now they stood tall and proud, and one day their branches will touch and form a wonderful arch. It will be my mark on Greenville and I thought what a fine legacy.

At the top of the hill I was tempted to stop and look back — one last look at Greenville — but I resisted. Through my tears I wouldn't have seen much anyway. Even though they say one should never look back, in writing this book I've been forced to. Now I only want to look forward and you know what . . . I am.

PS: As you read this I'm in the thick of renovations. I've bought the apartment next to mine and I'm knocking a hole in the wall, joining the two into a handsome new space. The walls will be white . . . I guess some things never change.

Acknowledgments

IF WRITING this book has at times been daunting, being faced with acknowledging all those who assisted me is even more so. There are so many who helped, encouraged and, in some cases, bullied and shoved me into this project that I fear this humble list is simply inadequate. But here goes ...

My sincere thanks go first to my daughter Brooke, who kick-started me with taped interviews of several family members and friends.

To my daughter Amanda and my friend Barbara Turnbull, who just kept saying, 'Get on with it.'

To Susan Mitchell, who always believed I could do it, and ultimately showed me how to find my way back over the years, collate my thoughts and practise the discipline of writing.

To Mary Beasley, Vicki Jones, Ken Stevens, Georgie and Snow Swift for their constant encouragement.

To my special friend Peter Weiss, who read my hesitant first pages and enthusiastically said, 'Go for it.'

To my dear sisters Nancy Paterson, Joan Clark and Betty Royans, who all contributed to recalling my childhood.

To Natalie Pike, Mavis Pozza, Ross Luck and Jill Robb, who gave of their time to clarify names, dates and happenings of those early Adelaide days.

To Charles Tabberer who kindly supplied photographs from our marriage.

To Bernard Leser for illuminating my era in *Vogue*.

To Helen Homewood and Janice Wakely, who walked me back through the Melbourne modelling days.

To Stuart Wagstaff and Graham McPherson, who contributed 'Beauty and the Beast' anecdotes — not all have made it into the book, but believe me it's wiser!

To my stepson Nicolas Prossimo, who generously and honestly helped me to remember both the good and bad times I shared with his father.

To Jan Geary, Rhonda Sayer Jones, George Gross, Harry Watt and John Cooper, who reminded me about the many days of 'Life's a Parade' at MTA.

To my solicitor Lyndon Sayer Jones, for both his recall of the many houses I've bought and sold and his wise counsel on some difficult decisions.

To Pam Darraugh for facts, figures and laughs about Maggie T experiences.

To Greg Barrett, who was both encouraging and kind, for allowing so many of his photographs to appear and photographing the cover. 'It will be an honour,' he said.

To Helmut Newton for generously allowing so many of his wonderful photographs to be included in this book.

To my manager Harry Miller, who tried to get me started on this book a long, long time ago, but who concedes that the extra living probably delivers a meatier read.

To Jane Burridge, who always believed it would be.

To Gill Harvie, who grappled with my appalling spelling and typed my original manuscript.

To Deb Brash, who designed the book but bowed to my pleas for black and white on the cover . . . everything!

And to all at Allen & Unwin for their enthusiastic and most professional support.

I am terrified of course that I have forgotten someone. If I have, I beg your forgiveness and ask that you simply realise that I'm too old, too tired and too talented to be perfect.

Maggie Tabberer, 1999

Index